# Timber frame construction

Stocking Lane   Hughenden Valley

High Wycombe  Buckinghamshire

HP14 4ND   UK

Tel:        +44 (0)1494 569600

Fax:        +44 (0)1494 565487

email: information@trada.co.uk

**www.trada.co.uk**

**Third edition 2001**

ISBN 1900510 32 4

# About TRADA Technology and TRADA

TRADA Technology is the leading independent timber research, consultancy and information provider for the construction industry.

TRADA, the Timber Research and Development Association is a membership-based organisation working to develop new market opportunities for timber and to protect existing ones.

Together, TRADA Technology and TRADA create a centre of excellence serving the timber industry generally and the timber frame industry in particular, together with its designers and customers.

TRADA's involvement in providing design guidance on timber frame and prefabrication dates from 1944 with the publication of a Red Booklet entitled  Prefabricated Timber Houses. This was revised in 1947.

A loose-leaf publication, the TRADA Timber Frame Design Guide was produced in sections over the years 1965 - 67.

The first edition of Timber Frame Construction was published in 1988 and the second edition in 1994.

**Published by TRADA Technology Ltd**

# Contents

# Introduction and scope

Since the last edition of Timber Frame Construction in 1994, there have been a number of changes to Standards and Regulations. Increasing concern about energy conservation and environmental issues, coupled with the need for greater efficiency in the building industry is making timber frame a favoured option for construction.

It is now widely recognised that timber is one of the few environmentally benign constructional materials. It is a renewable resource and uses little energy in production. The timber frame method of building allows easy incorporation of high levels of insulation and since timber itself is a natural insulator, the risk of cold bridges in highly insulated constructions is low.

The Latham Report, *Constructing the Team* and the Egan Report, *Rethinking Construction* concentrated on increasing the efficiency of the construction process. Off-site prefabrication is recognised as a major contributor in this area in terms of:

♦ speed of erection for reduced construction time

♦ reduced wastage on site

♦ minimum defects at handover

♦ increased productivity.

The level of timber frame prefabrication in the UK ranges from factory-produced 'open' timber frame wall panels - studs, sheathing and breather membrane, through 'closed' panels - including insulation, linings and even joinery and cladding, to full volumetric units.

UK timber frame construction has now matured to a stage where the timber frame wall - comprising studs with a wood-based sheathing material on the outside, protected by a breather membrane, insulation between the studs and a vapour control layer behind a plasterboard internal lining - is now regarded as a 'conventional' timber frame stud wall. The introduction of new materials and design approaches has led to the development of a number of alternative designs in recent years. The relaxation, in 1991, of the England and Wales Building Regulation fire requirements for non-combustible constructions over three storeys in height, has opened up the scope for timber frame buildings of four to seven storeys high – so called 'medium rise' timber frame. Chapter 4, which deals with wall design and construction considers some of the alternatives for the design of timber frame walls and provides guidelines to be followed when designing.

Energy efficient design is not solely concerned with the insulation levels in the fabric of the structure but impinges upon the whole design strategy. This is covered in a companion volume *Energy efficient housing- a timber frame approach* which covers the principles of energy efficiency, regardless of the form of construction. This was first published in 1989 but is equally relevant today.

The details in this book illustrate typical solutions to the design of platform frame construction to show the principles involved. It is not intended to provide a single prescriptive solution for timber frame design and other designs and details may be equally valid. Changes in Building Regulation requirements, for example to improve thermal and acoustic performance of buildings, can be met easily using a number of timber frame design options and details. The versatility of timber framing allows designers, manufacturers and fabricators the scope to develop appropriate solutions for their individual requirements. TRADA Technology can assist professional practices and companies to tailor timber frame to their needs.

The detailed requirements of Building Regulations and Building Standards differ slightly around the UK and are subject to change. The current requirements should always be checked. Housing warranty and guarantee authorities, such as the National House-Building Council (NHBC), Zurich Municipal and Housing Association Property Mutual (HAPM), also lay down their own requirements and the current edition of the appropriate manual should always be checked. The engineering calculations required for timber frame design are not covered here. Designers should refer to the relevant codes of practice: *BS 5268-2 The structural use of timber. Permissible stress design, materials and workmanship* and *BS 5268-6 Code of practice for timber framed walls* or *DD ENV 1995-1-1Eurocode 5 Design of timber structures Part 1.1 General rules and rules for buildings* and *DD ENV 1995-1-2 General rules. Structural fire design.*

# 1 Timber frame construction: An overview

Timber frame is a method of construction. It is not a system of building although there are a number of well researched systems which use timber frame as a basis. Timber frame construction uses timber studs and rails, together with a wood-based sheathing, to form a structural frame which transmits all vertical and horizontal loads to the foundations. The exterior cladding is non-loadbearing, although it may contribute to wind resistance; it is used to weatherproof the building and to provide the desired external appearance.

In the UK, timber frame construction generally uses factory-manufactured wall frames and roof trusses, or, in some cases, roof panels, with only a few specialist companies making and erecting frames on site. The extent of factory prefabrication can and does vary considerably; from so-called 'open panels' consisting of simple sheathed stud panels with a breather membrane, to 'closed panels' which include insulation and internal linings and may also include components such as joinery and sometimes also cladding. Floor and roof panels may also be factory-prefabricated as open panels with simple joists or rafters and sheathing panels, or as closed panels with insulation, linings etc fitted in the factory. The selection of an appropriate arrangement is an early decision in the design process.

Timber frame primarily developed in the UK for house building although it is also widely used for buildings such as hotels, hostels, clinics, nursing homes, student accommodation, offices and similar structures.

## 1.1 Methods of construction

**Platform frame** is the most commonly used method in the UK. Each storey is framed with **floor-to-ceiling** height panels and the floor deck of one floor becomes the erection platform of the next (Figure 1.1). This publication concentrates on the design and construction principles of the platform frame method.

**Figure 1.1 Platform frame construction**

The **prefabricated wall panels** can be either small units (up to approximately 3.6 m in length), designed to be manhandled into place (Figure 1.2) or up to full elevation-width panels incorporating ancillary components for placing with a crane (Figure 1.3).

**Figure 1.2 Platform frame: Small panel construction**

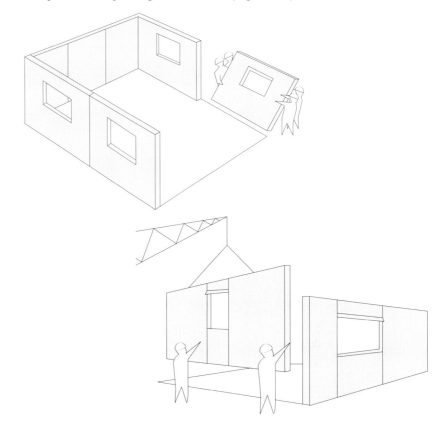

**Figure 1.3 Platform frame: Large panel construction**

Other types which may be used include:

**Floor-to-floor panel frame**: this is an erection method whereby the wall panels (except for the topmost storey) are floor-to-floor, or **storey height**, rather than floor-to-ceiling and the intermediate floors are hung inside the wall panel, see Figure 1.4. This reduces cross-sectional shrinkage of timber in the external wall and enables the insulation and vapour control layer to be continuous up the wall face.

**Figure 1.4 Storey height panels (may be large or small)**

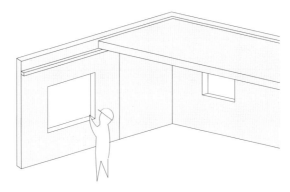

**Volumetric**: involves the factory fabrication of box units which can form individual rooms, or larger spaces, complete with finishes and services and which require crane erection (Figure 1.5). This is best suited to repetitive units, such as hotels, hostels or nursing homes.

**Figure 1.5 Volumetric construction**

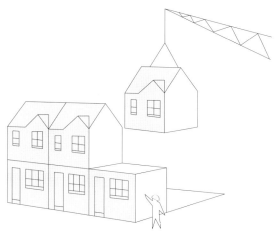

**Post and beam**: comprises a loadbearing system of posts and beams with lightweight timber or glazed infill panels (Figure 1.6). In the UK, this tends to be used in the specialist 'traditional appearance' market but there are modern timber frame systems using post and beam elsewhere in Europe.

**Figure 1.6 Post and beam construction**

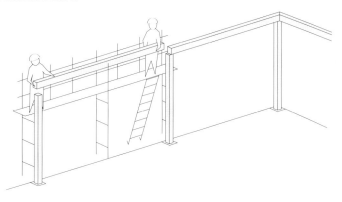

Timber frame panels and other components are usually obtained from a specialist manufacturer/fabricator although they can, less commonly, be manufactured by the contractor, either off site or in a temporary factory on the site. Most fabricators have developed their own method of fitting together the timber frame components and are able to offer a full building kit to their own designs or to designs produced by their clients. Some produce components to details supplied to them and leave responsibility for the structural or constructional detailing of the final building to the designer. Whatever the procurement method used, it is important that the client and supplier agree exactly what the timber frame package will comprise, even down to supply and/or fix of loose items such as noggings and strutting.

This chapter provides a broad introduction to timber frame construction; more detailed consideration is given to particular aspects in subsequent chapters.

## 1.2 Structural components

Platform frame external wall panels are constructed from vertical studs, normally at 400 mm or 600 mm centres, nailed with simple butt joints to top and bottom rails. Strength graded timber must always be used; 89 x 38 mm and 140 x 38 mm are the most common sizes but 97 x 47 mm sections are also used. With the increasing need for energy efficiency even deeper studs are being specified. The size of panels dictates the method of construction, eg whether to use a crane for erection. Wind bracing is usually provided by a wood-based board material, normally nailed to the external face of the frame (Figure 1.7a) or in certain cases, by cross-bracing combined with internal plasterboard. Alternative wall designs, using either wood-based boards, mineral fibre boards or fibre reinforced gypsum boards, fixed on the internal face of the studs, to provide the wind bracing, have also been developed (Figure 1.7b) and are discussed in more detail in Section 4.4.

**Figure 1.7 a Typical wall construction: sheathing on external face of frame**

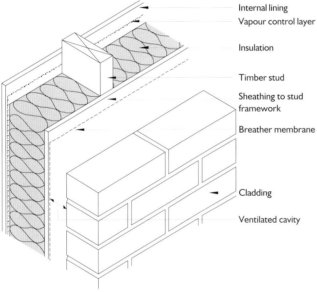

Internal lining
Vapour control layer

Insulation

Timber stud

Sheathing to stud framework

Breather membrane

Cladding

Ventilated cavity

**Figure 1.7 b Typical wall construction: sheathing on internal face of frame**
See Section 4.4 for details of condensation control

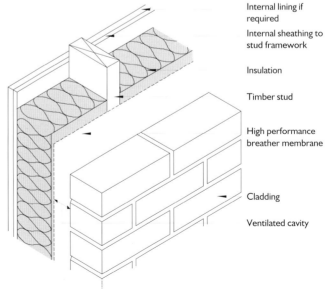

Internal lining if required

Internal sheathing to stud framework

Insulation

Timber stud

High performance breather membrane

Cladding

Ventilated cavity

External claddings can be chosen from a wide range of materials, including brickwork, cement rendered blockwork, tiling, slating, timber boarding, cement render on battens or proprietary claddings.

Internal loadbearing and non-loadbearing walls may be constructed simply by using a stud frame lined on both sides with plasterboard or other sheet material. Compartment or separating walls are generally constructed from two separate stud frames with room linings of at least 30 mm of plasterboard applied in two or more layers with staggered joints. It is also possible to construct compartment walls with a brick or concrete block core between the two timber frames; this is a convenient method for supporting masonry cladding to walls at steps (changes of level) between buildings.

Floor and roof framing are similar to other forms of construction, although the junction detailing is different. The intermediate floors and the roof provide structural diaphragms which, by means of structurally efficient connections to the walls, contribute to the overall stability of the building.

## 1.3 Performance of timber frame construction

### 1.3.1 Thermal performance

The overall thermal resistance of the building envelope is the main factor in determining its energy requirement, although other factors such as ventilation control, the building form, orientation and efficiency of the heating system, all influence the cost of achieving comfortable conditions. These aspects are considered in detail in a companion TRADA publication, *Energy efficient housing - a timber frame approach*.

Timber frame construction incorporates high levels of insulation within the structural elements (Figure 1.7) and can achieve U values significantly better than the minimum requirements of the Building Regulations. In order to reduce the amount of water vapour entering the wall, which may condense as a result of the temperature differential across the structure, it is normal practice to ensure that the internal face (lining) of the wall has more resistance to water vapour than the external face of the frame. This is usually achieved by a vapour control layer on the inside face of the stud frame, behind the wall lining but on the warm side of the insulation.

There are no differences between timber frame and other forms of construction so far as roof or ground floor insulation is concerned.

In common with all forms of construction, windows and doors should be draught-sealed and lobbies should be provided where possible to reduce ventilation heat loss. Small cracks and gaps at junctions, eg between windows and walls should be sealed. A minimum requirement for winter ventilation should be the provision in all rooms of trickle ventilators, usually fitted in the window frame, together with provision for higher ventilation rates in bathrooms, kitchens and utility rooms, eg by installing extract fans or passive ventilation systems.

Insulated timber frame construction has relatively low thermal capacity and therefore a fast response to heat input. In housing where heating is intermittent, this fast response can result in increased comfort and energy savings. However, the most important factor in energy saving, in all construction types, is to ensure that the heating system is compatible with the building fabric response and the predicted occupancy pattern. Consideration should always be given to using the sun as a supplementary heat source using passive solar design techniques. Since occupants can have a significant effect on the energy efficiency of buildings, designers should provide an operation manual to enable them to obtain maximum benefit from the energy efficiency measures included.

## 1.3.2 Fire performance

The fire resistance of a timber frame structure is achieved by a combination of the internal lining material, the timber structure and the insulation. Fire resistance requirements for elements of construction are defined in national Building Regulations.

Fire resistance performance is determined by tests carried out to the requirements of *BS 476 Fire tests on building materials and structures* Parts 20 to 22 (or Part 8 for tests carried out prior to the dates specified in the Building Regulations) by a UKAS (United Kingdom Accreditation Service) approved fire test laboratory. The commonly used forms of construction described in this book have been successfully tested to these criteria.

Note: BS 476 fire resistance tests will be replaced by BS EN 1363, 1364 and 1365 tests in due course. UK Building Regulations will provide the new classification requirements when this occurs and the relevant documents should be consulted.

There are three other ways of demonstrating fire resistance performance:

+ calculations in accordance with BS 5268-4 Section 4.2 *Recommendations for calculating for resistance of timber stud walls and joisted floor constructions*

+ constructions included in the BRE Report BR 128 *Guidelines for the construction of fire resisting structural elements*

+ an assessment of the construction which is acceptable to the building control authority.

Thirty and sixty minutes fire resistance are the current normal requirements for low rise buildings. The greater resistance is usually obtained by the use of a double layer of plasterboard with the joints staggered. Plasterboard is the most commonly used lining material due to its economy, ease of working, and good fire performance. Other materials can be used provided an appropriate fire test or assessment has been carried out.

The current Building Regulations in England and Wales, Northern Ireland and the Building Standards in Scotland have differing requirements in respect of the use of timber construction, depending upon the Purpose Group and size.

In many timber frame constructions, cavity barriers are required between the timber frame and the cladding to restrict the passage of flames and hot gases if a fire were to occur in this outer cavity. The requirements for these are different in Scotland compared with other parts of the UK.

In addition to fire resistance, it is necessary to control the potential for the linings of walls and ceilings to contribute to a developing fire. Prior to the introduction of European test methods, the reaction to fire properties of construction materials are based on *BS 476-6 Method of test for fire propagation for products* and *BS 476-7 Method of test to determine the classification of the surface spread of flame of products*. In some situations, Building Regulations call for a performance superior to those defined in BS 476-7. This is designated Class O and also includes results from BS 476-6. Table 1.1 shows typical flame spread ratings for cladding and lining materials.

BS 476-6 and −7 test methods will be replaced by BS EN reaction to fire test methods in due course. UK Building Regulations will provide the new classification requirements when this occurs and the relevant documents should be consulted.

**TABLE 1.1 Typical surface spread of flame ratings for commonly used timber frame cladding and lining materials**

| Classification to BS 476-7 (and BS 476-6) | Material |
| --- | --- |
| Class 0 | Brickwork<br>Cement render<br>Tile and slate hanging<br>Cement-bonded particleboard<br>Fibre cement boards<br>Plasterboard<br>Treated* wood-based materials eg softwood, hardwood, plywood, OSB, chipboard, mediumboard, mdf, hardboard, softboard |
| Class 1 | Treated* wood-based materials, eg softwood, hardwood, plywood, OSB, chipboard, mediumboard, mdf, hardboard, softboard |
| Class 3 | Timber or wood-based boards with a density greater than 400 kg/m$^3$ (painted or unpainted) |

* 'Treated' may consist of solid timber impregnated with flame retardant chemicals or coated with a flame retardant finish or wood-based panel products to which treatments are applied during or after manufacture, by impregnation of the fibres or the finished board, by the incorporation of dry chemicals into particle coatings and adhesives or by the application of surface coatings to the board

There is continual development of suitable products. The TRADA Wood Information Sheet 2/3-3 *Flame retardant treatments for timber* contains details.

There may also be requirements to control external surface spread of flame in certain buildings. This is, to some extent, affected by building height and use, but is primarily governed by the distance of the building from the boundary.

## 1.3.3 Sound insulation

Timber frame structures rely to a large degree upon structural separation to achieve sound reduction, rather than incorporating mass into the structure.

Building Regulations require walls and floors separating dwellings from another building, another part of the building, or another dwelling, to resist airborne sound. Floors above a dwelling, which separate it from another dwelling or from another part of the same building, not used exclusively as part of the dwelling, are required to resist impact sound.

Sound insulation of walls between two adjoining occupancies is achieved mainly by the use of two separate stud walls, plasterboard faced, with an air space containing sound absorbent materials between them (see Chapter 5). Reduction of airborne sound through floors separating dwellings is also achieved by the use of an absorbent blanket in the structural floor, a heavy plasterboard ceiling, plus a floating upper layer. This floating layer also serves to reduce the transmission of impact sound (see Chapter 7).

Sound transmission through non-compartment timber floors can be upgraded by the incorporation of an absorbent blanket in the structural floor and if required, by the use of additional plasterboard on the ceiling.

Sound transmission levels through external walls are normally governed by the presence and relative size of window and door openings, the effectiveness of weatherstripping and the form of multi-glazing. An imperforate timber frame external wall can achieve 45 to 50 decibels sound reduction, depending upon the cladding used. Internal airborne sound transmission between rooms can be reduced by the use of multiple linings and/or sound absorbing materials, such as mineral wool, in the stud cavity.

## 1.3.4 Durability

The long-term durability of any construction must always be considered as part of the design process. For timber, the potential for decay, arising from high moisture content levels, is usually the major consideration. Timber which remains at a moisture content of 20%, or less, is below the decay threshold. Timber assessed as being at risk of remaining above this moisture content level for prolonged periods should either be a naturally durable species or be treated with preservatives. Preservative treatment may be specified as an insurance where timber components are inaccessible or difficult to replace.

The vast majority of low rise timber frame buildings in the UK uses softwoods rated as non-durable (see Appendix 1) for the structural components. However, properly designed and constructed timber frame buildings do not rely upon preservative treatments for durability. The wall framework is designed so that it will maintain an equilibrium moisture content comfortably lower than that which could allow fungal growth. It is, however, common practice for the structural components in the external wall to be preservative-treated as an insurance against any future failure of the weather resistant cladding which might allow water to penetrate to the timber structure. The Building Regulations require softwood roofs in certain areas of England to be treated with a 'suitable' preservative against the house longhorn beetle.

There is no specific requirement to preservative-treat suspended timber ground floor components although these are also sometimes treated to reduce the risk of deterioration if, for example, ventilation air paths are inadvertently blocked during the life of the building.

Timber cladding and any supporting battens are normally treated with suitable preservatives unless the timber used is sufficiently durable and contains no sapwood. External joinery should be manufactured from Durability Class 3 (moderately durable) timber species or better, or from other suitable joinery species treated with preservatives.

For further information on preservative treatments see Appendix 1, section A1.5.

# 1.4 Dimensional discipline

## 1.4.1 The structural grid

The regular spacing of studs, joists and roof members in a timber frame construction leads naturally to the use of a simple planning grid at the design stage. Since most sheathing, lining and flooring materials are supplied in sheets 2400 mm long and 1200 or 600 mm wide, the most obvious structural grids are 400 mm or 600 mm.

The modular grid can, if desired, also be applied to the planning of the building. This can be advantageous in reducing cutting and wastage of sheet materials but may prove a difficult discipline, especially in small buildings. A 100 mm sub-grid is commonly used for internal planning which fits neatly with the standard sizes of most second fix components, eg kitchen units.

When buildings of non-modular sizes are planned, it is normal practice to set out the stud discipline from one end and have a non-modular make up at the opposite end (Figure 1.8).

**Figure 1.8 Using a structural grid on a non-modular building**

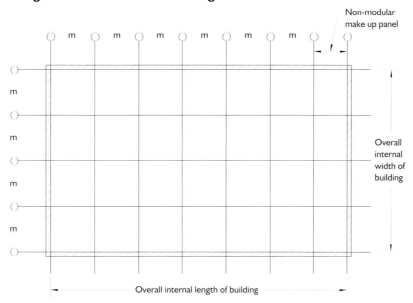

When walls are set out to the grid pattern, it is necessary to decide whether the wall lining or the structural face is located on the grid line. There are advantages and disadvantages in both methods. Whichever method is selected it is recommended that the discipline is clearly noted and followed throughout the building process. Manufacturers of timber frame components may predetermine the discipline, unless otherwise instructed.

Placing the finished wall face on the grid gives clear finished spaces of modular dimensions which allows the simple fitting of standard components such as staircases, doorsets and kitchen units. The disadvantage is that setting out dimensions are more complex since allowance should be made for the thickness of wall linings on all component sizes at junctions (see Figure 1.9).

### Figure 1.9 Finished wall face grid on module

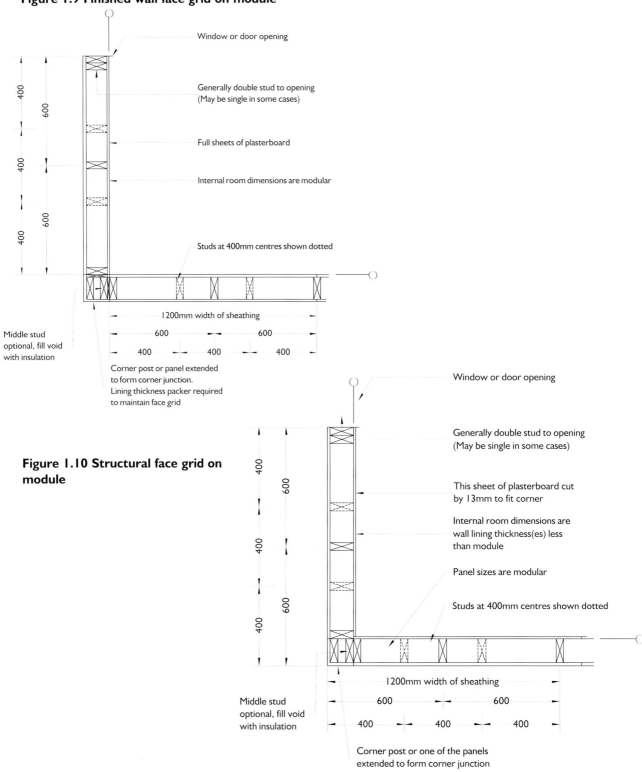

### Figure 1.10 Structural face grid on module

Placing the internal structural face of panels on the grid simplifies setting out dimensions but produces finished spaces less than the full modular size, see Figure 1.10. It is, however, the most commonly used method. The grid discipline also affects the use of plasterboard and sheathing materials.

## 1.4.2 Vertical dimensions

Figure 1.11 shows the relevant aspects which control the vertical height of a timber frame building. In setting out the vertical dimensions those aspects considered most important to a particular design should be defined:

**Datum:** Usually finished floor level - all floors.
**Floor-to-floor:** Typical floor-to-floor height in housing is 2.6 m.
**External joinery:** Standard size is 2.1 m from datum to head of door or window openings.
**Brick cladding:** 4 courses = 300 mm, which also suits external joinery head at 2.1 m. Coursing can normally be adjusted above this level with little visual impact.

**Figure 1.11 Vertical heights**

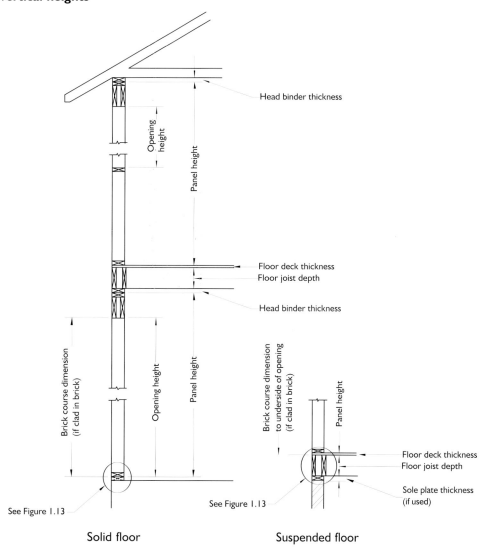

Solid floor                    Suspended floor

Wall panel heights can be determined by:

♦ Floor-to-floor dimension

♦ Floor thickness - depth of joist, thickness of floor deck and ceiling

♦ Floor-to-ceiling height

♦ The depth of lintel required over openings

♦ The use of uncut sheathing panels

♦ The use of head binders (see Chapter 4).

It is common practice to standardise the panel height and the depth of floor joists in order to maintain constant floor-to-floor dimensions. The variation in joist span capacity is adjusted by altering the joist spacing and/or by using joists of a higher strength class timber or structural timber composites.

Vertical dimensions of wall panels can be arranged to make use of standard sheet materials where possible, and various methods are available to the designer to achieve this. If cutting is necessary, arguably it is preferable to accept cutting the external sheathing to the required size if this enables the internal lining to be in uncut sheets.

Figure 1.12 a, b, c and d illustrate four examples with different cutting arrangements for sheathing and lining in conjunction with a separate head binder and 195 mm deep joists, where different criteria are used to determine the vertical dimensions.

**Figure 1.12 a Example of storey height dimensions when floor-to-floor height governs**

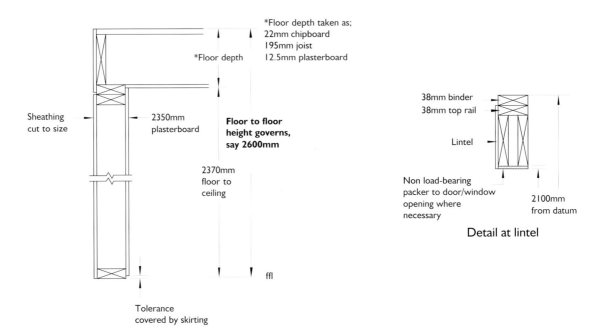

**Figure 1.12 b Example of storey height dimensions when floor-to-ceiling height governs**

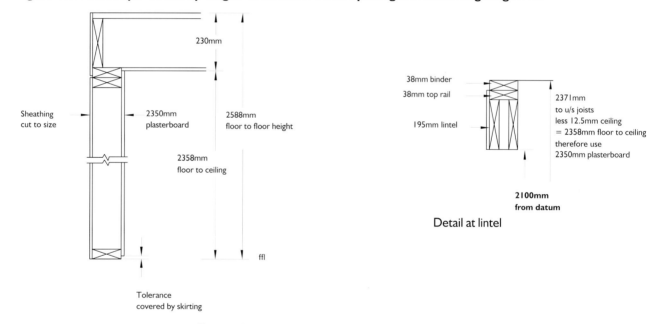

230mm

Sheathing and
plasterboard lining
cut to size

**2312mm
inc 12mm
allowance for
possible deflection**

2542mm
floor to floor

Note, if brick cladding
is used, 2550mm is
preferable as this is a
brick coursing dimension

ffl

38mm binder
38mm top rail

Max lintel depth
148mm-may limit
max allowable
opening width

2324mm

2100mm
from datum

Detail at lintel

**Figure 1.12 c Example of storey height dimensions when opening and lintel heights govern**

230mm

Sheathing
cut to size

2350mm
plasterboard

2588mm
floor to floor height

2358mm
floor to ceiling

ffl

Tolerance
covered by skirting

38mm binder
38mm top rail

195mm lintel

2371mm
to u/s joists
less 12.5mm ceiling
= 2358mm floor to ceiling
therefore use
2350mm plasterboard

**2100mm
from datum**

Detail at lintel

In certain circumstances it is possible to avoid the need to cut sheathing panels by allowing the top and/or bottom edge to project past the sole plate or head binder and cover the interface joint. Projecting sheathing edges of this type should use only rigid sheathing materials and care is required to protect the projecting edge during transportation and handling.

Another option is to use non-standard thickness head binders so that standard sheet lining materials may be used without on-site cutting. The head binder can also be omitted, but special care is then required to ensure that joist, beam, trimmer or truss loads occur over a stud or studs.

Standard door and frame components are 2.1 m high (other heights are available) and when combined with the lintel depth, plus panel top rail, may influence panel or room height dimension. See Figure 1.12c.

**Figure 1.12 d Example of storey height dimensions when sheathing panel size governs**

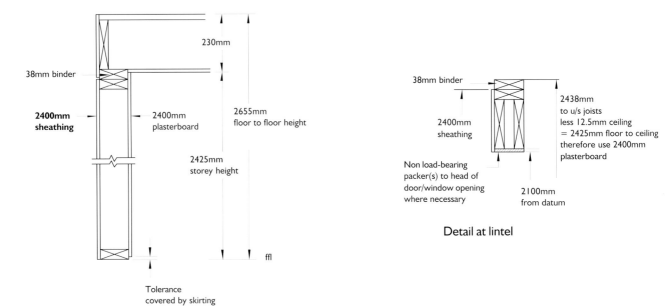

Detail at lintel

### Brick cladding

The 2100 mm dimension from datum (finished floor level) to the underside of the lintel fits an increment of 300 mm or 4 brick courses. Careful consideration of the brick coursing at the base is therefore necessary for the coursing to line through at door head level. See Figure 1.13.

If the first floor level datum is also a brick course (eg 2550 mm, 2625 mm and 2700 mm), it enables the coursing to run unchanged to the heads of upper floor openings. However, this is not essential since it causes no difficulty for the coursing above 2.1 m to be gauged to suit non-standard brick dimensions up to the head of the upper floor windows. In this case, coursing at window sills can be dealt with by inserting sub-sills, see Chapter 9.

Changes in level at steps between adjoining buildings should correspond with brick coursing dimensions to enable the coursing to continue across adjoining buildings.

Most other claddings are not affected by vertical dimension rules.

## Figure 1.13 Vertical dimensions: detail at ground floor level

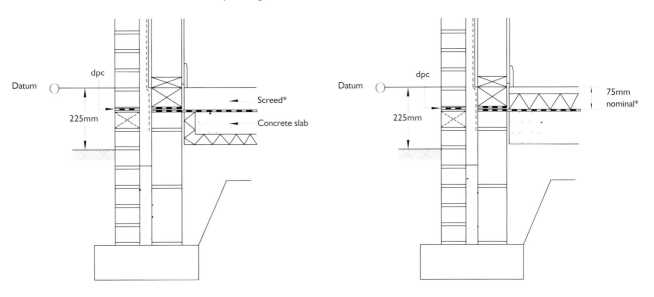

\* If dimension from datum to the top of slab is
less than 75mm a shallower sole plate is used
and the height of the dpc in the inner skin is
raised by inserting cut bricks or blocks

Brick cladding with an insulated concrete floor slab

Brick cladding with a floating floor deck

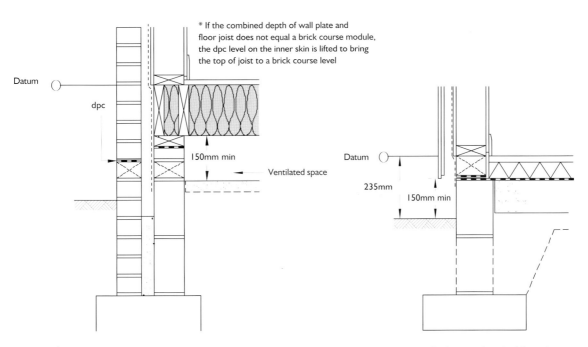

\* If the combined depth of wall plate and
floor joist does not equal a brick course module,
the dpc level on the inner skin is lifted to bring
the top of joist to a brick course level

Brick cladding and a timber ground floor

Lightweight cladding (insect screen not
shown for clarity)

# 2 Foundations

## 2.1 Design requirements

Timber frame superstructures can be erected from almost any type of foundation. Building Regulations require foundations to be of sufficient depth and constructed so as to sustain and transmit to the ground the combined dead load and imposed load in such a manner that the total or differential settlement of the building will not impair the stability of, or cause damage to, the whole or any part of the building.

*BS 8004 Code of practice for foundations* includes information on design and construction for the normal range of buildings.

The most common types of foundation used are conventional strip footings or trench fill. Other types which have been used include reinforced concrete rafts, short bored piles and ground beams, concrete pads with ground beams and fully pre-cast systems.

Timber frame constructed without masonry cladding can allow considerable economies to be made in the design of foundations, especially on ground with low bearing capacity. For example, the approximate load per metre run of a two storey timber-clad timber frame house supporting half the upper floor and half the roof load is likely to be in the region of 10 to 20 kN/m run. A similar two storey superstructure with brick cladding would have a linear load of approximately 20 to 35 kN/m run.

In addition to meeting the Design Requirements, the successful completion and quality of the timber frame building is dependent on good on-site practice in terms of accuracy in setting out and erecting components. Guidance is given in Appendix 3 Site Supervisor's Checklist.

## 2.2 Sequence and setting out

Foundation design for timber frame buildings should be considered in respect of the sequence of construction as this differs significantly from masonry construction.

When using prefabricated panels, these should ideally be delivered to site so that they can be placed into their final position with the minimum of handling and storage. This requires the foundations (and ground floor bases when they are used) to be completed prior to delivery of the timber frame components. Manufactured components, when assembled to form wall elements, require the base dimensions to be accurate in length and to be square and level; the wide variations common to masonry construction cannot be tolerated. However, the effort made at this stage is important because an uninterrupted work flow to achieve a weathertight shell can then be assured.

When brick cladding is to be used, the cavity dimension below the dpc should be nominal 50 mm plus the thickness of the sheathing.

## 2.3 Strip foundations

Concrete strip foundations should not normally be less than 150 mm thick and should project at least 150 mm either side of the foundation wall.

The foundations should be located centrally below the foundation wall as shown in Figure 2.1a and b. Although the minimum width could be less than 600 mm, this is often impracticable since bricklayers find it difficult to work in trenches narrower than this.

Strip foundations may step in level to suit ground contours but the minimum overlap should not be less than either twice the height of the step or the thickness of the foundation, or 300 mm, whichever is greater.

Unreinforced concrete strip foundations should not be used on made up ground or ground with wide variation in types of subsoil below the loadbearing level as these could impair the stability of the structure.

### Figure 2.1 a Strip foundations where brick or block cladding is used

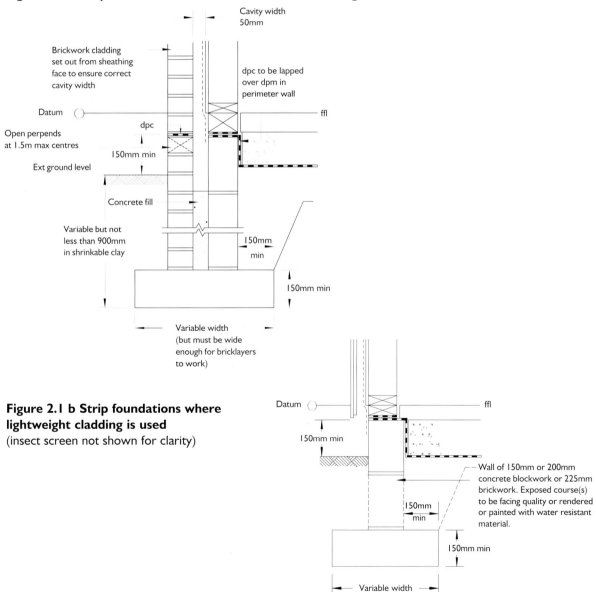

### Figure 2.1 b Strip foundations where lightweight cladding is used
(insect screen not shown for clarity)

## 2.4 Trench fill

Timber frame buildings, due to their relatively light loading on foundations, can make use of narrow mass concrete foundations on soils of low bearing pressure. These foundations cannot be less than the width of the wall they support and because mechanical bucket excavators are used, the average trench width is usually at least 450 mm. Accurate setting out of such narrow foundations is therefore very important.

Trench fill foundations are usually excavated after the site top soil has been removed or a level bed prepared. The trenches are filled to the top with mass concrete; the accuracy in levelling the top of the concrete is critical because of the few courses of brickwork before facework is exposed. See Figure 2.2. Depending upon the type of ground floor construction specified and the thickness of the finished floor construction, vertical adjustment of the foundation walling may be necessary for the brick cladding to course out at the finished floor level (datum) required for brick coursing to suit standard 2.1 m door and frame dimensions. See Figure 1.13.

The choice between strip foundations and trench fill is usually determined by costs, ground conditions, or simply preference.

**Figure 2.2 Trench fill foundation**

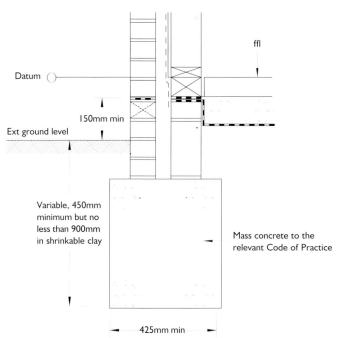

## 2.5 Reinforced concrete ground beams

These special foundations are generally considered only for very poor bearing conditions or in highly shrinkable clays, particularly close to existing healthy trees. They offer the best foundation solution in such situations but require specialist design and construction and are not in common use. The lighter weight of timber frame can gain significant cost savings with this type of specialised foundation design.

## 2.6 Concrete rafts

Reinforced concrete rafts (Figure 2.3) are designed to accept ground movement. They are therefore suitable for use with timber frame structures, especially in areas having known subsidence problems and when lightweight claddings can be used. Concrete raft design, in common with reinforced concrete ground beams and piles, requires specialist advice.

**Figure 2.3 Concrete raft foundation** (insect screen not shown for clarity)

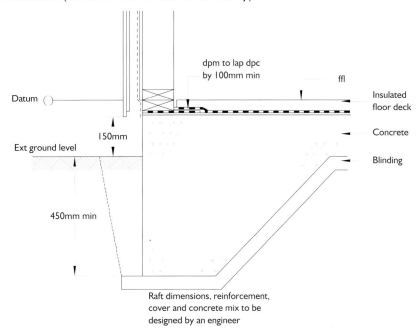

## 2.7 Proximity to trees

Building on sites close to existing healthy trees, or where new planting is proposed, should be carefully examined in relation to foundation damage. *BRE Digest 298 The influence of trees on house foundations in clay soils* and the housing warranty and guarantee authorities offer guidance on building near trees with advice on distances from named trees and precautions that should be taken.

Care should also be taken if building on sites which have recently been cleared of established trees, particularly in shrinkable clay areas, when ground heave could cause serious problems.

## 2.8 Basements

Timber frame superstructures can be constructed over basements or semi-basements and this is common practice in North America and Scandinavia. The floor between the basement storey and the ground floor may be either of timber or concrete construction depending upon the structural design of the basement. Full 30 minutes fire resistance is required for this floor even when modified 30 minutes fire resistance is allowable for the floor between ground and first floor level. Loadbearing walls at ground floor level should be supported at basement level by loadbearing walls or beams. If the basement is of masonry or *in situ* concrete construction, loadbearing internal walls in the basement should also be of masonry to avoid problems of differential movement. A Building Regulations Approved Document *Basements for dwellings* is published by the British Cement Association and the National House-Building Council.

In North America it is allowable to construct basements of treated timber and these are included in the building codes. In the UK the use of timber basement structures would need to be discussed with the building control department to establish their acceptability.

# 3 Ground floors

## 3.1 Design requirements

Suspended timber, suspended concrete and ground-supported in situ concrete floors can all be used with timber frame superstructures. The selection of the appropriate type for any specific project will usually depend upon factors such as end user requirement, site bearing pressure and contours, insulation standards required, specifier's preference, labour availability and cost.

A floor next to the ground should prevent moisture reaching the upper surface of the floor and prevent excessive heat loss to the ground or into the ventilated space beneath a suspended floor. Building Regulations include requirements for damp proof membranes for both suspended and ground-supported floors, requirements for the ventilation of the space beneath suspended floors and define the minimum requirements for thermal insulation.

There are no requirements for fire resistance for ground floors.

In certain areas of the country, special precautions are necessary to reduce the entry of radon or landfill gases. Details of geographical areas where this is necessary are obtainable from the DETR. Precautions are described in the *BRE Report No 211 Radon: guidance on protective measures for new dwellings* and *No 212 Construction of new buildings on gas contaminated land*.

Access for disabled users of buildings requires a level threshold to at least one entrance, see Section 3.6.

The housing warranty and guarantee authorities lay down specific requirements for items such as the moisture content of structural timber, the use of ground supported floors in respect of the depth of hardcore and blinding and for the ventilation of the space beneath suspended timber and concrete floors. These may differ from the Building Regulations and the current requirements should be checked.

Some water authorities require joints and bends in pipes to be accessible.

In addition to meeting the Design Requirements, the successful completion and quality of the timber frame building is dependent on good on-site practice in terms of accuracy in setting out and erecting components. Guidance is given in Appendix 3 Site Supervisor's Checklist.

## 3.2 Integration with the timber frame superstructure

Timber superstructures are generally quick to erect, dimensionally accurate and are of dry construction. A timber ground floor is normally provided by the supplier of the other timber components and is constructed sequentially with the timber frame superstructure.

A concrete slab or precast concrete ground floor is usually constructed whilst the timber components are being fabricated. On larger sites, a number of floor slabs may be laid in advance of the shell erection, thus avoiding the possibility of subsequent delays due to inclement weather when it may not be possible to lay concrete but when timber construction could continue. Precast concrete floors may have a longer delivery period than the timber structure, possibly obviating some of the time advantage of timber frame.

The use of 'dry' types of floor finish has several advantages. It reduces the time lost while screeds are laid and set, avoids introducing a wet process into an otherwise dry method of construction, thereby avoiding the possible moisture content and cracking problems which can result from subsequent drying out.

## 3.3 Floor insulation

Floor insulation is comparatively cheap and easy to install. However, the calculation of the thermal resistance of floors is a relatively complex procedure. The greater part of floor heat loss occurs at the edges so that the size of the floor (ie perimeter length to area ratio) influences the U value. For this reason, floor values are normally taken from tables giving averaged figures (see Table 3.1), based on the calculations given in *BS EN ISO 13370 Thermal performance of buildings. Heat transfer via the ground*. Calculation methods and values are given in the *Chartered Institution of Building Services Engineers (CIBSE) Guide A3 Thermal properties of building structures*.

**Table 3.1 Typical U values for ground floors**

| Floor type | Insulation | Typical U value of 6m x 6m floor W/m²K |
|---|---|---|
| Suspended timber with 10% joists | 100 mm mineral wool | 0.28 |
| | 200 mm mineral wool | 0.19 |
| Concrete with floating floor | 50 mm extruded polystyrene | 0.30 |
| | 75 mm extruded polystyrene | 0.25 |

## 3.4 Timber suspended ground floors

Timber floors may be supplied by the manufacturer of the timber frame superstructure as precut joist components, as floor panels, or they can be site-cut to the relevant sizes and constructed by the contractor. The floor can be designed to form a platform at ground level (similar to intermediate floors) or can be fitted within the building, allowing its installation to be delayed until the shell is erected and it is protected from the weather. A suspended timber ground floor is particularly appropriate for timber frame housing since it is constructed by the same trades as the main structure, is of dry construction and can be readily insulated to similar high standards as the walls and roof.

The floor joists may span between the foundations of the loadbearing walls or may be supported at closer centres by means of sleeper walls. The latter allows smaller section joists but increases the amount of substructure required.

The types of suspended timber ground floors are shown in Figure 3.1 and the details for each type in Figures 3.2 to 3.8.

## Figure 3.1 Types of suspended timber ground floors

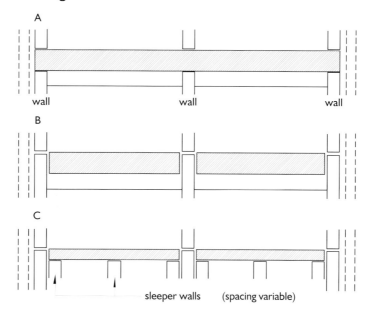

Type A
Floor joists spanning over loadbearing external and internal walls: suitable for prefabricated floor panels using on-site crane assembly

Type B
Floor joists on joist hangers spanning between external and internal loadbearing walls

Type C
Floor joists spanning over sleeper walls, independent from external and internal loadbearing walls

Points to watch

Joist depth as intermediate floor: may add to differential movement; increases height of floor above adjacent ground level

Floor joists independent of walls in terms of sequence of construction and differential settlement

As Type B but smaller depth joists: minimum height of floor above adjacent ground level

Regardless of floor type, it is important to maintain a uniform support for the main superstructure to avoid differential settlement

All Building Regulations require the ground beneath the floor to be covered to restrict the passage of moisture and to prevent plant growth. Specific requirements vary but the ground cover may be:

♦ sand or smooth gravel at least 50 mm thick laid on a polythene sheet at least 300 microns thick turned up at the edges, with all joints lapped by 150 mm and taped, laid on 25 mm thick sand blinding (see Figure 3.2a).

♦ 50 mm concrete laid on at least 300 micron thick polythene and sand blinding as above (see Figure 3.2a).

♦ 100 mm of concrete laid on a clean, inert hardcore bed at least 100 mm thick.

♦ a damp proof membrane in accordance with Section 3 of *CP 102 Code of practice for the protection of buildings against water from the ground* on 100 mm minimum clean, inert hardcore.

## Figure 3.2 Suspended timber floor at external wall: Type A floor.
### (a) Joists parallel with wall
(Insulation not shown for clarity)
Note: Void between header and inner joist should be filled with insulation

### (b) Joists at right angles to wall

## Figure 3.3 Suspended timber floor at internal loadbearing wall: Type A floor.
### (a) Joists at right angles to wall (Insulation between blocking not shown for clarity)

### (b) Joists parallel with wall
(Insulation between double joists not shown for clarity)

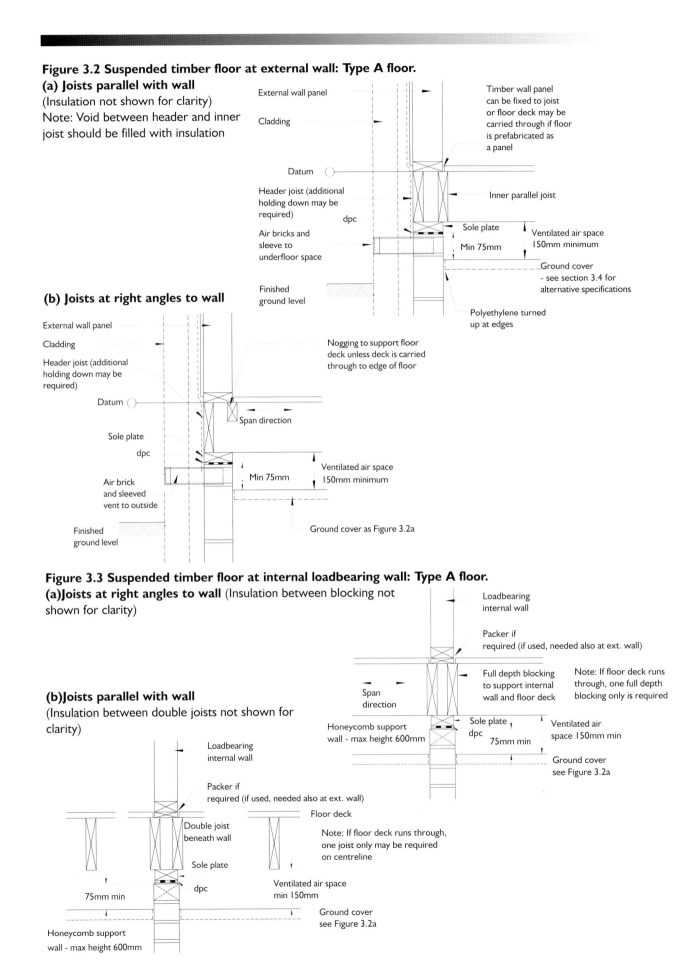

**Figure 3.4 Suspended timber floor at external wall: Type B floor; Joists supported on joist hangers**

**Figure 3.5 Suspended timber floor at internal loadbearing wall: Type B floor; Joists supported on joist hangers**

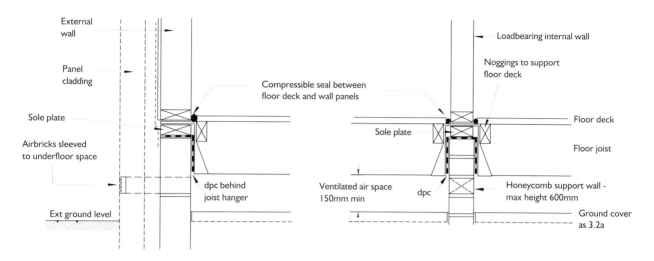

Detail at external wall

Detail at loadbearing internal wall

**Figure 3.6 Suspended timber floor at external wall: Type C floor; Joists supported on sleeper walls**

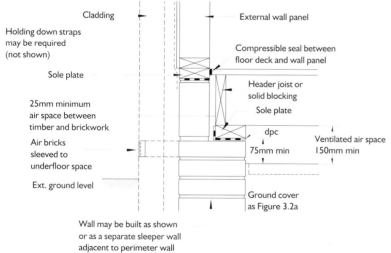

**Figure 3.7 Suspended timber floor at internal loadbearing wall: Type C floor; Joists supported on sleeper walls**
Note: Floor joist and deck must not run across sleeper walls at loadbearing internal walls since this would create increased differential movement

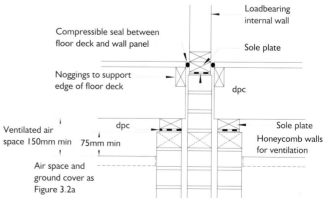

35

**Figure 3.8 Suspended timber floor at sleeper wall: Type C floor** (Insulation not shown for clarity)

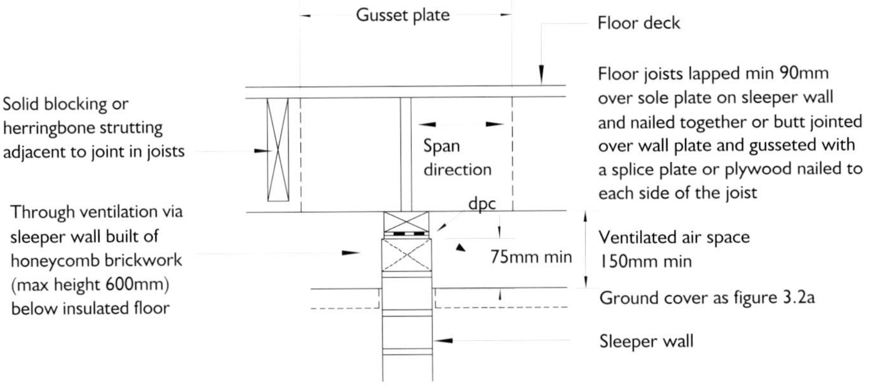

Gusset plate

Floor deck

Solid blocking or
herringbone strutting
adjacent to joint in joists

Span
direction

dpc

Through ventilation via
sleeper wall built of
honeycomb brickwork
(max height 600mm)
below insulated floor

75mm min

Floor joists lapped min 90mm
over sole plate on sleeper wall
and nailed together or butt jointed
over wall plate and gusseted with
a splice plate or plywood nailed to
each side of the joist

Ventilated air space
150mm min

Ground cover as figure 3.2a

Sleeper wall

To prevent water collecting on the ground cover, either the top surface of the ground cover (the polythene sheet when used in conjunction with sand or gravel) should be above the level of the surrounding ground or should fall to a drainage outlet above the lowest level of the adjoining ground.

It is essential that the void beneath the floor is adequately ventilated and that the ventilating air has a free path across the floor void. Ventilation should be the equivalent of 1500 mm$^2$ per metre run of two opposite sides of the floor or 500 mm$^2$ per m$^2$ of floor area, whichever is the greater. Vents should be not more than 450 mm from the corners and at maximum 2 m centres. The minimum dimensions between the top of the ground cover and the underside of the floor construction are shown in Figure 3.2.

A common method of insulating a timber floor is to support the insulation on galvanized wire, plastic mesh or a breather membrane sheeting which can be stapled to the sides of the joists to form a trough to accept the insulation. Other materials should not be used for support without first checking to establish whether there is a condensation risk due to the relatively high vapour resistance of the material compared with that of the decking.

Where floors are prefabricated as panels or where access is possible beneath the floor, mesh, breather membrane or impregnated softboard can be fixed to the underside of the joists to support the insulation, or rigid insulation can be fixed to the underside of the joists.

Rigid plastic insulation may also be supported by battens or clips fixed between the joists. This method requires care to ensure a tight fit with the joists since failure to do so can result in cold bridges at these points. This degree of accuracy is achievable in factory prefabrication but may not be possible on site where joist setting out is unlikely to be sufficiently accurate, and would require each piece of insulation to be cut to fit. The manufacturers of these materials offer guidance on suitable specifications.

Vapour control layers are not normally required in insulated timber suspended ground floors. It is preferable to allow water vapour to diffuse freely through the floor to be dispersed by the underfloor ventilation. Figure 3.9 illustrates typical floor insulation arrangements.

**Figure 3.9 Alternative methods of incorporating insulation in a suspended timber ground floor**

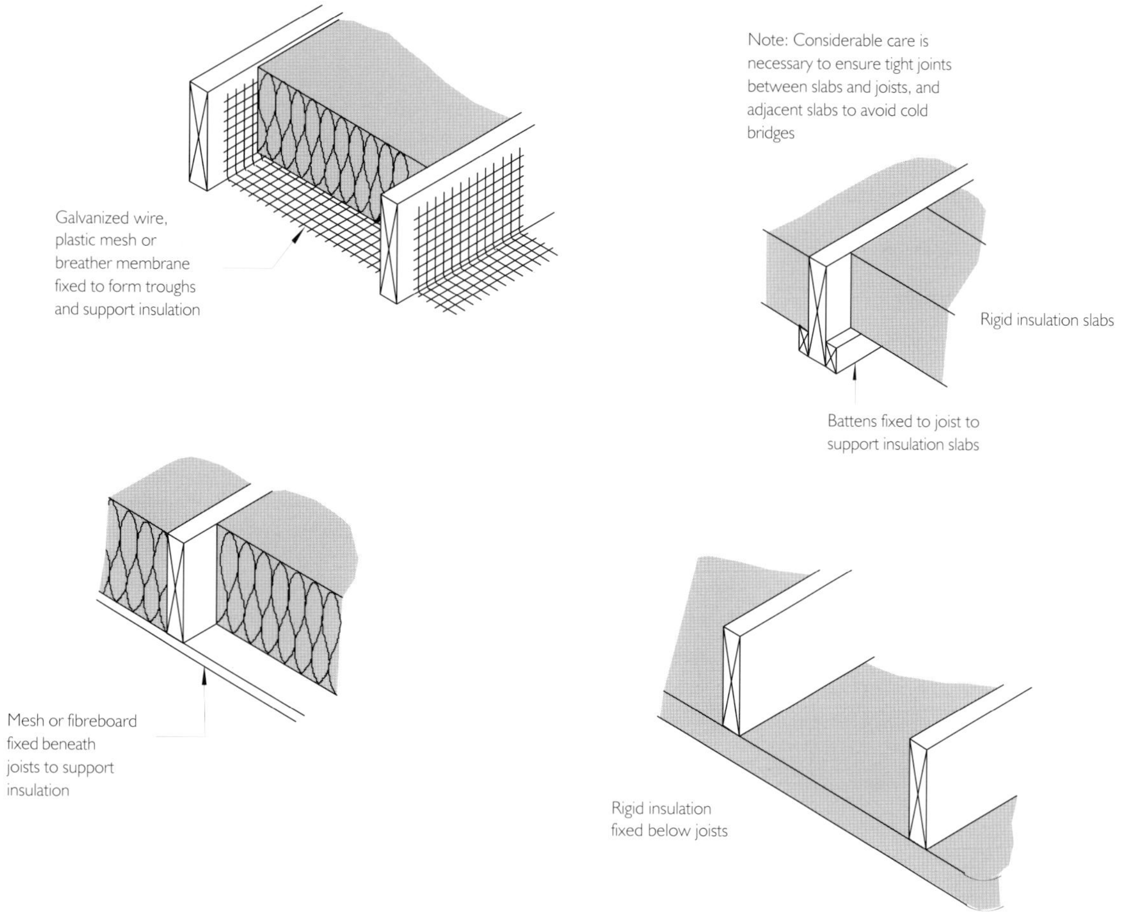

Galvanized wire, plastic mesh or breather membrane fixed to form troughs and support insulation

Note: Considerable care is necessary to ensure tight joints between slabs and joists, and adjacent slabs to avoid cold bridges

Rigid insulation slabs

Battens fixed to joist to support insulation slabs

Mesh or fibreboard fixed beneath joists to support insulation

Rigid insulation fixed below joists

## Timber joists

*BS 5268-2 The structural use of timber. Code of practice for permissible stress design, materials and workmanship* recommends that timber joists should be strength graded and installed at an average moisture content of not more than 20%.They should be marked with the strength grade and/or strength class and stamped DRY or KD (see Appendix 1). *BS 5268-5 Code of practice for the preservative treatment or structural timber* indicates that from a risk analysis, floor joists of a timber species classified as non-durable or better can be used without preservative treatment. The ground cover and ventilation provisions incorporated into the floor construction will normally ensure that moisture content of the timber remains below the decay threshold. However, treatment of non-durable species may be considered as an insurance.

Timber joist sizes may be selected from span tables in Building Regulations documents, *BS 8103-3 Structural design of low-rise buildings. Code of practice for timber floors and roofs for housing* or can be calculated in accordance with BS 5268-2.

Joints in joists should only occur over sleeper walls or walls supporting a loadbearing internal timber frame wall. Joists which overlap on sleeper or supporting walls should be nailed together and should not project more than 100 mm beyond the wall. Joists which are butt jointed over a sleeper or supporting wall should be joined mechanically to both sides of the joists using solid timber, plywood (to *BS EN 636-2 Plywood for use in humid conditions*) or OSB 3 or 4 (to *BS EN 300 Oriented strand boards. Definitions, classification and specifications*) gussets or galvanised or stainless steel proprietary nailed plates. The gussets or nail plates should extend to at least three quarters of the joist depth and be nailed with at least four 3 mm minimum diameter nails into each side of each joist, see Figure 3.8.

### Figure 3.10 Supporting non-loadbearing internal walls

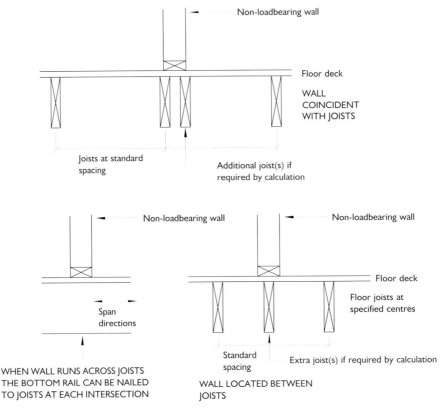

Where joists are required to support non-loadbearing internal walls, running either parallel to or across the joists, additional joists may be required or the joist span amended as required. See Figure 3.10 and Section 6.4 for further information.

The depth to breadth ratio of joists should be checked to ensure there is no risk of buckling under design load. BS 5268-2 recommends the maximum depth to breadth ratios shown in Table 3.2.

### TABLE 3.2 Maximum depth to breadth ratios

| Degree of lateral support | Max depth to breadth ratio of joist |
|---|---|
| Ends held in position and compression edge held in line by direct connection of sheathing, deck or joists | 5 |
| Ends held in position and compression edge held in line by direct connection of sheathing, deck or joists, together with adequate bridging or blocking spaced at intervals not exceeding 6 times the joist depth | 6 |
| Edges held in position and both edges held firmly in line | 7 |

Solid timber at least 38 mm thick and three-quarters the joist depth, timber herringbone strutting or proprietary struts can be used to provide the required lateral restraint.

Regardless of the depth to breadth ratio of the joists, they should be strutted using timber herringbone strutting, solid blocking or proprietary struts as shown in Table 3.3. Timber herringbone strutting should be at least 38 mm x 38 mm, solid blocking should be at least 38 mm thick and extend at least three quarters of the joist depth.

**TABLE 3.3 Strutting recommendations**

| Joist span (m) | Rows of strutting |
|---|---|
| up to 2.5 | none |
| 2.5 to 4.5 | One at mid span |
| over 4.5 | Two at 1/3 points |

Strutting between joists provides not only lateral restraint but stiffens floors against vibration. These strutting recommendations are the same as those for intermediate timber floors where the ceiling lining provides additional stiffness. Consideration should therefore be given to closer spacing of the strutting in longer span suspended timber ground floors to compensate for the absence of a plasterboard ceiling.

Notching and drilling of joists should comply with the limits given in Section 10.2, except where the sizes of notches and/or holes are calculated in accordance with BS 5268-2.

## 3.4.1 Decking for suspended timber floors

Designers must avoid supporting heavy internal wall loads by floor decking materials only. Guidance on the support of internal walls is given in Figure 3.10 and Section 6.4. Further information on timber and wood-based boards is given in Appendix 1.

### 3.4.1.1 Tongued and grooved boarding

Softwood timber boards for flooring should comply with *BS 1297 Specification for tongued and grooved softwood flooring*. It should not be fixed until the building is weathertight unless specific protection is provided. This is to avoid excessive increase in the moisture content of the boards, resulting in expansion problems and possibly later, a greater degree of shrinkage on drying out.

The moisture content of the boarding should not exceed 19% at the time of laying. In a normally heated building, the boards will eventually attain a moisture content of around 10%, so some shrinkage will be inevitable. Where the boarding is proposed as a decorative feature it should not be laid until the building is completed and has dried out and the moisture content of the boards should be 12% +/-2%. It may be preferable to install a structural floor to allow the decorative flooring to be added later.

For tongued and grooved boards, the finished face widths usually correspond to board thicknesses, eg a 16 mm finished thickness board usually has a face width of 65 mm; a 19 mm board a face width of 90 mm; and a 21 mm board a face width of 113 mm.

Table 3.4 gives recommended maximum joist centres for tongued and grooved floor boarding for domestic floor loadings.

**Table 3.4 Maximum spans for tongued and grooved floor boarding in domestic floors (1.5 kN/m$^2$).**

| Finished board thickness (mm) | Maximum span (centre to centre) (mm) |
| --- | --- |
| 16 | 500 |
| 19 | 600 |

Floor boards should be tightly butted together before nailing down and floor cramps are commonly used for this. Boards nailed down without cramping can result in excessive gaps between the boards when they dry to the equilibrium moisture content. Nail length is normally 2.5 times the board thickness and all nails should be punched below the level of the floor surface. Butt joints should be square and occur over joists with both boards adequately supported. Joints should be staggered so that they are at least two board widths apart and any board should span at least three joists.

### 3.4.1.2 Plywood floor decking

Plywood for flooring should be to *BS EN 636-2 Requirements for plywood for use in humid conditions* and should be one of the grades listed in BS 5268-2 for structural uses.

It is important to position plywood sheets in the correct direction for optimum panel strength, which is usually with the direction of the face grain at right angles to the joists. Some plywood is manufactured with the face grain at right angles to the shortest side, but for most, the face grain is parallel to the longest side. This determines whether the plywood long edge runs at right angles to, or parallel with, the joists.

Plywood for flooring is available as square edged or tongued and grooved edged sheets. Commonly only the long edges of the sheets have the tongued and grooved profile. Square edged sheets should be fully supported by joists or noggings at all edges. Tongued and grooved boards with square edged ends only need support at square edges and at the room perimeter. Supported ends should occur centrally over joists or noggings. Any cut sheet should span at least three joists.

The type of plywood specified will depend on the use required. Plywood which will form the finished surface (with a surface coating) should be sanded and have a better visual surface appearance than that to be covered. Where carpets, thin tiles or sheets are to be used, 'touch sanded tight faced' plywood should be specified, but where wood strips, blocks or other tiled finishes are to be used, an unsanded surface with lower face grades may be acceptable.

Table 3.5 gives recommended maximum spans for plywood flooring for domestic loadings.

**Table 3.5 Maximum spans for plywood flooring for domestic loadings (1.5 kN/m²).**

| | Maximum joist centres (mm) | |
| --- | --- | --- |
| | 450 | 600 |
| Plywood type | Required nominal thickness (mm) | |
| American construction and industrial plywood CD grade: Exterior : unsanded | 15 | 18 |
| American construction and industrial plywood CC grade: Exterior : unsanded | 15 | 18 |
| Canadian Douglas fir plywood Select tight face: Select and sheathing grades: unsanded | 15.5 | 15.5 |
| Canadian softwood plywood Select tight face: Select and sheathing grades: unsanded | 15.5 | 18.5 |
| Finnish birch faced plywood I/I, I/II etc, sanded | 15 | 18 |
| Finnish conifer plywood I/I, I/II etc, sanded | 15 | 18 |
| Swedish softwood plywood P30 grade: unsanded | 16 | 16 |

Tongued and grooved board joints should be pulled together (not cramped) before fixing and fixed with either screws or nails at the corners and at 150 mm maximum centres along edge supports and at 300 mm centres along intermediate supports. Fixings should be not closer than 8 mm to the board edge.

Nails should be improved/annular ring shank type. Nail length should be 2.5 times the board thickness and nail heads should be punched below the board surface.

Tongued and grooved board joints should be glued with a PVAC or similar adhesive and the joints between the joists and the boards should also be glued with PVAC to reduce the risk of creaking of the floor.

Where future access is required, eg by water authorities, purpose-designed screwed access panels should be provided.

### 3.4.1.3 Wood chipboard, oriented strand board and cement bonded particleboard floor decking

Flooring grade wood chipboard should be Type P5 or P7 in accordance with *BS EN 312-5 Particleboards – Specifications. Load bearing boards for use in humid conditions* and *BS EN 312-7 Heavy duty load bearing boards for use in humid conditions* respectively.

Oriented strand board (OSB) should be OSB 3 or OSB 4 manufactured in accordance with *BS EN 300 Oriented strand board.*

Cement bonded particleboard should comply with the requirements of *BS EN 634-2 Cement bonded particleboards. Specifications. Requirements for OPC bonded particleboards for use in dry, humid and exterior conditions.* Cement bonded particleboards tend to be used in specialist applications and supplied direct from the manufacturers. The manufacturer's recommendations for laying should be followed.

Guidance on the use of these board materials for flooring is included in *BS 7916 Code of practice for the selection and application of particleboard, oriented strand board (OSB), cement bonded particleboard and wood fibreboards for specific purposes.*

Flooring grades of chipboard are available with tongued and grooved edges on all four sides, or to the long edges only, or as square edged boards. OSB flooring is available with all edges tongued and grooved or square edged.

Chipboard has equal spanning capacity along and across the boards; OSB is stronger along the board than across the board. These characteristics affect the way in which the boards are laid over the supporting joists.

Tongued and grooved chipboard and OSB sheets are laid with long edges across the joists with the board ends located centrally on joists. Support is not necessary to the long edges except at perimeters of floors and to cut edges.

Square edged OSB is also laid across the joists and with the long edges supported by noggings between the joists.

Square edged chipboard is usually laid with the long edges on joists and the short edges supported by noggings between the joists.

All edges of square edged boards should be supported.

Both tongued and grooved and square edged boards should be laid with the end joints staggered. Any cut board should span at least three joists.

Table 3.6. gives the maximum recommended span when laid over joists or battens for domestic loadings.

**Table 3.6 Maximum spans for chipboard, OSB and cement bonded particleboard (Cbp) flooring for domestic loadings (1.5 kN/m$^2$)**

| Max joist centres (mm) | Minimum nominal thickness (mm) | | |
|---|---|---|---|
| | Wood chipboard | OSB | Cbp |
| 450 | 18 | 15 | 18 |
| 610 | 22 | 18 | 22 |

Boards should not be laid until the building is weatheright unless specific protection is provided, for example, by the use of boards pre-faced with protective film. Boards should be conditioned on site by laying them in place for at least 24 hours before fixing down. They should not be fixed to joists or noggings which have a moisture content greater than 20% as this can cause localised swelling. Board joints should be tightly pulled together before fixing and fixed along edge and intermediate supports with either screws or nails at board corners and at 300 mm centres. Fixings should be not less than 8 mm from the board edges.

Nails should be improved/annular ring shank type. Nail length should be 2.5 times the board thickness and nail heads should be punched below the board surface. Unless power nailing is used, cement bonded particleboard should be pre-drilled before nailing.

Tongued and grooved board joints should be glued with a PVAC or similar adhesive and the joints between the joists and the board should also be glued with PVAC to obviate possible creaking of the floor.

An expansion gap of at least 2 mm (divided between each end) per metre run of deck, or not less than 10 mm should be allowed between the decking and the perimeter wall in each room area. On large floor areas, board manufacturers may recommend intermediate expansion gaps.

Where future access is required, eg by water authorities, purpose-designed screwed access panels should be provided.

## 3.5 Concrete ground floors

Concrete ground floors for timber frame structures are generally similar to those used with other types of construction. They may be ground supported in situ concrete slabs or proprietary suspended concrete beam and block infill floors with either sand and cement screeds, or floating deck finish (See Section 3.5.1).

Figures 3.11 to 3.15 illustrate typical details for both in situ and suspended concrete floors.

The void beneath suspended concrete floors should be ventilated; the amount of ventilation is given by manufacturers. The minimum dimensions between the ground and the underside of the floor construction are shown in Figure 3.15.

The relatively light weight of a timber frame superstructure and its resistance to distortion when subjected to differential settlement make it especially suitable for sites with low ground bearing pressure when used with a reinforced concrete raft foundation or ground beams supported on piles.

The method of fixing down the timber frame superstructure and the slab edge detail are the only points where special details are required for timber frame, see Chapter 4.

**Figure 3.11 Concrete slab and screed with sub-slab insulation**

Note: A similar detail can be used with an insulated floating deck (as shown in Figure 3.12) when the sub-slab and edge insulation could be omitted.

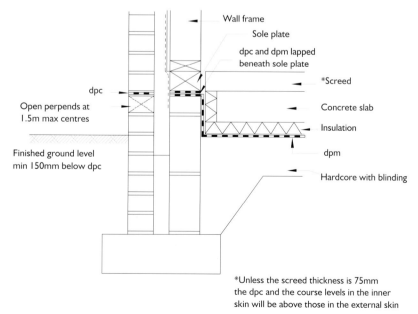

Wall frame
Sole plate
dpc and dpm lapped
beneath sole plate
*Screed
dpc
Open perpends at
1.5m max centres
Concrete slab
Insulation
Finished ground level
min 150mm below dpc
dpm
Hardcore with blinding

*Unless the screed thickness is 75mm
the dpc and the course levels in the inner
skin will be above those in the external skin

## Figure 3.12 Concrete slab and insulated floor deck

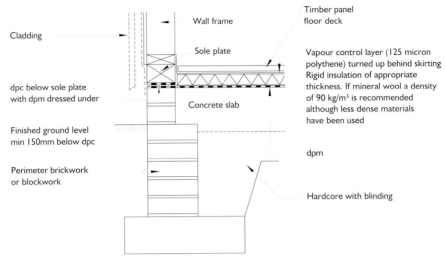

Cladding

Wall frame

Timber panel
floor deck

Sole plate

Vapour control layer (125 micron
polythene) turned up behind skirting
Rigid insulation of appropriate
thickness. If mineral wool a density
of 90 kg/m³ is recommended
although less dense materials
have been used

dpc below sole plate
with dpm dressed under

Concrete slab

Finished ground level
min 150mm below dpc

dpm

Perimeter brickwork
or blockwork

Hardcore with blinding

## Figure 3.13 Reinforced concrete raft with insulated floor deck. Note: When the slab edge is exposed, as in this detail, it is essential to use an insulated floor deck to avoid a cold bridge at the floor edge.

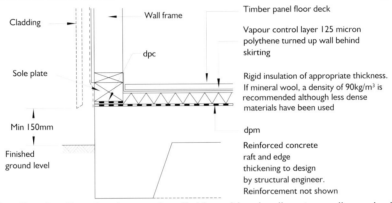

Cladding

Wall frame

Timber panel floor deck

Vapour control layer 125 micron
polythene turned up wall behind
skirting

dpc

Sole plate

Rigid insulation of appropriate thickness.
If mineral wool, a density of 90kg/m³ is
recommended although less dense
materials have been used

Min 150mm

dpm

Finished
ground level

Reinforced concrete
raft and edge
thickening to design
by structural engineer.
Reinforcement not shown

## Figure 3.14 Slab detail at loadbearing internal wall. Note: Non-loadbearing walls can be built directly from the concrete slab with a dpc beneath the sole plate (or bottom rail if no sole plate is used)

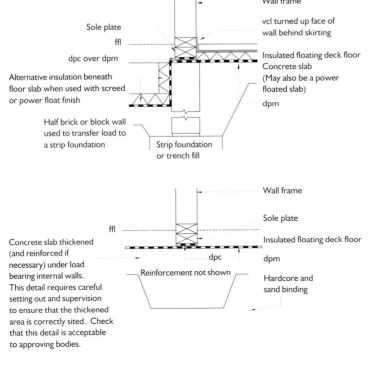

Sole plate

ffl

dpc over dpm

Alternative insulation beneath
floor slab when used with screed
or power float finish

Half brick or block wall
used to transfer load to
a strip foundation

Wall frame

vcl turned up face of
wall behind skirting

Insulated floating deck floor
Concrete slab
(May also be a power
floated slab)

dpm

Strip foundation
or trench fill

Wall frame

Sole plate

ffl

Insulated floating deck floor

Concrete slab thickened
(and reinforced if
necessary) under load
bearing internal walls.
This detail requires careful
setting out and supervision
to ensure that the thickened
area is correctly sited. Check
that this detail is acceptable
to approving bodies.

dpc

dpm

Reinforcement not shown

Hardcore and
sand binding

**Figure 3.15 Typical suspended beam and block ground floor.** Note: Precise details vary and manufacturer's recommendations should be checked

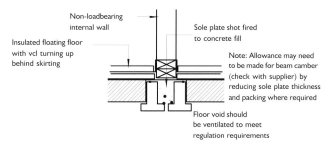

Non-loadbearing internal wall

Insulated floating floor with vcl turning up behind skirting

Sole plate shot fired to concrete fill

Note: Allowance may need to be made for beam camber (check with supplier) by reducing sole plate thickness and packing where required

Floor void should be ventilated to meet regulation requirements

Detail of support to non-loadbearing internal walls parallel to floor beams

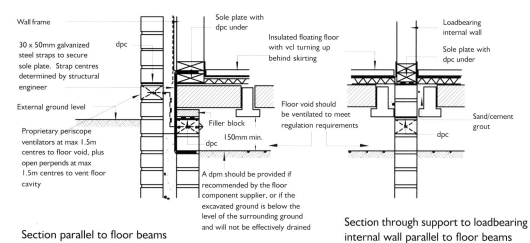

Wall frame

30 x 50mm galvanized steel straps to secure sole plate. Strap centres determined by structural engineer

External ground level

Proprietary periscope ventilators at max 1.5m centres to floor void, plus open perpends at max 1.5m centres to vent floor cavity

dpc

Sole plate with dpc under

Insulated floating floor with vcl turning up behind skirting

Filler block

150mm min.

dpc

A dpm should be provided if recommended by the floor component supplier, or if the excavated ground is below the level of the surrounding ground and will not be effectively drained

Floor void should be ventilated to meet regulation requirements

Loadbearing internal wall

Sole plate with dpc under

Sand/cement grout

dpc

**Section parallel to floor beams**

When floor block is built into wall as shown it must have sufficient compressive strength to carry the load from the superstructure to the foundations

**Section through support to loadbearing internal wall parallel to floor beams**

Thickness of brick/block wall may need to be increased if depth of floor void is greater than shown

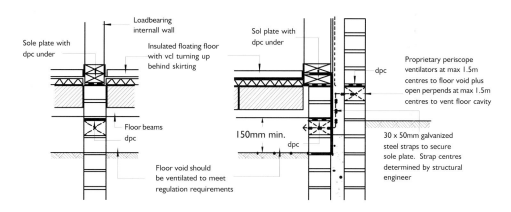

Sole plate with dpc under

Loadbearing internall wall

Insulated floating floor with vcl turning up behind skirting

Floor beams

dpc

Floor void should be ventilated to meet regulation requirements

Sol plate with dpc under

150mm min.

dpc

Proprietary periscope ventilators at max 1.5m centres to floor void plus open perpends at max 1.5m centres to vent floor cavity

dpc

30 x 50mm galvanized steel straps to secure sole plate. Strap centres determined by structural engineer

**Section through support to loadbearing internal wall at 90° to floor beams**

**Section at 90° to floor beams**

When brick or block infill is within external wall as shown, alternative methods of fixing the timber superstructure may be used. See Section 4.1.2

## 3.5.1 Floating ground floor decks

Floating ground floor decks are an alternative to using a screed if wet trades are to be minimised. A layer of rigid insulation is laid across the surface of the slab followed by a wood-based board material deck. The insulation should be of sufficient density to support the floor deck, especially at the edges. It provides insulation to the slab, reducing the overall heat loss of the building and obviates the need for edge insulation to avoid cold bridging. A number of companies produce proprietary composite boards combining the deck and the insulation specifically for this purpose.

When floating decks are used in conjunction with an in situ concrete floor it is important that the slab has sufficient time to dry out before the deck is applied. The damp proof membrane should be located on top of the concrete slab.

Floating floors can also be used with proprietary suspended precast concrete floors. When beam and block floors are used, the infilling blocks should be kept dry or allowed to dry out before the floating deck is laid.

With a layer of insulation being placed between the floor deck and the slab, with no means of ventilation, there is a risk of condensation occurring on the top surface of the slab. To obviate this, a vapour control layer should be laid over the layer of insulation. BS 7916 recommends 250 micron polythene with all joints lapped 150 mm and taped. The vcl should be turned up to just below skirting depth (minimum 38mm) around the perimeter of the floor, and fixed behind the skirting board.

Since it is important to prevent moisture penetrating floors of this type, consideration should be given to the provision of a waterproof floor finish and sealed upstand skirting in potentially wet areas such as bathrooms or utility rooms.

Common decking materials for floating ground floors are:

♦ Chipboard on continuous insulation support.
  Boards should be Type P5 or P7 to BS EN 312-5 and BS EN 312-7 respectively, 18 mm minimum thick, tongued and grooved with all joints glued.

♦ Plywood on continuous insulation support.
  Boards should be 15 mm minimum thick, to BS EN 636-2, tongued and grooved with all joints glued.
  (Note: BS 7916 does not recommend OSB as the floating overlay board on a continuously supported floating floor)

Both plywood and chipboard decks should be laid so that all end joints are staggered.

Loadbearing internal walls should be built directly off the structural floor and not off the floating deck. Internal non-loadbearing walls may be supported directly off the deck but the insulation must be of sufficient density to support the wall loads.

Movement of the floor deck should be allowed for by the provision of a gap, which will normally be covered by the skirting, between the edge of the deck and the perimeter wall or other abutment. This should be at least 10 mm or not less than 2 mm (divided between each end) per metre run of deck. On large floor areas, manufacturers may recommend intermediate expansion gaps.

## 3.6 Accessible thresholds

UK Building Regulations require that there is at least one entrance to all new buildings which is accessible to disabled people; either wheelchair users or ambulant disabled people. This can be provided with designed step access where wheelchair users are assisted but it is preferable to provide a notionally level threshold whereby unassisted disabled access is possible. Figures 3.16 – 3.18 show accessible threshold details for suspended timber floors, concrete slab on ground and suspended concrete floors. These details apply only at the entrance and ramped access up to this threshold will be required.

Additional information and details are available in the *DETR booklet Accessible thresholds in new housing*.

### Figure 3.16 Level threshold: Suspended timber floor with ramped access

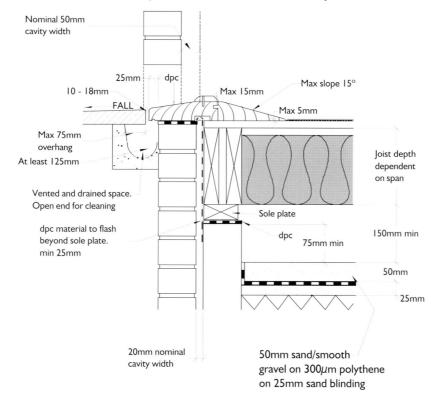

Nominal 50mm cavity width

25mm  dpc

10 - 18mm

Max 15mm

Max slope 15°

FALL

Max 5mm

Max 75mm overhang

At least 125mm

Joist depth dependent on span

Vented and drained space. Open end for cleaning

Sole plate

dpc material to flash beyond sole plate. min 25mm

dpc

75mm min

150mm min

50mm

25mm

20mm nominal cavity width

50mm sand/smooth gravel on 300$\mu$m polythene on 25mm sand blinding

**Figure 3.17 Level threshold: Concrete slab floor**

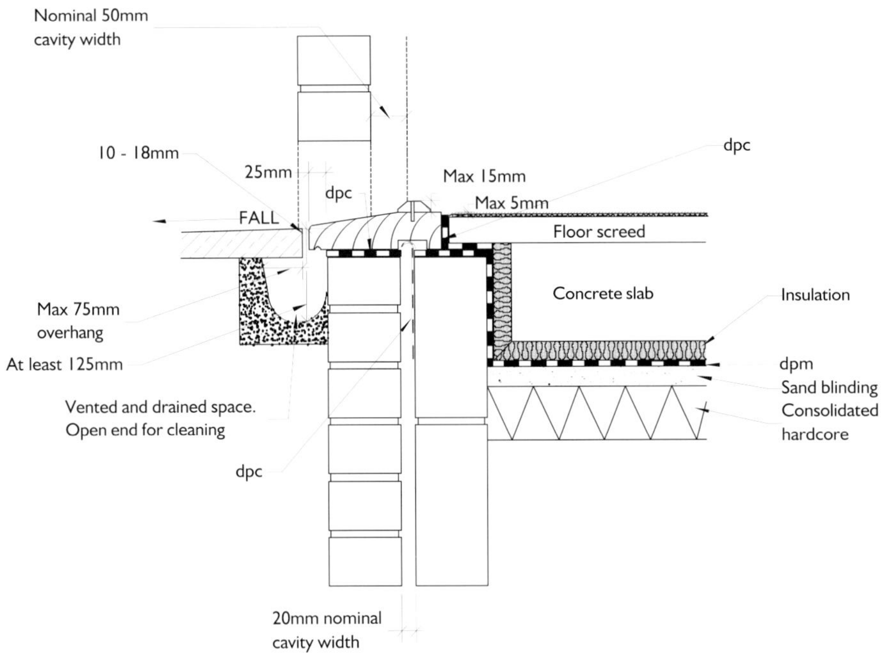

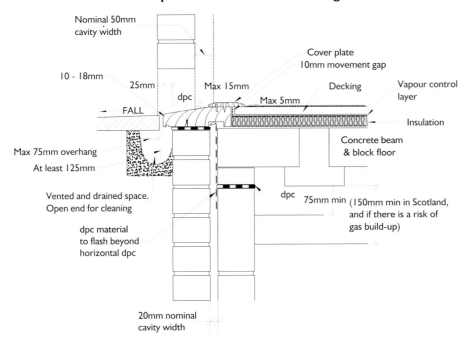

Nominal 50mm
cavity width

10 - 18mm

25mm

dpc

FALL

Max 15mm

Max 5mm

Floor screed

dpc

Concrete slab

Insulation

Max 75mm
overhang

At least 125mm

Vented and drained space.
Open end for cleaning

dpc

dpm
Sand blinding
Consolidated
hardcore

20mm nominal
cavity width

**Figure 3.18 Level threshold: Suspended concrete floor/ floating floor**

Nominal 50mm
cavity width

Cover plate
10mm movement gap

10 - 18mm

25mm

dpc

FALL

Max 15mm

Max 5mm

Decking

Vapour control
layer

Insulation

Max 75mm overhang

At least 125mm

Concrete beam
& block floor

Vented and drained space.
Open end for cleaning

dpc

75mm min (150mm min in Scotland,
and if there is a risk of
gas build-up)

dpc material
to flash beyond
horizontal dpc

20mm nominal
cavity width

# 4 Walls

## 4.1 External walls

### 4.1.1 Design requirements

Timber framed external walls are required to carry the dead and imposed loads (including wind loads) acting on the structure and transmit them to the foundations. The structural design should be in accordance with *BS 5268-2 The structural use of timber. Permissible stress design, materials and workmanship* and *BS 5268-6 Section 6.1 Code of practice for timber framed walls. Dwellings not exceeding four storeys.* For buildings of five storeys or more, the disproportionate collapse requirements of National Building Regulations need to be met.

External walls are required to have thermal performance levels (insulation and air-sealing) to meet the requirements of the Building Regulations.

Durability is an essential requirement and the walls also need to provide support for the cladding materials to be used.

External walls are required to have appropriate fire resistance and internal surface spread of flame (reaction to fire) characteristics see Section 1.3.2. Fire resistance requirements always relate to resistance from within the structure. When the building is within one metre of the relevant boundary, there are also requirements for external fire resistance and surface spread of flame (reaction to fire) characteristics. Full details are given in National Building Regulations.

The periods of fire resistance required vary depending upon the building's purpose group and height. National Building Regulations differ in detail and should be checked for specific requirements. Loadbearing walls must have equal fire resistance to the floors that they support.

As the timber frame shell will be erected quickly and construction work will continue internally whilst (or before) the external cladding is applied, the timber frame external walls should provide a weather resistant shell prior to the cladding being installed.

Housing warranty and guarantee authorities have specific requirements for aspects such as sheathing materials, breather membranes and the preservative treatment of external wall framing.

In addition to meeting the Design Requirements, the successful completion and quality of the timber frame building is dependent on good on-site practice in terms of accuracy in setting out and erecting components. Guidance is given in Appendix 3 Site Supervisor's Checklist.

## 4.1.2 External wall construction

The external wall consists of two parts:

♦ the loadbearing timber frame wall

♦ the outer cladding. This may be a heavyweight cladding, supported independently by the foundations, or a lightweight cladding attached to the timber frame.

This section deals with the loadbearing timber frame wall and its components. The outer cladding is covered in detail in Chapter 9 'Cladding'. Figure 4.1 shows a typical timber frame external wall with a brick outer cladding.

### Figure 4.1 Typical externally sheathed wall with brick cladding

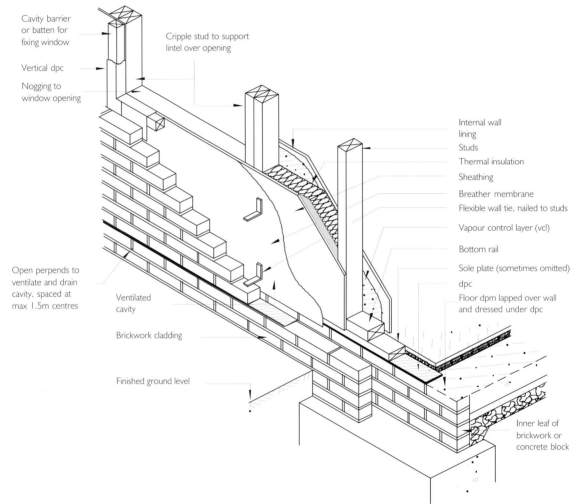

Cavity barrier or batten for fixing window

Vertical dpc

Nogging to window opening

Cripple stud to support lintel over opening

Internal wall lining
Studs
Thermal insulation
Sheathing
Breather membrane
Flexible wall tie, nailed to studs
Vapour control layer (vcl)
Bottom rail
Sole plate (sometimes omitted)
dpc
Floor dpm lapped over wall and dressed under dpc

Open perpends to ventilate and drain cavity, spaced at max 1.5m centres

Ventilated cavity

Brickwork cladding

Finished ground level

Inner leaf of brickwork or concrete block

### 4.1.2.1 Sole plate

The sole plate (see Figure 4.2):

♦ provides a level and accurately positioned base on which the superstructure will be fixed, including the floor in the case of suspended timber ground floors

♦ provides a nailing plate for the timber panels, or ground floor joists

♦ secures and protects the dpc.

**Figure 4.2 Bedding of sole plate**

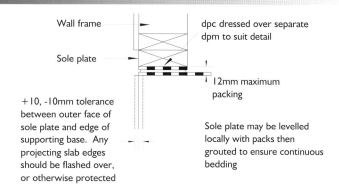

Wall frame

Sole plate

dpc dressed over separate dpm to suit detail

12mm maximum packing

Sole plate may be levelled locally with packs then grouted to ensure continuous bedding

+10, -10mm tolerance between outer face of sole plate and edge of supporting base. Any projecting slab edges should be flashed over, or otherwise protected

Sole plates are usually treated with preservative generally using water-borne treatments eg pressure impregnated CCA and less commonly, boron salts, double vacuum organic solvent treatment or water-based micro-emulsions. Where the sole plate is located below the upper surface of the screed or concrete slab, the use of vacuum pressure CCA treatment is recommended unless the dpc wraps up to protect the side face.

When a concrete slab is used in conjunction with insulation and a chipboard or plywood deck, the sole plate thickness may be determined by the combined thickness of insulation and decking material in order to keep the bottom rail of the wall panel above finished floor level and to allow for fixing the internal wall lining.

Sole plate fixings serve two purposes; to locate the plates accurately during construction to enable them to be used as an accurate jig for setting out the superstructure and to transfer wind loads to the foundations once the building is completed.

Sole plates may be fixed by shot-firing through the timber into a concrete slab through the dpc (Figure 4.3a). Many years of use in the UK and abroad have shown that no problems are caused by the small perforations from shot-fired pins since the dpc forms a satisfactory gasket around the nail. If larger diameter fixings, such as cast in bolts are used, a bituminised felt washer around the bolt should be used to seal the hole in the dpc.

An alternative solution is to use proprietary stainless steel sole plate fixing shoes (Figure 4.3b). These avoid nailing through the dpc and also move the fixing position away from the edge of a concrete slab, reducing the risk of spalling the concrete. Sole plates may also be fixed to a brickwork substructure using stainless steel straps (Figure 4.4a).

**Figure 4.3 Typical sole plate fixing to concrete slab/ edge beam:**
**(a) using nails (also suitable for nailable bricks)          (b) using shoes**

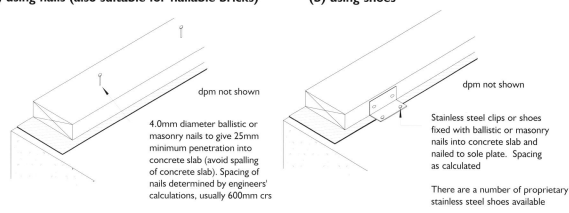

dpm not shown

4.0mm diameter ballistic or masonry nails to give 25mm minimum penetration into concrete slab (avoid spalling of concrete slab). Spacing of nails determined by engineers' calculations, usually 600mm crs

dpm not shown

Stainless steel clips or shoes fixed with ballistic or masonry nails into concrete slab and nailed to sole plate. Spacing as calculated

There are a number of proprietary stainless steel shoes available

In exposed localities or unusual design conditions, sole plates can be fixed with expanding bolts fitted into holes drilled through the timber into the concrete. Alternatively, sole plates can be temporarily fixed prior to the erection of the ground floor panels and holding down straps fixed to the wall panel studs and built into the masonry outer leaf as shown in Figure 4.4b.

**Figure 4.4 (a, left) Typical sole plate fixing to brick/block foundation walls using straps**

**Figure 4.4 (b, right) Holding down straps fixed to studs and built into external masonry cladding**

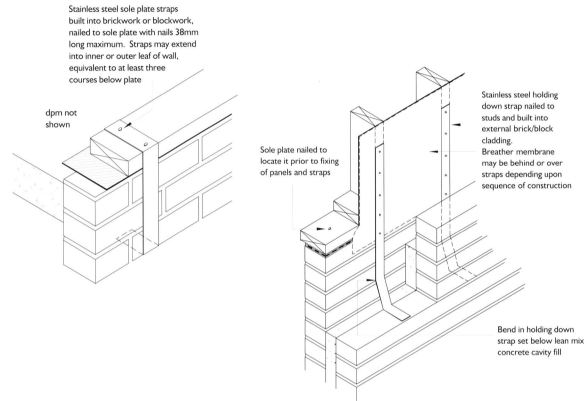

Stainless steel sole plate straps built into brickwork or blockwork, nailed to sole plate with nails 38mm long maximum.  Straps may extend into inner or outer leaf of wall, equivalent to at least three courses below plate

dpm not shown

Sole plate nailed to locate it prior to fixing of panels and straps

Stainless steel holding down strap nailed to studs and built into external brick/block cladding. Breather membrane may be behind or over straps depending upon sequence of construction

Bend in holding down strap set below lean mix concrete cavity fill

It is possible to omit the sole plate, (except when using a concrete ground floor with a screed) but all of its functions should then be performed by the bottom rail of the wall panels which are usually preservative treated to the same specification as a separate sole plate. Sole plate omission also makes the accurate location and fixing of the wall panels more difficult and the dpc becomes more vulnerable to accidental damage. Greater precision is also required in forming the base on which the panels sit, as local levelling is more difficult (see Appendix 3). The bottom rail of the panel may need to be increased in thickness in order to extend sufficiently above the top of the floor finish when a floating floor is used. Alternatively, an additional framing member may be inserted between studs to provide adequate bottom fixing for the lining material (see Figure 4.5).

**Figure 4.5 Detail at bottom of wall panel with noggings to provide fixing for internal wall linings**
* as an alternative solution, the thickness of the sole plate can be increased

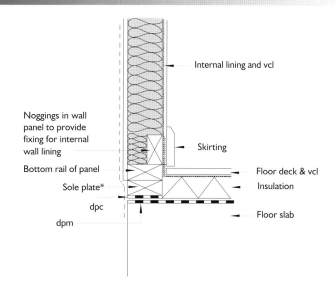

Internal lining and vcl

Noggings in wall panel to provide fixing for internal wall lining

Skirting

Bottom rail of panel

Sole plate*

dpc

dpm

Floor deck & vcl

Insulation

Floor slab

## 4.1.2.2 Stud framing

The stud framework is the vertical loadbearing skeleton of the external wall. Studs are usually placed at 400 or 600 mm centres, depending upon preference or, in specific cases, on the loads they are required to transmit. The studs:

♦ transmit vertical dead and imposed loads from the top of the wall to the bottom rail/ sole plate and ultimately to the foundations

♦ contribute to resisting wind loads on the wall

♦ provide a framework for fixing sheathing, internal linings, wall ties etc.

All loadbearing studs and rails must be of strength graded timber, the species, structural grade and size depending upon the combined vertical and wind loading. Structural calculations should be based on BS 5268-2. Detailed information on the methods for calculating the wind (racking) resistance of timber frame walls is included in BS 5268-6.

The top and bottom rails of the panel are normally of the same section as the studs and are fixed to the studs by two nails at each joint (Figure 4.6). They provide the required top and bottom fixings for wall sheathing and lining boards.

**Figure 4.6 Typical fixing of top and bottom rails to studs**

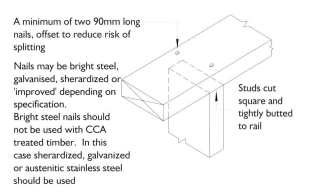

A minimum of two 90mm long nails, offset to reduce risk of splitting

Nails may be bright steel, galvanised, sherardized or 'improved' depending on specification.
Bright steel nails should not be used with CCA treated timber.  In this case sherardized, galvanized or austenitic stainless steel should be used

Studs cut square and tightly butted to rail

**TABLE 4.1 Typical sizes for sole plates\*, studs, rails and binders**

| Finished size | 72 x 47, 44, 38\*\* mm |
| --- | --- |
| | 97 x 75, 63, 47, 44, 38\*\* mm |
| | 122 x 75, 63, 47, 44, 38\*\* |
| | 145 x 75, 63, 47, 44, 38\*\* |
| | 170 x 75, 63, 47, 44, 38\*\* |
| **Surfaced sizes** (ALS/CLS) | 89 x 38 |
| | 114 x 38 |
| | 140 x 38 |
| | 184 x 38 |

\*  Sole plate thickness may need to be increased to 63 mm or 75 mm in some instances, see section 4.1.2.1
\*\* Surfacing to less than 37 mm thickness is not acceptable

Sizes for structural timber are defined in a National Annex to *BS EN 336 Structural timber – Coniferous and poplar. Sizes – Permissible deviations*. Further details are included in Appendix 1.

If a single top rail is used without an additional head binder, vertical point loads from joists or rafters should occur over the studs or may be offset from the centre line of the stud as shown in Figure 6.6. A double rail, ie top rail and head binder (Figure 4.7) allows normal loads from floor joists or rafters to occur between studs. Abnormal loads from trimmers, purlins or beams, or from long span trusses cannot always be supported in this way and extra studs may have to be inserted under such members, see Section 4.1.2.10.

**Figure 4.7 Head binder to panel junction (sheathing to frames not shown)**

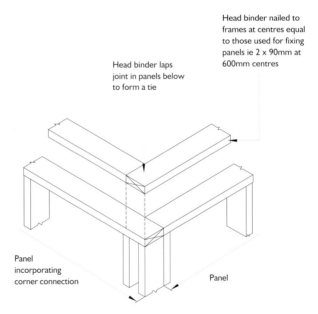

Head binder nailed to frames at centres equal to those used for fixing panels ie 2 x 90mm at 600mm centres

Head binder laps joint in panels below to form a tie

Panel incorporating corner connection

Panel

Although there are many examples of timber frame buildings in the UK, Scandinavia and North America where the wall framing has not been preservative treated with no adverse effect, *BS 5268-5 Code of practice for the preservative treatment of structural timber* includes external wall framing in risk category 2C (where the risk of fungal decay is low but where remedial work would be difficult and expensive). Treatment is considered optional or desirable and so the timber would commonly be treated. Treatment is generally with water-borne preservatives eg pressure impregnated CCA or boron salts; with double vacuum organic solvents or with water-based micro-emulsions. The latter two methods are usually preferred since the timber does not require redrying to an acceptable moisture content after treatment.

### 4.1.2.3 Noggings

Noggings are used in wall panels:

♦ to provide support for internal walls and/or plasterboard sheet edges occurring off the structural grid

♦ to minimise buckling of studs in heavily loaded unsheathed or unlined panels

♦ to provide fixing points for fittings and fixtures, including radiators, cupboard fittings and socket outlet boxes where these occur away from studs.

Noggings can be either site fixed or fixed in the factory. Where a variety of different types and heights of noggings are necessary, it is usually easier to fix these once the panels are in place on site. If the internal wall linings are factory fixed then noggings would also be factory fitted.

### 4.1.2.4 External sheathing

Figure 4.8 shows a typical externally sheathed wall panel.

The sheathing:

♦ provides the necessary panel stiffness to resist lateral (racking) forces due to wind loads (some materials, eg impregnated softboard may not provide full racking resistance on their own in all cases).

**Figure 4.8 Typical externally sheathed wall panel**

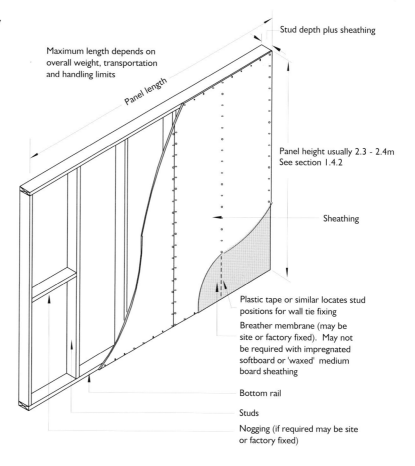

Stud depth plus sheathing

Maximum length depends on overall weight, transportation and handling limits

Panel length

Panel height usually 2.3 - 2.4m See section 1.4.2

Sheathing

Plastic tape or similar locates stud positions for wall tie fixing

Breather membrane (may be site or factory fixed). May not be required with impregnated softboard or 'waxed' medium board sheathing

Bottom rail

Studs

Nogging (if required may be site or factory fixed)

The internal lining material will normally also contribute to racking resistance

♦ reduces wind penetration of the structure and contributes to sealing against air movement from within the building

♦ enables rapid enclosure of the structure (with breather membrane fitted where necessary) before claddings are applied (ie weather-proofing and security)

♦ encloses and supports the insulation

♦ reduces the risk of damage or distortion of the panels prior to fixing

♦ provides a solid background for fixing breather membranes, cavity barriers, flashings etc.

Materials commonly used for sheathing are sheathing grade plywood, oriented strand board (OSB), medium board and impregnated softboard. Other materials such as tempered hardboard, moisture resistant chipboard and cement-bonded particleboard have also been used.

When considering a sheet material for sheathing, the following performance criteria should be considered:

♦ evidence of racking strength for calculation purposes derived from testing to the method in BS 5268-6.1

♦ evidence of durability in use

♦ vapour resistance should be significantly less than the combined resistance of the internal lining and vapour control layer - a factor of 1 to 5 is generally taken as an acceptable rule of thumb

♦ resistance to site and transport damage (impact damage)

♦ resistance to damage from wetting and rain penetration during erection

♦ availability in the required grade and suitable sheet sizes

♦ ease of cutting and fixing.

Plywood for sheathing should comply with BS EN 636-2, be one of those listed in BS 5268-2 and should be subject to third party quality assurance by one of the bodies included in BS 5268-2.

8 - 10 mm thick plywood is normally used for timber frame sheathing. The specific type will vary depending on the country of origin; the following types are those most frequently specified; they should be clearly marked with the relevant grade.

Plywoods included in BS 5268-2: 1996 are

♦ Unsanded Douglas fir Exterior Sheathing Grade C-C to CSA 0121 M1978 Standard

♦ Unsanded CSP (Canadian Softwood Plywood) SHG Sheathing Grade E-C to CSA 0151 - M1978 Standard

♦ American Plywood C-C Exterior bonded CCX or C-D Exterior CDX to US Product Standard PS 1.95

♦ Swedish Softwood Plywood Grade P30 or better.

Oriented strand board OSB 3 or OSB 4 should comply with BS EN 300. Typical OSB sheet thicknesses for sheathing are 8, 9 and 11 mm.

Impregnated softboards Type SB.HLS to BS EN 622-4 have less resistance to impact and racking loads than plywood or OSB but are generally more vapour permeable. The boards are most commonly impregnated with a bitumen emulsion which improves the adhesion of the fibres and reduces water absorption if the boards get wet. Boards are also available with an additional sprayed coating of bitumen on one face, which significantly increases the vapour resistance. 12 mm thick boards are normally used for timber frame sheathing. A breather membrane is not usually required with these sheathing boards (except in very exposed locations) but the joints between wall panels are sometimes sealed to increase weathertightness.

Tempered hardboard Type HB.HLA2 to BS EN 622-2 and Mediumboard Type MBH.HLS1 and MBH.HLS2 to BS EN 622-3 have good resistance to racking and impact forces and low vapour permeability. A breather membrane is normally required with these boards but certain 'waxed' medium boards can be used without a membrane.

Plywood, OSB, mediumboard, and hardboard sheathing is normally fixed to the stud framing by nailing at 150 mm centres along board perimeters and at 300 mm centres to intermediate studs with corrosion resistant nails approximately 50 mm in length. Impregnated softboard normally requires closer centres, commonly 75 mm spacing at board perimeters and 150 mm elsewhere.

Whilst the nailing pattern for the relevant sheathing material given above is common, it must be determined by calculation or testing in accordance with BS 5268-6. Enhanced racking values may be obtained for sheathed panels when nailed at closer centres and/or by using thicker sheathing material.

### 4.1.2.5 Vapour control layers

In common with all building structures, it is necessary to ensure that under normal conditions, surface mould on walls and condensation within the construction are avoided. In timber frame walls, thermal insulation is packed between studs, maintaining internal surface temperatures above dewpoint level and thus avoiding surface condensation.

To avoid the risk of harmful condensation within a wall with external sheathing, a vapour control layer (vcl) is fixed between the inner wall surface, eg plasterboard, and the warm side of the thermal insulation. This may be a separate membrane or combined with the wall lining, its function being to control the amount of water vapour passing through the wall due to different internal and external vapour pressure levels. Materials commonly used as vapour control layers include:

- 125 micron polythene sheet (Reconstituted polythene should only be used if it has been independently assessed for this purpose)

- Vapour control plasterboard comprising a metallised polyester film bonded to the back face of a plasterboard sheet.

As a guide, harmful condensation will not occur in timber frame walls when the vapour resistances of materials on the warm side of the insulation are at least five times greater than those on the cold side of the insulation. If this rule is not met then a calculation of wall condensation risk will be required. The vapour resistivity values of some common wall materials are shown in Appendix 2.

Sheet membranes should overlap at studs by approximately 100 mm and any horizontal joints should be taped or sealed. Tears should be repaired and holes formed tightly around service connections. Services passing through vcls should be sealed. If a sheet gets seriously damaged it should be removed and replaced. Vcls should be carefully cut and dressed into door and window reveals, should overlap similar vcls in insulated ground floors, and be folded and extended into ceilings by a minimum of 75 mm.

Calculations assume an imperforate vcl which may not always be possible. Test evidence under a wide range of conditions shows that under normal circumstances, harmful condensation is unlikely to occur within the wall as a result of small tears or perforations, although every effort should be made to locate and repair these to increase the safety margin.

When services are concentrated on external walls (see also Chapter 10), perforating the vcl can be avoided by battening the internal lining away from the wall studs and forming a service zone on the warm side of the vcl (see Figure 10.4). The cost of labour and additional material may be partly offset by the time saved in resealing service joints. However, consideration should be given to the normal sequence of construction, since it is common practice for the services first fix to be done before vcls are fitted. To avoid the subjective feeling of 'hollow construction', it is recommended that the service cavity is filled with insulation.

In adopting this approach the performance requirements of the wall, eg fire resistance, must be maintained. It is therefore important to ensure that the lining material is supported by the battens in compliance with the manufacturer's instructions to satisfy the fire resistance requirements.

### 4.1.2.6 Breather membranes

It is normal practice to cover the outer face of the wall panels with a breather membrane (except for impregnated softboard and some medium board sheathed panels when it may only be required in very exposed locations). The breather membrane is usually fixed to the panels in the factory with the necessary laps to cover the joints but it may be applied on site as soon as the shell of the building is erected. Its primary function is to protect and weatherproof the building until the cladding is completed but, in the preferred option of factory fixing, it provides important protection to panels during transport and erection. It also provides a second line of defence against any wind driven rain that may penetrate the cladding during the life of the building. The breather membrane may also contribute to air sealing the wall and reducing ventilation heat losses.

Breather membranes need to combine a high degree of wet strength and water resistance with very low vapour resistance. A maximum vapour resistance value of 0.6 MNs/g is required but commonly available membranes are well below this. It is recommended that high performance breather membranes: Type 1 to *BS 4016 Specification for flexible building membranes (breather type)* are specified in all cases.

The breather membrane is normally fixed to the sheathing with stainless steel staples. A reinforcing tape is frequently used which both strengthens the fixing and identifies the position of the studs in the wall panel to simplify the subsequent fixing of brick ties or battens for other claddings. If reinforcing tape is not used, the stud positions should be identified in some other way. Staple fixings should be at 300 mm centres at stud positions and 150 mm centres around openings, at eaves, at the top and bottom of panels and at membrane joints.

Breather membranes should be fitted from the sole plate or bottom rail upwards so that the upper membrane overlaps the lower to prevent water which may run down the wall face from running behind the membrane. Horizontal laps should be at least 100 mm and vertical laps 150 mm (Figure 4.9). Breather membranes should extend at least 25 mm below the lowest timber member in the wall (usually the sole plate), lap over the dpc at the bottom of walls, heads of openings and under dpcs at jambs and sills.

When a breather membrane is not required, it is common practice in severe exposure locations, to tape or seal the wall panel joints to enhance the weather resistance of the junctions.

**Figure 4.9 Horizontal and vertical joints in breather membrane**

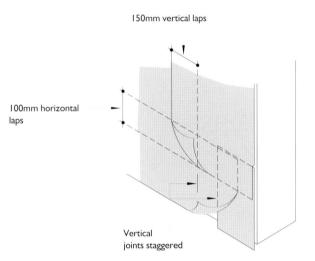

150mm vertical laps

100mm horizontal laps

Vertical joints staggered

### 4.1.2.7 Thermal insulation

The most common types of thermal insulation in timber frame construction are:

♦ mineral wool (glass or rock) fitted in the voids between studs. This can be in the form of rolled quilts or semi-rigid batts. Rolled material may need to be stapled to the studs to hold it in place. Semi-rigid batts can be friction fitted without stapling

♦ blown cellulose fibre.

As statutory requirements for levels of thermal insulation continue to increase, designers may specify rigid foam insulation materials between studs to minimize the stud depth and reduce overall wall thickness. If this option is selected, care is required to cut the rigid insulation accurately to fit each stud cavity. Any gaps can result in cold bridges with potential for surface condensation.

The area between studs should be completely filled with insulation to avoid cold areas. Although insulation is incorporated primarily to reduce heat loss, it also contributes towards airborne sound insulation and to the fire resistance of the external wall.

The thermal conductivity values of the most common types of insulation are included in Appendix 2.

Heat losses through components can be compared by their U values; the higher the U value, the greater the loss of heat through the material; ie the lower the number, the better the insulation.

Table 4.2 shows values which have been adjusted to take account of the solid timber element of the walls. The insulation material is such a dominant part of the wall's thermal performance that varying the specification of sheathing, lining and cladding materials makes little difference to the overall wall U value.

## TABLE 4.2 Typical wall U values

Note: the figures are based on generic thermal conductivity values, see Appendix 2 for more information. For individual products, manufacturers' data may give more precise values

| Mineral wool or cellulose fibre insulation (mm) | U value W/m$^2$ K (15% frame) | Rigid foam insulation (mm) with $\lambda$ not greater than 0.02 W/m K | U value W/m$^2$ K (15% frame) |
|---|---|---|---|
| | | 70 (with reflective cavity) | 0.30 |
| 90 | 0.42 | 90 | 0.27 |
| 97 | 0.39 | 97 | 0.26 |
| 122 | 0.33 | 122 | 0.22 |
| 140 | 0.30 | 140 | 0.19 |
| 170 | 0.25 | 170 | 0.16 |

In conventional timber frame walls the maximum thickness of insulation is controlled by the stud dimensions. It is normal practice to fill the full depth of the stud cavity with insulation, providing thermal performance beyond the minimum requirements of the regulations without affecting costs significantly. There is no advantage in compressing a quilt into a cavity since the effective thermal insulation would be only equal to the compressed thickness and could cause bowing of the internal linings.

When increased thicknesses of insulation are required it is either necessary to use deeper studs in the wall frame or to fix battens to the internal or external face of the walls to obtain increased wall thickness. The use of low conductivity rigid foams can reduce the need to increase the stud depth. If a service zone is provided on the internal face of the wall, this should be sealed at its perimeters to prevent air currents within the zone partially negating the wall insulation. An alternative and the recommended solution is to fill the service zone with insulation (see Figure 10.4) thereby increasing the overall insulation value of the wall.

Very energy efficient buildings can be achieved with timber frame and it may be possible to recoup at least part of the increased insulation cost by reducing heating plant costs.

There are alternatives to installing insulation between studs; further information is included in Section 4.4.

Sealed unit double glazing will improve the overall energy performance of the building, reduce the incidence of condensation on windows and give increased comfort to users of the building. The use of low emissivity coated insulating glass offers a further method of improving the performance of double glazed windows. Glazed panel doors typically have a similar U value to windows. A 44 mm solid timber door will have a U value of approximately 2.0 W/m$^2$K. Insulated doors can achieve U values in the region of 0.5 W/m$^2$K. Table 4.3 illustrates typical window U values.

**Table 4.3 Typical U values for windows**

| Window | U value (W/m$^2$K) |
|---|---|
| Double glazed (20 mm units) | 2.6 |
| Triple glazed | 2.0 |
| Double glazed with low emissivity glass | 1.9 |

### 4.1.2.8 Forming openings

Openings in loadbearing wall panels should include a timber lintel at the head of the opening to transmit loads to the flanking studs and cripple studs. The number of cripple studs required depends on the size of the opening and on the load being carried by the lintel (see Figure 4.10a). The only situation where no lintel is required is when there is no vertical load (including cladding load) applied to the head of the panel (Figure 4.10b).

**Figure 4.10 a
Openings
requiring lintels**

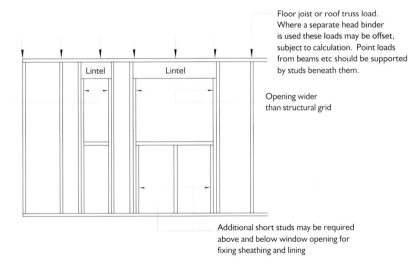

Opening located across structural grid

Lintel

Lintel

Floor joist or roof truss load. Where a separate head binder is used these loads may be offset, subject to calculation. Point loads from beams etc should be supported by studs beneath them.

Opening wider than structural grid

Additional short studs may be required above and below window opening for fixing sheathing and lining

**Figure 4.10 b Openings not requiring lintels**

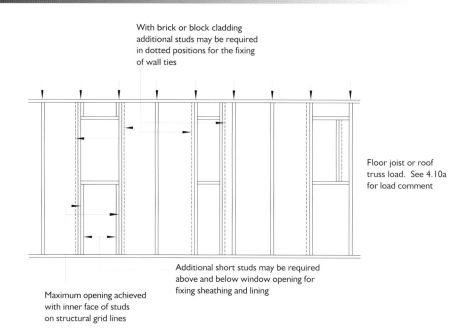

With brick or block cladding additional studs may be required in dotted positions for the fixing of wall ties

Floor joist or roof truss load.  See 4.10a for load comment

Additional short studs may be required above and below window opening for fixing sheathing and lining

Maximum opening achieved with inner face of studs on structural grid lines

Where possible it is preferable to select opening widths which are a multiple of the structural grid and locate the openings on grid. Where they occur off grid, additional framing is needed and cutting and possible waste of sheathing and lining materials may result. Irrespective of where such additional studs occur, the main studs should still be located at the structural grid line to provide regular fixing positions for lining, sheathing, wall ties and/or cladding battens (Figure 4.11).

**Figure 4.11 Modular openings** (see also 4.10 a for loading comment)

### (a) On grid

Floor joist or roof truss load

### (b) Off grid

Floor joist or roof truss load

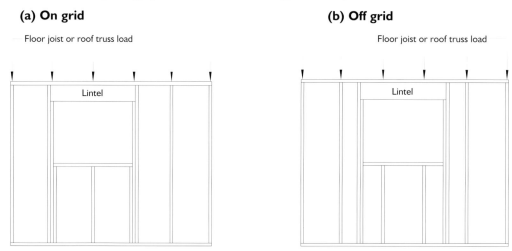

Lintel

Lintel

Where non-modular openings are required, eg 900 mm for doors or windows, it is still preferable to locate the opening with one side on the structural grid since this uses fewer studs. (Figure 4.12).

Staggered window openings at different storeys (see Figure 4.13) may result in lintels to the ground floor openings being heavily loaded and hardwood lintels or structural composite beams may be needed. Structural calculation will determine the precise requirements.

**Figure 4.12 Preferred location of non-modular openings** (see also Figure 4.10 a for loading comment)

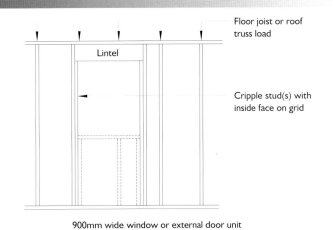

900mm wide window or external door unit

**Figure 4.13 Staggered openings in external wall**

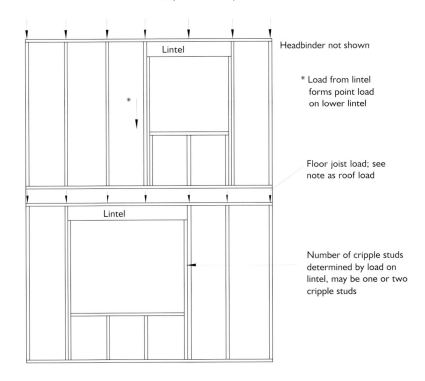

#### 4.1.2.9 Lintels

Softwood lintels are sufficient for the majority of domestic loads and spans. The dimension between the base of the panel and the underside of the lintel is normally 2100 mm, to suit standard door heights. Depending upon the size of the lintel, packing may be required to the underside to form an opening of precise dimensions (see Figure 4.14).

The design of lintels will be determined by the dead load (uniform or combined uniform and point load), the span, availability of the required size and strength class of timber and the deflection limit imposed (particularly over large span openings), usually 0.003 of the span as defined in BS 5268-2. Lintel deflection over large openings may affect the operation of, for example sliding patio doors, and should preferably be limited by a specified dimension. Figure 4.15 shows typical lintel types.

**Figure 4.14 Typical lintel arrangement for door opening in loadbearing wall**

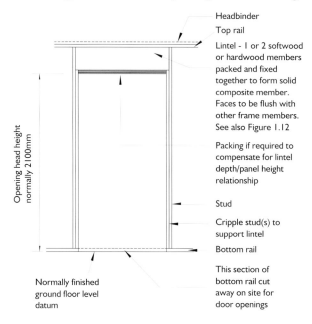

Headbinder

Top rail

Lintel - 1 or 2 softwood or hardwood members packed and fixed together to form solid composite member. Faces to be flush with other frame members. See also Figure 1.12

Packing if required to compensate for lintel depth/panel height relationship

Stud

Cripple stud(s) to support lintel

Bottom rail

This section of bottom rail cut away on site for door openings

Opening head height normally 2100mm

Normally finished ground floor level datum

**Figure 4.15 Typical lintels**

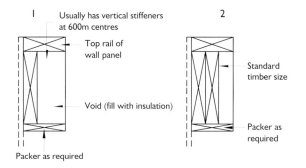

1
Usually has vertical stiffeners at 600m centres

Top rail of wall panel

Void (fill with insulation)

Packer as required

2
Standard timber size

Packer as required

**1** Lightly loaded
Fill void with thermal insulation. Cripple stud to extend to underside of lintel member

**2** Standard lintel
Cripple studs to extend to underside of lintel member

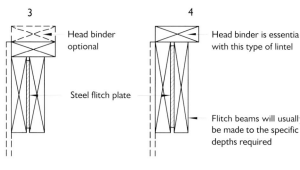

3
Head binder optional

Steel flitch plate

4
Head binder is essentia with this type of lintel

Flitch beams will usuall be made to the specific depths required

**3** Heavy load
Structural hardwoods or softwood and steel flitch, sized in depth to allow for timber shrinkage, bolts recessed into lintel members

**4** Heavy load, large span
Top rail omitted. Requires head binder and end fixing into wall studs to restrain lintel against overturning. Can incorporate steel flitch if structurally required

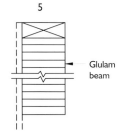

5
Glulam beam

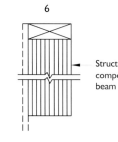

6
Structural composite beam

**5** Glulam beam
Structurally laminated softwood, refer to manufacturer's literature for span details

**6** Structural composite beam (eg lvl beam)
Proprietary fabricated beam, refer to manufacturer's literature for span information.

Multi-member lintels should be fixed together in accordance with the structural design. Dimensional constraints are shown in Figures 1.11 and 1.12.

Independent steel or concrete lintels are required to carry external brick or block cladding, see Section 9 'Cladding'. Under no circumstance should the weight of masonry walls be transferred to the timber frame wall. Steel lintels should be independently assessed for supporting brickwork cladding to timber frame.

### 4.1.2.10 Support for point loads

Point loads from beams, eg trimmers carrying joists, should be transmitted directly to the foundations by the use of additional studs (Figure 4.16), the exact number being determined by calculation. Deep beams require pockets to be formed within the wall panels as shown in Figure 4.17. Support for beams should be followed through all panels and floor framing to foundation level.

**Figure 4.16 Support for trimmer beams within floor depth**

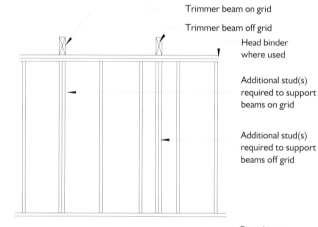

Trimmer beam on grid

Trimmer beam off grid

Head binder where used

Additional stud(s) required to support beams on grid

Additional stud(s) required to support beams off grid

**Figure 4.17 Support for deep beams**

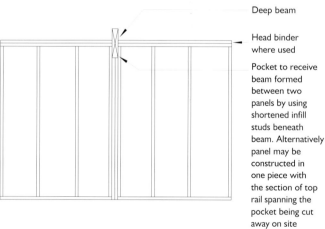

Deep beam

Head binder where used

Pocket to receive beam formed between two panels by using shortened infill studs beneath beam. Alternatively panel may be constructed in one piece with the section of top rail spanning the pocket being cut away on site

### 4.1.2.11 Spandrel panels to gable walls

Spandrel panels to gable ends are nailed directly to the top rail or the head binder of the external wall panel. The bottom rail of the spandrel panel may double as the head binder to the wall panel, and the details in this section are based on this arrangement (Figure 4.18).

The Building Regulations assume that gable end walls at roof level form part of the roof where the roof space is limited to access for repair and maintenance only. If the roof space is used for habitable purposes, that part of the gable is assumed to form part of the external wall.

**Figure 4.18 Typical roof gable spandrel panel sheathed externally with wood-based sheet material**

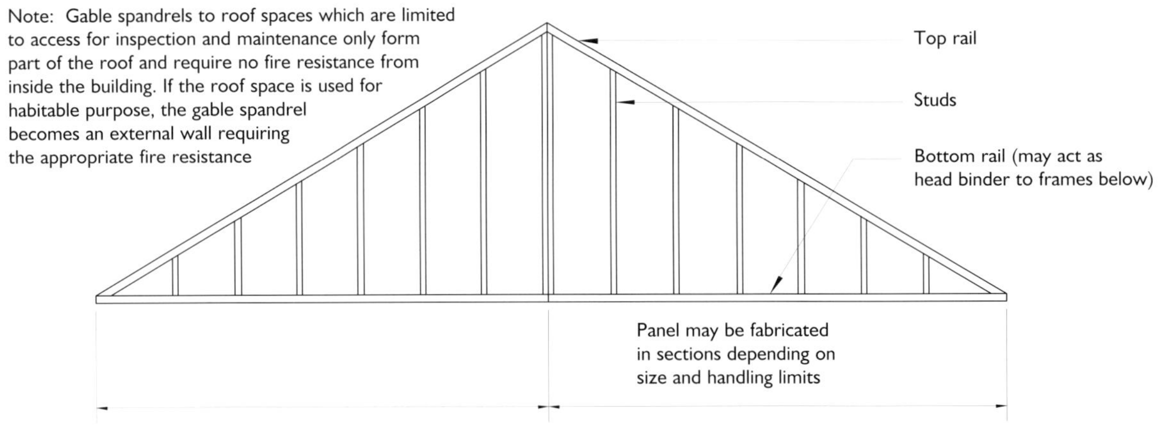

Note:  Gable spandrels to roof spaces which are limited
to access for inspection and maintenance only form
part of the roof and require no fire resistance from
inside the building. If the roof space is used for
habitable purpose, the gable spandrel
becomes an external wall requiring
the appropriate fire resistance

Top rail

Studs

Bottom rail (may act as
head binder to frames below)

Panel may be fabricated
in sections depending on
size and handling limits

It is common to sheath and fit a breather membrane to gable end spandrel panels to achieve early weather protection, panel strength and stability. In order to produce spandrel panels which are accurately made, the manufacturers require detailed information about the roof construction and verge details. For example, the decision to use a gable ladder affects the height of the spandrel panel as shown in Figure 4.19. An alternative method of framing is to use a trussed rafter with supplementary framing and breather membrane.

**Figure 4.19 Verge formed (left) with gable ladder     (right) with spandrel panel**

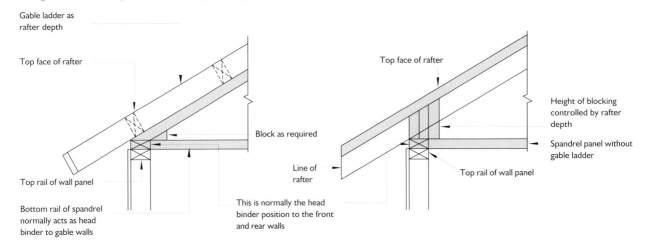

Gable ladder as
rafter depth

Top face of rafter

Top rail of wall panel

Bottom rail of spandrel
normally acts as head
binder to gable walls

Block as required

Line of
rafter

This is normally the head
binder position to the front
and rear walls

Top face of rafter

Height of blocking
controlled by rafter
depth

Spandrel panel without
gable ladder

Top rail of wall panel

In the case of a trussed rafter roof, the spandrel panel should be made either by using a trussed rafter as a jig, or by reference to a drawing supplied by the truss manufacturer, since the depth of the rafter member of the trussed rafter may affect the dimensions of the spandrel panel.

In a building which contains both gable and compartment wall spandrel panels, the detailing of both should be considered to ensure that when the roof trusses are fully loaded the resulting truss deflection does not induce distortion in the roof at gable ends and over compartment walls. A rule of thumb figure for deflection of loaded trusses is approximately 1 mm per metre span of truss at the apex and zero at the eaves. Allowance should be made in the vertical dimensions of the spandrel panel.

Verge details are shown in Section 8.8.2.

# 4.2 Internal walls

This section should be read in conjunction with Section 4.1 'External walls', Section 4.3 'Wall linings' and with Section 3.3 'Suspended ground floors' and Chapter 6 'Intermediate floors' for details of support for internal walls.

## 4.2.1 Design requirements

Timber framed internal walls may be loadbearing and may contribute to the wind resistance of the structure. The structural design should be in accordance with BS 5268-2 and BS 5268-6.

Loadbearing internal walls will require the same fire resistance as the external walls. The periods of fire resistance required vary depending upon the building's purpose group. Fire resistance periods for buildings other than dwellings generally also depend upon the height, floor area and/or cubic capacity of the building.

In larger buildings, loadbearing and/or non-loadbearing internal walls may be provided to compartmentalise the building and will require the prescribed fire resistance for this purpose. Walls of this type are described in Chapter 5 'Compartment walls'.

Loadbearing and non-loadbearing internal walls will be required to satisfy the surface spread of flame (reaction to fire) requirements set out in the Building Regulations. Information on surface spread of flame characteristics is included in Section 1.3.2.

Internal walls are not generally required to provide thermal insulation except when they form a semi-exposed wall between heated and unheated areas. Thermal performance data for timber frame walls is included in Section 4.1.2.

Internal walls may also have to provide sound insulation between adjacent rooms. Current Regulations should be checked. The housing warranty and guarantee authorities have specific requirements for aspects such as sound insulation between rooms containing wcs and other rooms. Figure 4.22 lists the sound insulation performance of some common constructions.

In addition to meeting the Design Requirements, the successful completion and quality of the timber frame building is dependent on good on-site practice in terms of accuracy in setting out and erecting components. Guidance is given in Appendix 3 Site Supervisors' Checklist.

## 4.2.2 Internal wall construction

There is, in practice, little difference in construction between loadbearing and non-loadbearing stud framed internal walls. The stud size required for non-loadbearing walls may be smaller than those used to carry loads but it is common practice to use the same section for ease of manufacture and to standardise detailing of other elements.

When sole plates and head binders are used on external walls it is good practice to use them also with loadbearing internal walls. This equalises shrinkage, allows a constant stud length to be used throughout each storey and can, subject to check by calculation, enable joists and rafters to be positioned without regard to the stud positions in loadbearing internal walls, except for heavy concentrated loads when additional studs may be required. It is common practice to fix preservative-treated sole plates beneath non-loadbearing internal walls in order to delineate their position and, if necessary for loadings, to provide solid support for walls when insulated deck floors are laid. Setting out and fixing of internal walls is simplified when sole plates are already in place.

Internal walls should not be supported by floating floor decks or on the decking of timber floors unless adequate support is provided, see Chapters 3 and 6. Actual deflections of roofs or floors, particularly long spans, may impose loads onto non-loadbearing elements, unless deflections are taken into account. Normally deflected elements are assumed as 0.003 of span (m) under full design load.

Internal walls are constructed similarly to external wall panels with studs at either 400 or 600 mm centres and with noggings as required (Figure 4.20). Sheathing is not used except in situations when the external wall sheathing alone does not provide adequate racking resistance. In this case, selected loadbearing internal walls may be sheathed on one or both faces and may also require special holding down fixings.

**Figure 4.20 Typical internal wall framing: may be supplied with temporary cross bracing**

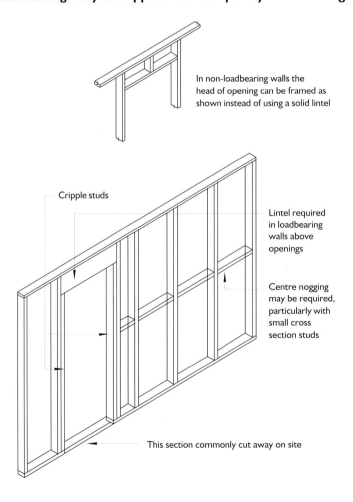

In non-loadbearing walls the head of opening can be framed as shown instead of using a solid lintel

Cripple studs

Lintel required in loadbearing walls above openings

Centre nogging may be required, particularly with small cross section studs

This section commonly cut away on site

Non-loadbearing internal walls are often fitted after the main structure is erected and will require a fitting tolerance. To facilitate lining of ceilings by reducing cutting, non-loadbearing internal walls can be of reduced height to allow plasterboard to fit between the head of the wall and the underside of joists.

Wall linings (see Section 4.3) are usually site fixed although some component suppliers pre-fix them on one or both faces. When internal walls are supplied lined on both faces, they can be fixed by skew nailing along the bottom edge into a sole plate, or fixed using proprietary shoes or clips. Fixings are subsequently covered by the skirting. Figures 4.21a and 4.21b show typical arrangements.

**Figure 4.21 Non-loadbearing internal walls with pre-fixed linings:**
**a (right) Typical arrangements**

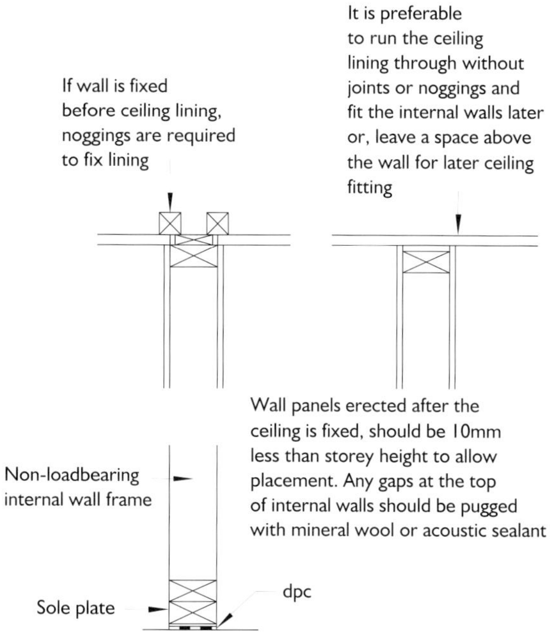

**b (below) Typical shoe fixings**

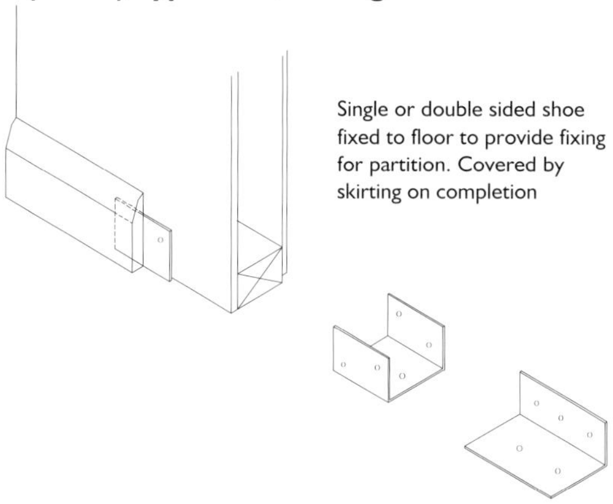

If wall is fixed before ceiling lining, noggings are required to fix lining

It is preferable to run the ceiling lining through without joints or noggings and fit the internal walls later or, leave a space above the wall for later ceiling fitting

Single or double sided shoe fixed to floor to provide fixing for partition. Covered by skirting on completion

Non-loadbearing internal wall frame

Wall panels erected after the ceiling is fixed, should be 10mm less than storey height to allow placement. Any gaps at the top of internal walls should be pugged with mineral wool or acoustic sealant

Sole plate

dpc

Loadbearing internal frames are manufactured by the supplier of the superstructure. Non-loadbearing wall frames are usually also provided or alternatively, frame components can be delivered cut to length for site assembly. To reduce the risk of distortion of unsheathed wall frames during handling and erection, it is recommended that 'improved' nails (with better withdrawal resistance) are used.

Loadbearing walls should be able to maintain their loadbearing capacity for the required period of fire resistance. Where walls have no fire separating function, no requirement for integrity or insulation fire performance exists. Figure 4.22 illustrates typical timber frame partitions and gives details of their fire performance. Internal walls also need to be fire resisting where they provide fire compartmentation. In addition to any loadbearing requirements, these compartment walls will also need to provide fire integrity and insulation performance from both sides separately, see Chapter 5.

The sound insulation of an imperforate timber framed, plasterboard lined internal wall is around 30 dB which is usually considered adequate for domestic or similar purposes. Improved sound insulation can be achieved, if required, by alternative specifications. Figure 4.22 shows typical sound reduction figures for various constructions.

Air gaps at the top and bottom edges of walls are potential weak links for sound transmission. Attention should be given to closing any indirect sound paths over or around internal walls by sealing gaps with pugging of mineral wool, gypsum plaster or proprietary acoustic sealant. The sound insulation will be lower if the wall contains a standard internal door of 15 dB performance with perimeter gaps. The overall wall insulation will be about 25 dB, but with door edge treatment may be raised to around 28 dB.

Non-loadbearing walls in timber frame buildings may also be of proprietary laminated or hollow core plasterboard construction. Provisions for supporting and restraining all internal walls within timber frame structures are similar to other types of construction, but the manufacturer's instructions should always be followed.

## Figure 4.22 Internal timber stud partitions: typical acoustic and fire performance

| Construction | Specification | Sound reduction index (dB) * 100-3150 Hz Rw | Overall thickness (mm) | Average weight (kg/m$^2$) | Fire resistance (minutes) |
|---|---|---|---|---|---|
| 1 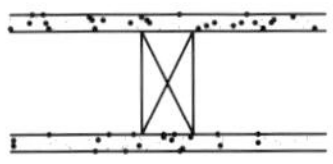 | 12.5 mm plasterboard 75 x 38 mm studs at 600 mm centres 12.5 mm plasterboard | 35 | 100 | 19 | 30 |
| 2 | as 1 with 25 mm glass wool in cavity | 36 | 100 | 19 | 30 |
| 3 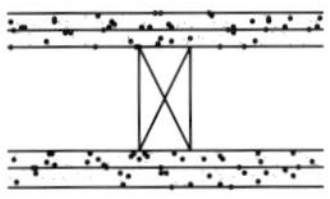 | 2 x 12.5 mm plasterboard 75 x 38 mm studs 2 x 12.5 mm plasterboard | 38 | 126 | 36 | 60 |
| 4 | as 3 with 25 mm minimum glass wool in cavity | 40 | 126 | 36 | 60 |
| 5 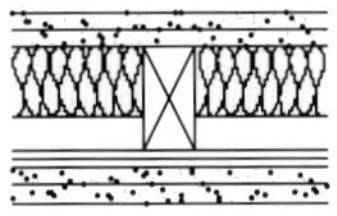 | 2 x 12.5 mm high density plasterboard 75 x 38 mm studs at 600 mm centres with 50 mm glass wool in cavity Resilient bars fixed horizontally to one side at 600 mm centres 2 x 12.5 mm high density plasterboard | 55 | 140 | 46 | 60 |

* Minor variation in stud dimensions will have negligible effect on sound insulation performance
Results extracted from British Gypsum 'White Book'

In assessing the sound insulation performance, the values can be compared with the privacy provided, eg

| Mean Rw (dB) | Degree of privacy |
|---|---|
| 20 | Normal speech can easily be overheard |
| 25 | Loud speech can be heard clearly |
| 30 | Loud speech can be distinguished |
| 35 | Loud speech can be heard but not distinguished |
| 40 | Loud speech can be heard faintly |
| 45 | Loud speech or shouting difficult to hear |

# 4.3 Wall linings

This section should be read in conjunction with Section 4.1 'External walls' and Section 4.2 'Internal walls'

## 4.3.1 Design requirements

The internal lining of the timber frame wall may be required to perform three functions:

♦ to provide the finish or a substrate to accept the finish on the inner face of external walls and to both faces of internal walls

♦ to contribute to the racking resistance of the wall on external and loadbearing internal walls

♦ to contribute to the fire resistance of the wall.

BS 5268-6 includes information on the criteria for racking strength contribution.

The Building Regulations, in addition to specifying the required periods of fire resistance, require surface spread of flame (reaction to fire) provisions for walls to rooms and circulation spaces, see Section 1.3.2.

In addition to meeting the Design Requirements, the successful completion and quality of the timber frame building is dependent on good on-site practice in terms of accuracy in setting out and erecting components. Guidance is given in Appendix 3 Site Supervisor's Checklist.

## 4.3.2 Lining materials

The most commonly used material for wall lining is plasterboard, but wood-based boards, such as medium density fibreboard (MDF), mediumboard, plywood, OSB, wood chipboard and cement-bonded particleboard, as well as timber boarding can also be used.

It is possible to skim coat the plasterboard face as an alternative to taping and filling but this introduces a wet trade to an otherwise dry building process and experience shows that skim coated walls are more prone to hairline cracking at the joints than dry lined walls.

Plasterboard fixing should comply with the manufacturer's instructions. Nails are usually smooth shank galvanized with a flat round head although other types are available and the use of powered screwdrivers has encouraged the increased use of screw fixing of plasterboard. Nails should be at maximum 150 mm centres at board edge and intermediate supports. Screws should be at 230 mm centres.

The use of timber and wood-based boards may be limited by surface spread of flame (reaction to fire) requirements. Surface coatings or impregnation treatments can be applied to enhance the performance of these materials, see Section 1.3.2. When walls which are lined with timber or wood based sheet materials require fire resistance, test evidence to show compliance with the relevant requirement will be needed.

Wood-based boards can be fixed by nailing or screwing, the latter generally requiring predrilling. Nail length is normally 2.5 times the board thickness. All board edges should be supported by studs or noggings. Most types of wood-based board require conditioning to a moisture content appropriate to the eventual equilibrium moisture content in service; the manufacturer's advice should be sought.

Plasterboard linings can support light loads if proprietary cavity fixings are used as shown in Figure 10.3. Wall hung cupboards and other heavy fittings should be supported by fixing direct into the vertical studs or to bearers fixed to the studs. Boilers and other similar heavy wall hung components may require additional framing built into the standard wall frames. The manufacturer's instructions should be followed. See Chapter 10.

When timber frame external walls are internally sheathed (see Section 4.4), the sheathing board may provide the racking strength, contribute to fire resistance, comply with surface spread of flame (reaction to fire) classification and provide the internal decorative surface. These sheathing/lining boards will need careful selection but could include cement-bonded particleboard, fibre reinforced gypsum board, mineral fibre boards, and flame spread-treated plywood, OSB and chipboard.

### 4.3.3 Framing and lining junctions

See Figure 4.23 for junctions providing 30 minutes fire resistance and Figure 4.24 for junctions using multiple boards and providing 60 minutes fire resistance.

**Figure 4.23 Wall and ceiling lining junctions: 30 minutes fire resistance**

All plasterboard 12.5 mm thick, fixed in accordance with manufacturers' instructions, with joints backed by solid timber and taped and filled.
Note vapour control layers, insulation and breather membrane have been omitted for clarity.

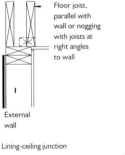

Floor joist, parallel with wall or nogging with joists at right angles to wall

External wall

Lining-ceiling junction

1 Where wall linings abut ceiling linings it is normal practice to trap the ceiling board with the wall board.

Edges of plasterboard must be supported by noggings or joists

Internal loadbearing wall

2 All cut edges of ceiling linings should be backed and supported by noggings or joists, except if 15 mm or thicker plasterboard is specified.

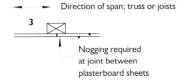

Direction of span; truss or joists

Nogging required at joint between plasterboard sheets

3 Board joints in ceilings should be supported by noggings, except if 15 mm or thicker plasterboard is specified.

**Figure 4.23 Wall and ceiling lining junctions: 30 minutes fire resistance (continued)**

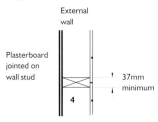

**4** All lining board junctions should occur on studs or noggings.

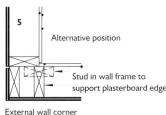

**5** Internal and external corner junctions should be arranged to provide support to both lining boards and may require an additional stud for this purpose. Void between studs at corner should be filled with insulation

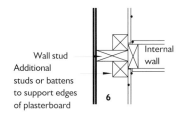

**6** When internal wall junctions occur at the stud centre line, additional studs or battens are required to support adjoining board edges. Where it is possible, offsetting the internal wall by approximately 50 mm allows the joint to be made using only one additional stud as shown in detail 7.

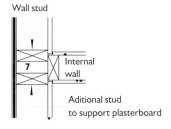

**7** Internal wall offset to use one additional stud only to support plasterboard. Note that a nogging (or a third stud) may also be necessary between the studs to provide a fixing for the end of the internal wall panel. The void should be filled with insulation.

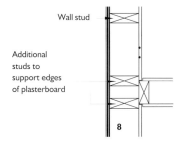

**8** When the junction occurs between studs, two additional studs should be inserted to fix the internal wall and support the adjacent board edges. Void between studs should be filled with insulation.

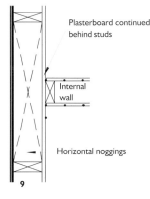

**9** Alternatively, the wall can be supported by horizontal noggings set between the studs. Nogging spacing to comply with lining fixing requirements for fire resistance.

Proprietary plasterboard fixing clip

**10** If fire resistance is not required it is possible to use proprietary steel clips at approx 150 mm centres to retain the wall lining board which is then trapped in place by the adjacent board.

## Figure 4.24 Wall and ceiling lining junctions: 60 minutes fire resistance

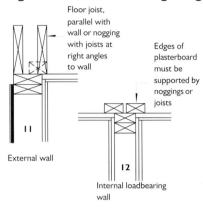

External wall

Floor joist, parallel with wall or nogging with joists at right angles to wall

Edges of plasterboard must be supported by noggings or joists

Internal loadbearing wall

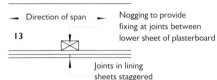

Direction of span

Nogging to provide fixing at joints between lower sheet of plasterboard

Joints in lining sheets staggered

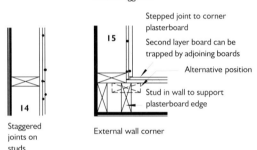

Staggered joints on studs

External wall corner

Stepped joint to corner plasterboard

Second layer board can be trapped by adjoining boards

Alternative position

Stud in wall to support plasterboard edge

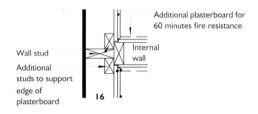

Wall stud

Additional studs to support edge of plasterboard

Additional plasterboard for 60 minutes fire resistance

Internal wall

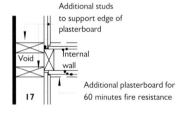

Additional studs to support edge of plasterboard

Void

Internal wall

Additional plasterboard for 60 minutes fire resistance

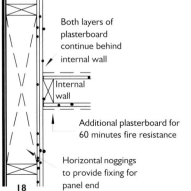

Both layers of plasterboard continue behind internal wall

Internal wall

Additional plasterboard for 60 minutes fire resistance

Horizontal noggings to provide fixing for panel end

All plasterboard 12.5 and/or 19 mm thick as appropriate should be fixed in accordance with manufacturers' instructions. Joints should be staggered and those in outer layers should be backed by solid timber and taped and filled. Note: Vapour control layers, insulation and breather membrane omitted for clarity.

**11** Where wall linings abut ceiling linings it is normal practice to trap the ceiling boards with the wall boards and fix the boards with a break joint (avoiding a straight joint between the layers).

**12** All edges of ceiling linings should be backed and supported by noggings or joists to provide support and fixings for the outer layer of plasterboard, unless this layer is at least 15 mm thick.

**13** Board joints to the outer layer of plasterboard in ceilings should be supported by noggings, except if this layer is at least 15 mm thick.

**14** Board joints should be staggered and all layers fully nailed in accordance with the manufacturer's instructions.

**15** Wall corner joints should be formed so that a straight joint is avoided between lining boards. The void should be filled with insulation.

**16** Where internal walls occur at an external wall stud, additional studs are required to fully support both layers of wall lining board.

**17** Where internal walls occur between external wall studs, additional studs should be provided to support both edges of the lining board. Note that a nogging (or a third stud) may also be necessary between the studs to provide a fixing for the end of the internal wall panel. The void should be filled with insulation.

**18** Alternatively, horizontal noggings can be used to fix the internal wall. Nogging spacing to comply with lining fixing requirements for fire resistance.

# 4.4 Alternative wall constructions

The drive for energy efficiency, the development of new materials and the increasing awareness of the overall environmental impact of materials and buildings is leading to the development of alternative timber frame wall designs. This section examines some of the options, giving an overview of the alternative approaches. Only the basic wall construction is considered here; the detail design may have implications for junctions, for example between the walls themselves, at floor and at roof level. The range of alternatives is wide; designers and manufacturers are developing their own details and some have been developed into complete building systems.

In this section, the technical options for meeting the design performance requirements are examined.

## 4.4.1 Structure

**Studs**

The most common option is to increase the depth of the studs to more than 140 mm to allow more insulation to be incorporated. Studs up to 200 mm deep have been used. For sections deeper than 200 mm, the use of solid timber is unlikely to be economic and designers should consider a timber based structural composite. There are a number of different types on the market in addition to glued laminated timber, which has been available for many years (see Appendix 1). These take the form of laminated strands or laminated veneers which are manufactured as rectangular structural sections. They are produced by a number of manufacturers in Europe and in North America under a variety of trade names. In addition, there are a number of I-section components with solid timber or composite material flanges and sheet material, eg plywood or oriented strand board webs (See Figure 4.25).

For very thick walls, double stud or planted batten systems, (Figure 4.26) may be more economic than composite sections. The ratio of insulation inside the vapour control layer to that outside should be 1:4.

**Figure 4.25 Studs as I-sections. Typical U values 0.17 – 0.12 W/m²K** (See Section 4.4.2)

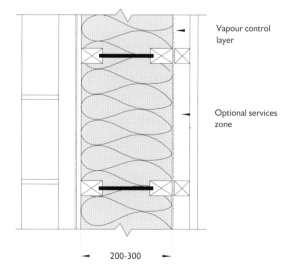

Vapour control layer

Optional services zone

200-300

**Figure 4.26 Battens planted on both sides of standard construction. Typical U value 0.18 W/m²K**

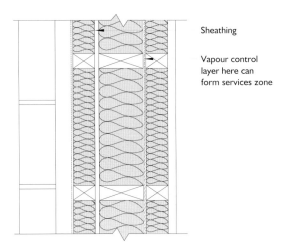

Sheathing

Vapour control layer here can form services zone

## Sheathing

Most alternative wall constructions will still employ some form of wood-based board sheathing as wind bracing. However, its position in the wall can be varied. A common option is to fix the sheathing to the inside of the wall, where in certain cases it can also perform as a vapour control layer, allowing the polythene membrane or proprietary plasterboard vcl to be omitted, see Figure 1.7b. Where sheathing is fixed to the inside face, the depth to breadth ratio of the studs, together with requirements for lateral restraint should be checked.

A most important consideration in relation to the positioning of the sheathing material is adherence to the '5 times' rule for vapour resistance for condensation control, ie the vapour resistances of the materials on the warm side of the insulation should be at least 5 times greater than those on the cold side of the insulation. Values for the vapour resistivities of commonly used materials are given in Appendix 2. For example, if plywood or OSB sheathing is fixed to the inside face of the wall beneath a plasterboard lining and the outside is sheathed with an impregnated softboard or breather membrane, the 5 times rule is met.

## Breather membranes

A breather membrane will normally be required on any of the alternative wall constructions unless secondary weather protection is provided in some other way. For example, certain materials, such as impregnated softboard, some medium boards and moisture resistant sheathing plasterboard, are inherently weather and moisture resistant and do not require a breather membrane although the joints may require protection using proprietary tape.

## Insulation

All the insulation options available to conventional timber frame are equally suitable for filling the stud cavities in alternative designs. One alternative which is wholly concerned with insulation is the 'warm wall'. In this design, a rigid insulation material is fixed to the outside face of a conventional frame leaving a clear stud void, see Figure 4.27.

In a variant of the warm wall, the stud cavity is also filled with insulation. However, condensation control and the need for a vapour control layer within the construction should be checked.

**Figure 4.27 Typical warm wall construction** (see Section 4.4.2)

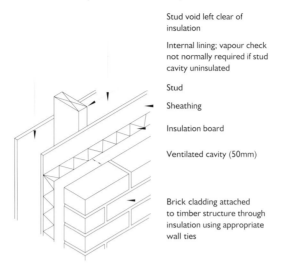

Stud void left clear of insulation

Internal lining; vapour check not normally required if stud cavity uninsulated

Stud

Sheathing

Insulation board

Ventilated cavity (50mm)

Brick cladding attached to timber structure through insulation using appropriate wall ties

## 4.4.2 Fire performance

Fire resistance in alternative constructions is achieved in a similar manner as that for conventional timber frame construction. The innermost lining is typically a gypsum-based board at least 12.5 mm thick (for 30 minutes fire resistance) and the studs and insulation will contribute in the same way as they do in conventional frame.

Wood-based board materials used as sheathing on the inside will provide some additional fire resistance in addition to that provided by the gypsum-based board lining.

Where highly engineered small section structural composites are used, eg I-sections, the inner lining may be required to provide a greater contribution to fire resistance than in conventional frame, as their smaller sectional area has a lower tolerance to charring than solid rectangular sections.

Where insulation other than mineral wool is used, the lining may also be required to provide additional fire resistance unless the insulation is able to provide similar fire protection to the studs as mineral wool. The fire resistance of warm wall designs with no insulation in the stud cavities should be checked.

**Cladding**

The types of cladding available for use with conventional frame techniques (see Chapter 9) are all equally suitable for use with alternative walls.

The use of an alternative wall design to bring significant savings in costs and improvements in quality is demonstrated in the TRADA Technology *Report 2/2000 Timber frame: Re-engineering for affordable housing*.

# 4.5 Medium rise construction

Medium rise construction in timber frame is taken as meaning four or more storeys. The upper limit is not defined but is probably seven to ten storeys.

This section highlights those aspects of timber frame design which need special consideration when designing medium rise structures. It does not provide prescriptive solutions since these will be governed by the detailed design of the building. Most of the considerations are structural.

The increased height of the building results in higher cumulative vertical loads acting on the lower storey walls than would be the case with low-rise construction. Therefore it is likely that studs larger than those required for low-rise building will be required. Alternatively similar sized studs may be placed at closer centres or used as multiple studs in the lower walls. Structural composite materials, such as those described in Section 4.4.1 may be used as studs where appropriate.

Since wind speeds increase with height, the sheathing requirements will be different from those for low-rise buildings, for example:

- thicker sheathing or closer nailing to the sheathing may be required

- internal walls and compartment walls may require sheathing

- the contribution made to stability by plasterboard or similar linings may be taken into account.

If the sheathing is thicker than that used in low-rise construction it is important that the condensation risk is checked using the 5 times rule or full risk calculations.

Higher wind speeds also mean that the measures to counteract wind uplift on roofs may need to be increased, for example by the use of holding down straps.

At five storeys or more, in addition to the normal vertical and lateral load calculations required, the designer needs to provide calculations for disproportionate collapse. Disproportionate collapse means that in the event of accidental damage to the building, the structure not directly affected by the accident must not collapse excessively in relation to the severity of the accidental event.

If masonry cladding is used, the normal measures to accommodate differential movement between the frame and cladding may require modification. For example, the conventional wall ties may not provide sufficient flexibility above three storeys and specially designed ties may be needed. These include ties which are designed to slot into a channel fixed to the studs in the wall. The gaps required below windows in the upper storeys could be more than 30 mm which could require special detailing to avoid visual impairment and rainwater penetration problems. The differential movement between stairs (a dry joinery item) and the frame structure will also require special consideration at the design stage.

Most differential movement problems can be avoided by adopting one of several approaches. For example low moisture content timber can be specified. This should be close to the moisture content which it will be in service, which for floor joists is likely to be 10% or lower. Super-dried timber at 12% moisture content is available and is acceptable in this context. Since it is not always practicable to use timber at this level of moisture content, the use of structural composites which are manufactured and supplied at low moisture contents can be considered for use in the floor zone. Alternatively differential movement can be significantly reduced by reducing the amount of cross-sectional timber in the external walls. This can be achieved through the use of some form of storey-height panel, see Figure 1.4 or by hanging floor joists off a dry ring beam.

# 5 Party walls

## 5.1 Design requirements

'Party' walls are described in National Building Regulations as Separating or Compartment walls, depending upon the function being considered and the area of the country. See the Regulations for details. There are three types of party walls. These are:

♦ Walls which separate dwellings from other dwellings and from other parts of the same building which are not used as dwellings.

♦ Walls which separate different purpose groups or occupancies (excluding dwellings) within a building.

♦ Walls required to subdivide a large building into compartments of specified size or volume for fire safety.

Timber party walls may be loadbearing and may need to contribute to the wind resistance of the structure.

All party walls are required to have specified periods of fire resistance. These are determined by the purpose group, location, height, floor area and volume of the building. National Building Regulations should be checked for details.

Party walls which separate dwellings or occur between a dwelling and other parts of the same building are required to resist the passage of sound to an acceptable degree. No other compartment walls currently have a mandatory requirement for sound resistance, although in 'Other Residential' buildings, eg hotels and hostels, this is normally a design requirement and may become mandatory in future.

There are no thermal performance requirements for party walls except where steps and/or staggers occur. The area of party wall which becomes an external wall should meet the thermal insulation requirements for external walls, have the required surface spread of flame (reaction to fire) rating on the external face of the wall and have the appropriate fire resistance from both sides.

In England and Wales and Northern Ireland, party walls may be of timber construction in all building types. Currently in Scotland, party walls to houses and flats may be of timber construction; all other party walls are required by the regulations to be of non-combustible materials, precluding the use of timber. Additionally, in Scotland party floors must be of non-combustible materials when over a certain height, effectively limiting timber construction to buildings below this height. Section 5.2 of this Chapter deals with party walls for dwellings. Party walls required for fire compartmentation of buildings or separation of non-residential uses are dealt with in Section 5.3.

In addition to meeting the Design Requirements, successful completion and quality of a timber frame building depends on good on-site practice in terms of accuracy in setting out and erecting components. Guidance is given in Appendix 3 Site Supervisor's Checklist. Good workmansip is especially important in achieving expected levels of fire and acoustic performance

# 5.2 Party walls for dwellings

Party walls may be constructed using any materials and methods providing they meet the requirements of the Building Regulations for stability, fire resistance and sound insulation. When constructions not specifically included in the regulations are proposed, test evidence of fire and sound resistance will be required by building control authorities.

Party walls (loadbearing and non-loadbearing) for dwellings are required to provide 60 minutes fire resistance from either side separately. The wall should form a complete vertical barrier to fire, including the roof space and where relevant, the basement. Where floors or other structural elements which have a lesser fire resistance requirement abut the party wall, the detail design should enable the full fire resistance of the wall to be maintained. Party walls are required to meet the same surface spread of flame (reaction to fire) requirements as the other walls of the building.

Resistance to the passage of sound is obtained in a timber framed party wall by the use of two independent wall frames with only minimal ties between them and an insulating material in the cavity. Documents associated with National Building Regulations include prescriptive details of this type of wall and allow alternative constructions to be developed and tested.

Details of acoustic tests undertaken on the 'standard' timber frame party wall and on a similar wall including additional OSB sheathing are detailed in TRADA Technology *Report 1/2000 Acoustic performance of party floors and walls in timber framed buildings*. The results showed that the walls met an 'enhanced+' level of performance – well above the current requirements of the Building Regulations.

## 5.2.1 Party wall construction

Timber framed party walls are normally formed by two independent wall frames; see Figure 5.1. The combined width of the timber frames should not be less than 200 mm, but a greater dimension (say 250 mm) is beneficial for the acoustic performance of the wall. The two leaves are unconnected for the full height except for 3 mm (max) thick, light metal restraint straps tying the two leaves together. These straps should be spaced at approximately 1.2 m horizontal centres, one row per storey height at or near ceiling level, to stiffen the frames during construction and to assist in maintaining the stability of the wall in the event of an intermediate floor collapse.

An alternative timber frame party wall incorporates a solid masonry core between the two wall frames. This construction is mostly used at steps between dwellings where brickwork is exposed above the lower roof area. See Section 5.2.8.

## 5.2.2 Structural stability

The twin party wall frames with plasterboard linings usually provide adequate resistance to wind load on the front and rear walls. However, additional bracing can be introduced in the wall if structural calculations

## Figure 5.1 Typical party wall construction with 60 minutes fire resistance for dwellings

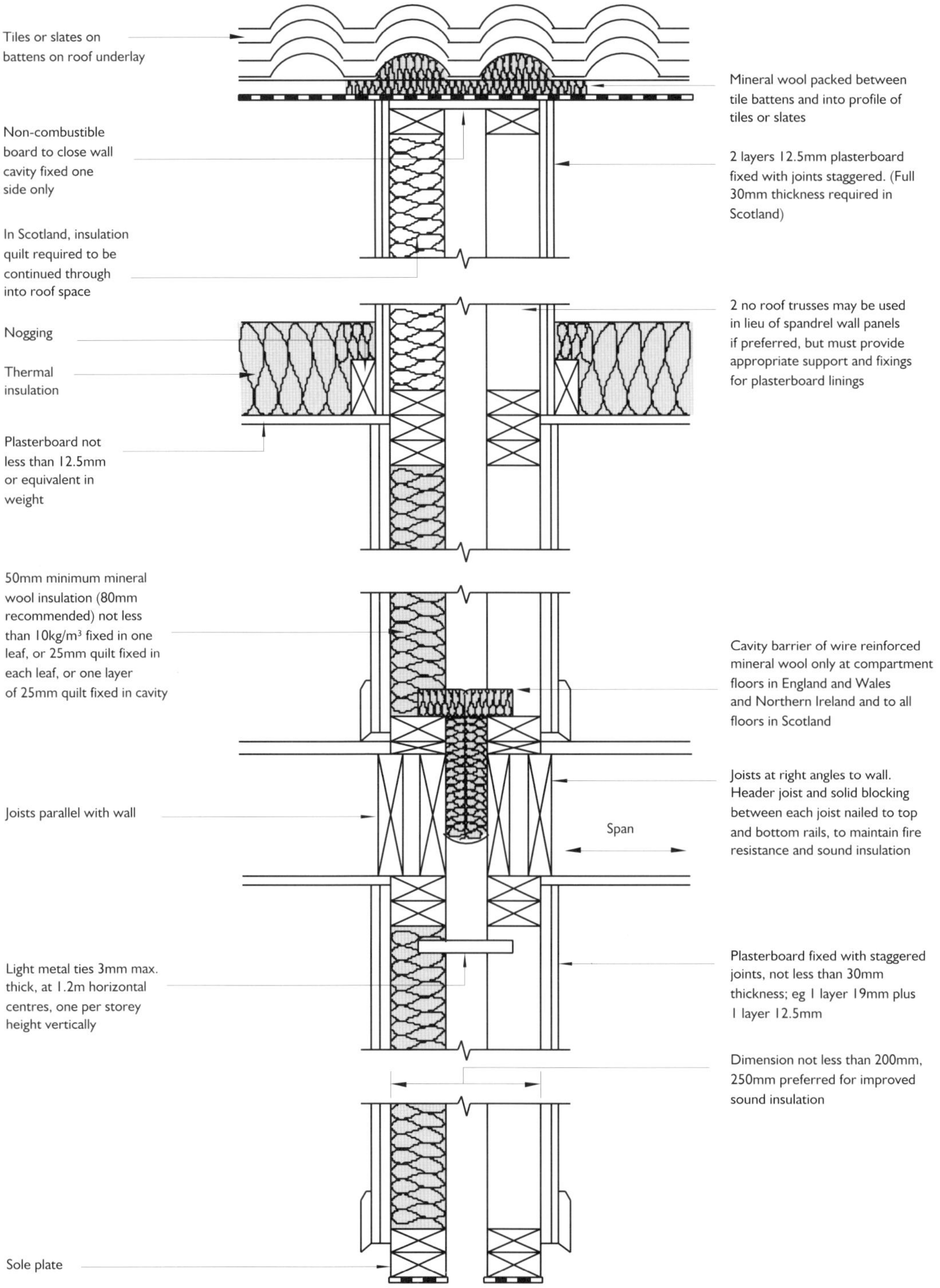

Tiles or slates on battens on roof underlay

Non-combustible board to close wall cavity fixed one side only

In Scotland, insulation quilt required to be continued through into roof space

Nogging

Thermal insulation

Plasterboard not less than 12.5mm or equivalent in weight

50mm minimum mineral wool insulation (80mm recommended) not less than 10kg/m³ fixed in one leaf, or 25mm quilt fixed in each leaf, or one layer of 25mm quilt fixed in cavity

Joists parallel with wall

Light metal ties 3mm max. thick, at 1.2m horizontal centres, one per storey height vertically

Sole plate

Mineral wool packed between tile battens and into profile of tiles or slates

2 layers 12.5mm plasterboard fixed with joints staggered. (Full 30mm thickness required in Scotland)

2 no roof trusses may be used in lieu of spandrel wall panels if preferred, but must provide appropriate support and fixings for plasterboard linings

Cavity barrier of wire reinforced mineral wool only at compartment floors in England and Wales and Northern Ireland and to all floors in Scotland

Joists at right angles to wall. Header joist and solid blocking between each joist nailed to top and bottom rails, to maintain fire resistance and sound insulation

Span

Plasterboard fixed with staggered joints, not less than 30mm thickness; eg 1 layer 19mm plus 1 layer 12.5mm

Dimension not less than 200mm, 250mm preferred for improved sound insulation

Note:    Where timber joists are at right angles to the party wall, full joist-depth blocking should be installed between each joist on the line of the edge of the lining to the wall to block air paths. The blocking should be nailed to the wall plates above and below. The outer joists should be blocked tightly to the perimeter walls

indicate the safe racking resistance of the plasterboard lining is exceeded. This can be achieved with diagonal bracing fixed to the cavity side of the wall frames, care being taken to ensure that any applied bracing does not contact the opposite wall frame. Alternatively, sheathing materials can be fastened to the party wall frames. The position of this additional sheathing is determined by the amount of extra stiffening required. If the whole length of the party wall requires sheathing it can be fixed to the room side of the frames and then covered with the required thickness of plasterboard. In this instance, at least one of the wall frames will have to be skew nailed to the sole plate through the sheathing, or metal shoes will be required for holding down. Alternatively, the sheathing can be applied on the cavity side of the wall on opposite faces. This narrows the space within the wall at each end but has little adverse effect on the acoustic performance of the wall (see Figure 5.2). In many cases, partial sheathing of the wall can provide adequate stiffness.

**Figure 5.2 Typical arrangement for sheathing party walls for additional stiffness**

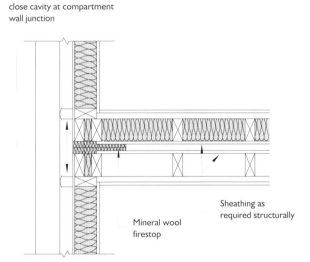

Vertical cavity barriers to close cavity at compartment wall junction

Mineral wool firestop

Sheathing as required structurally

### 5.2.3 Fire resistance

The two leaves should form a complete barrier to fire, including in the roof spaces. This is usually achieved with plasterboard in two or more layers to contribute to the 60 minutes fire resistance required. The complete fire barrier includes not only the wall itself, but the junctions with the floor, the roof and the external walls and any penetration of the wall permitted under the regulations. Correct installation of cavity barriers and firestops is essential.

### 5.2.4 Sound insulation

Airborne sound insulation is achieved in lightweight walls by combining structural discontinuity, dense wall linings and absorbent insulation in the cavity.

The specification requires a minimum of 30 mm thickness of plasterboard on both wall faces; usually one layer of 19 mm plasterboard plank and one layer of 12.5 mm plasterboard fixed with joints staggered. In England

and Wales this thickness can be reduced to two layers of 12.5 mm plasterboard in the roof space when a 12.5 mm plasterboard ceiling is used. This is not allowed in Scotland or Northern Ireland where the full 30 mm plasterboard thickness should continue to the underside of the roof.

An alternative specification which has been used in conjunction with non-habitable roof spaces in England and Wales provides a single leaf wall in the roof space, with two 12.5 mm plasterboard layers on each side. This is particularly useful when the party wall occurs at roof intersections as shown in Figure 8.18a and b. At similar intersections in Scotland or Northern Ireland, the detail shown in Figure 8.18c is appropriate.

The sound absorbent insulation in the party wall is normally unfaced mineral wool quilt of not less than 10 kg/m$^3$ density; 25 mm thick if suspended in the cavity between the two frames, 25 mm in each frame or 50 mm thick if fixed to one of the frames. However, many designers and contractors install thicker and denser mineral wool material in the party wall to simplify installation and to rationalise the number of types of insulation needed on site. Acoustic test evidence would be necessary for insulation other than mineral wool.

Currently, use of the specifications set out in Regulations does not rely on acoustic test evidence to show compliance with the requirements. However, testing may be required (check National Regulations for details). This requires measurements to be taken in completed buildings in accordance with *BS EN ISO 140-4 Field measurements of airborne sound insulation between rooms* to determine the Standardized Level Difference (DnT) for airborne sound transmission. The weighted standardized level difference (DnT,w) for airborne sound is then calculated as defined in *BS EN ISO 717-1 Acoustics. Rating of sound insulation in buildings and of building elements*. Airborne sound insulation. Current England and Wales Regulations also include a method of testing in a test chamber by a UKAS accredited laboratory which may be used to show that a proposed solution meets the test requirements for similar construction.

Spectrum adaptation terms can be applied to the $D_{nT,w}$ values to better indicate sound insulation performance against specific types of noise. Those relevant in this context are:

$C_{tr}$ This value is added to $D_{nT,w}$ to give an indication of airborne sound insulation against low frequency bass music and traffic noise. There is evidence that the combined value better represents the insulation against airborne noise nuisance than $D_{nT,w}$ alone. Note: $C_{tr}$ is normally a negative number, making the combined value numerically smaller.

## 5.2.5 Proximity of windows

There are no restrictions in the current England and Wales or Scottish Regulations on the proximity of windows to timber framed party walls in timber framed dwellings. Test evidence shows that the close proximity of windows (when closed) does not generally affect the overall sound insulation performance of a timber party wall. In Northern Ireland there is a requirement for a dimension of 650 mm between window openings adjacent to party walls irrespective of their construction.

## 5.2.6 Junctions with other elements

### 5.2.6.1 Junction with the roof

The top of the party wall frames should be covered with a non-combustible board or similar fire resistant material tightly butted at joints and fixed to one top rail only.

The space between the roofing underlay, which is continued over the wall, and the roofing tiles should be filled with mineral wool for the full width of the wall. See Figures 5.3 and 5.4. Additional details are shown in Section 8.8.3.

**Figure 5.3 Typical junction of party wall with roof**

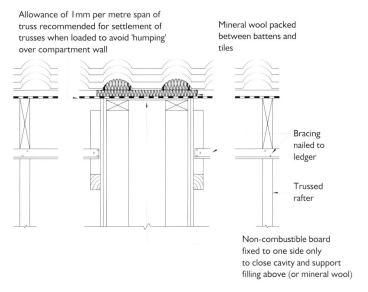

Allowance of 1mm per metre span of truss recommended for settlement of trusses when loaded to avoid 'humping' over compartment wall

Mineral wool packed between battens and tiles

Bracing nailed to ledger

Trussed rafter

Non-combustible board fixed to one side only to close cavity and support filling above (or mineral wool)

### 5.2.6.2 Junction at the eaves

The void formed by the slope of the rafter and the horizontal soffit to the eaves should be firestopped at each party wall position. This can be achieved by fixing a non-combustible board to all faces of the projecting spandrel frames or by filling the space with mineral wool. If a board is used, it should be cut to suit the profile of the roof slope and be tightly butted to the soffit and fascia board.

**Figure 5.4 Party wall/eaves junction**

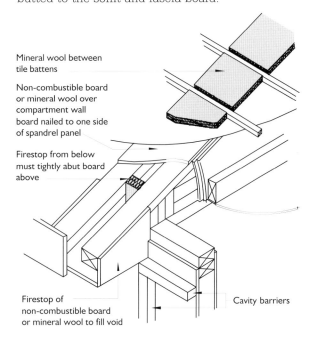

Mineral wool between tile battens

Non-combustible board or mineral wool over compartment wall board nailed to one side of spandrel panel

Firestop from below must tightly abut board above

Firestop of non-combustible board or mineral wool to fill void

Cavity barriers

The party wall firestop should project out to the fascia line and the vertical stop between the two frames should continue up to form a tight joint. Even small gaps at these junctions could create a flue effect, inducing vertical spread of smoke and flame in the event of a fire. See Figure 5.4.

### 5.2.6.3 Junction with external walls

There are no restrictions on the type of cladding passing across the ends of party walls. The cavity behind the cladding should be sealed with a cavity barrier at the party wall. This confines cavity fire within the boundaries of one occupancy or compartment.

In addition to vertical cavity barriers, a vertical fire stop seals the junction of the two timber frame leaves at the external cavity. This is usually a 50 mm thick wire reinforced mineral wool quilt stapled or nailed to one side. Alternatively it could be a non-combustible board fixed to the face of one of the two wall frames. Figure 5.5 shows a typical detail with brick cladding; a similar detail using tile hanging is shown in Figure 9.13.

**Figure 5.5 Junction of party wall with external wall**

Cavity barrier, With thinner claddings fixed to the panel face it is common practice to use a section of mineral wool quilt to close the cavity.  See Figure 9.13

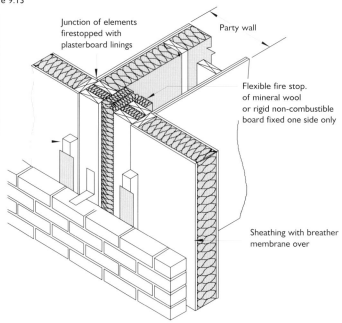

Junction of elements firestopped with plasterboard linings

Party wall

Flexible fire stop. of mineral wool or rigid non-combustible board fixed one side only

Sheathing with breather membrane over

### 5.2.6.4 Internal junctions

The integrity of the party wall against fire spread and sound paths should be maintained. This is usually achieved by inserting additional vertical studs to fully support any plasterboard joint, or by running the layers of plasterboard through. See Figure 5.6.

**Figure 5.6 Party wall junction
with internal walls**

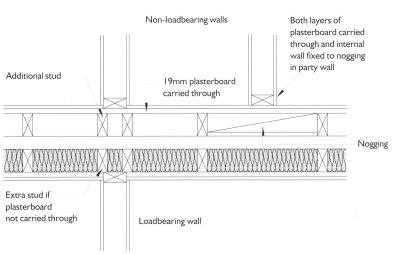

In practice, loadbearing internal walls are usually fixed directly to the party wall frames (so that the total structure can be erected prior to any lining materials being fitted) whilst non-loadbearing internal walls may be nailed to horizontal noggings fixed between the studs. Using this method, the plasterboard should run through before fixing the internal wall framing to ensure a sealed connection.

In some plan forms it is necessary for several party walls to abut. Figure 5.7 illustrates a junction between four party walls as a typical example of this junction.

**Figure 5.7 Junction between
party walls**

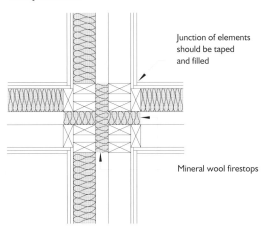

## 5.2.7 Penetration of linings

Current Regulations in Scotland and Northern Ireland do not permit services in the void formed by the party wall. The England and Wales Regulations permit wall linings to be penetrated and services run in the void, subject to the integrity of the wall for fire resistance and sound insulation being maintained.

Wherever possible, however, services should be routed away from the party wall or should be surface mounted if positioned on it.

Electrical socket outlets, switches or other service ducts in party walls should not be fixed back to back and the boxes should be protected at the back by plasterboard or other material equal in performance to that used on the wall surface. Any hole cut into the wall lining (eg for outlet boxes) should be as tight as possible around the service connection and sealed with mineral wool pugging or similar. See Chapter 10 'Services'.

Water services should not be contained within the party wall but may be fitted in a specially designed service duct. See Chapter 10 for further details.

## 5.2.8 Steps and staggers

Changes in floor level because of ground contours often occur at party walls. Adjoining buildings may also stagger in plan, with or without steps. These conditions give rise to special requirements in detailing.

With all steps and staggers, especially if they are substantial in dimension, the structural stability of both units should be checked with particular regard to wind forces acting on the party walls where they effectively become external walls.

As the party wall is formed using two independent frames, it is necessary to clad the exposed wall area above the lower roof level with lightweight cladding. The cladding should have the required surface spread of flame (reaction to fire) performance and provide the appropriate fire resistance from outside to the upper building. See Figures 5.8, 5.9 and 5.10.

**Figure 5.8 Plan at stagger or step and stagger: Timber frame party wall**

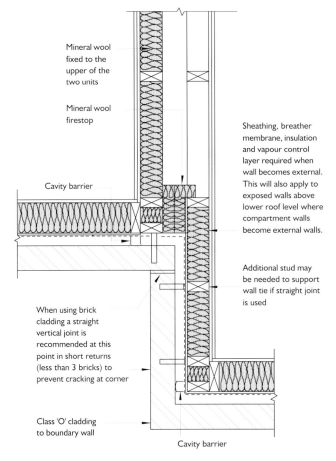

Mineral wool fixed to the upper of the two units

Mineral wool firestop

Cavity barrier

Sheathing, breather membrane, insulation and vapour control layer required when wall becomes external. This will also apply to exposed walls above lower roof level where compartment walls become external walls.

Additional stud may be needed to support wall tie if straight joint is used

When using brick cladding a straight vertical joint is recommended at this point in short returns (less than 3 bricks) to prevent cracking at corner

Class 'O' cladding to boundary wall

Cavity barrier

## Figure 5.9 Section showing stepped buildings: Timber frame party wall

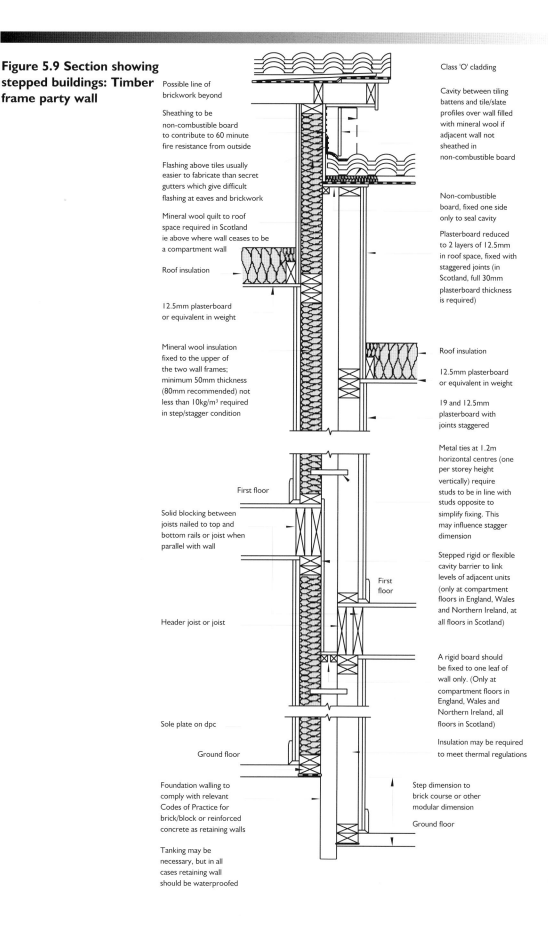

Possible line of brickwork beyond

Sheathing to be non-combustible board to contribute to 60 minute fire resistance from outside

Flashing above tiles usually easier to fabricate than secret gutters which give difficult flashing at eaves and brickwork

Mineral wool quilt to roof space required in Scotland ie above where wall ceases to be a compartment wall

Roof insulation

12.5mm plasterboard or equivalent in weight

Mineral wool insulation fixed to the upper of the two wall frames; minimum 50mm thickness (80mm recommended) not less than 10kg/m³ required in step/stagger condition

First floor

Solid blocking between joists nailed to top and bottom rails or joist when parallel with wall

Header joist or joist

Sole plate on dpc

Ground floor

Foundation walling to comply with relevant Codes of Practice for brick/block or reinforced concrete as retaining walls

Tanking may be necessary, but in all cases retaining wall should be waterproofed

Class 'O' cladding

Cavity between tiling battens and tile/slate profiles over wall filled with mineral wool if adjacent wall not sheathed in non-combustible board

Non-combustible board, fixed one side only to seal cavity

Plasterboard reduced to 2 layers of 12.5mm in roof space, fixed with staggered joints (in Scotland, full 30mm plasterboard thickness is required)

Roof insulation

12.5mm plasterboard or equivalent in weight

19 and 12.5mm plasterboard with joints staggered

Metal ties at 1.2m horizontal centres (one per storey height vertically) require studs to be in line with studs opposite to simplify fixing. This may influence stagger dimension

Stepped rigid or flexible cavity barrier to link levels of adjacent units (only at compartment floors in England, Wales and Northern Ireland, at all floors in Scotland)

A rigid board should be fixed to one leaf of wall only. (Only at compartment floors in England, Wales and Northern Ireland, all floors in Scotland)

Insulation may be required to meet thermal regulations

First floor

Step dimension to brick course or other modular dimension

Ground floor

When it is a design requirement that the exposed wall at the step or stagger is brick clad, it is normal practice to provide a masonry core between party wall frames to support the exposed brickwork above the lower roof level. It imposes few problems but the sequence of operations should allow for the additional time in constructing the core wall and for different trades to be involved at the erection phase. It does, however, simplify junction details as the brickwork can be projected forwards or backwards on plan to form the external wall cladding to staggered situations as well as downwards to provide a retaining wall (in part) at steps in the ground. See Figures 5.10 and 5.11.

**Figure 5.10 Plan at stagger or step and stagger: Timber frame with brick/block core wall**

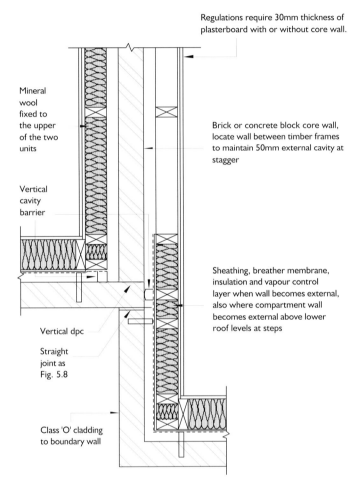

Regulations require 30mm thickness of plasterboard with or without core wall.

Mineral wool fixed to the upper of the two units

Vertical cavity barrier

Brick or concrete block core wall, locate wall between timber frames to maintain 50mm external cavity at stagger

Sheathing, breather membrane, insulation and vapour control layer when wall becomes external, also where compartment wall becomes external above lower roof levels at steps

Vertical dpc

Straight joint as Fig. 5.8

Class 'O' cladding to boundary wall

## Figure 5.11 Section showing stepped buildings: Timber frame with brick/block core wall

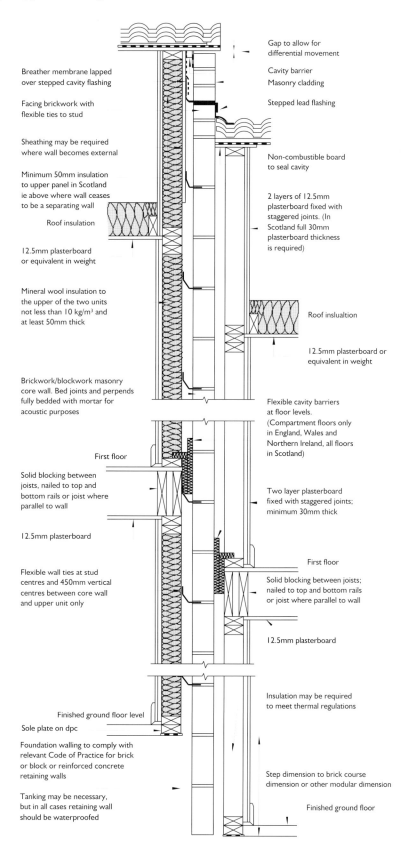

Breather membrane lapped over stepped cavity flashing

Facing brickwork with flexible ties to stud

Sheathing may be required where wall becomes external

Minimum 50mm insulation to upper panel in Scotland ie above where wall ceases to be a separating wall

Roof insulation

12.5mm plasterboard or equivalent in weight

Mineral wool insulation to the upper of the two units not less than 10 kg/m³ and at least 50mm thick

Brickwork/blockwork masonry core wall. Bed joints and perpends fully bedded with mortar for acoustic purposes

First floor

Solid blocking between joists, nailed to top and bottom rails or joist where parallel to wall

12.5mm plasterboard

Flexible wall ties at stud centres and 450mm vertical centres between core wall and upper unit only

Finished ground floor level

Sole plate on dpc

Foundation walling to comply with relevant Code of Practice for brick or block or reinforced concrete retaining walls

Tanking may be necessary, but in all cases retaining wall should be waterproofed

Gap to allow for differential movement

Cavity barrier

Masonry cladding

Stepped lead flashing

Non-combustible board to seal cavity

2 layers of 12.5mm plasterboard fixed with staggered joints. (In Scotland full 30mm plasterboard thickness is required)

Roof insulaltion

12.5mm plasterboard or equivalent in weight

Flexible cavity barriers at floor levels. (Compartment floors only in England, Wales and Northern Ireland, all floors in Scotland)

Two layer plasterboard fixed with staggered joints; minimum 30mm thick

First floor

Solid blocking between joists; nailed to top and bottom rails or joist where parallel to wall

12.5mm plasterboard

Insulation may be required to meet thermal regulations

Step dimension to brick course dimension or other modular dimension

Finished ground floor

91

### 5.2.8.1 Dimensions for steps and staggers

The module of the external wall cladding, eg brick coursing, is likely to be the governing factor at steps between claddings. Although not essential, it is preferable to stagger buildings on plan so that the stud positions in the party wall frames are directly opposite each other. This simplifies the installation of the metal ties required to connect the two wall frames together (and any vertical cavity barrier required in separating walls).

Steps and staggers can be dimensioned so that a change in roof plane occurs on both pitches or a common roof plane is maintained on one side of a dual pitch roof. It is important to ensure adequate roof separation for the correct detailing of verges and flashings. A small change in roof plane is difficult to weatherproof adequately and is better avoided. See Figure 5.12a.

**Figure 5.12 Step and stagger dimensions**

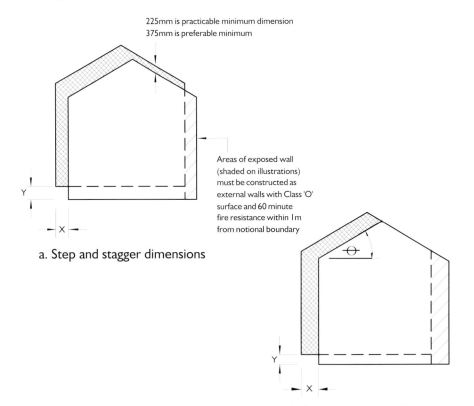

225mm is practicable minimum dimension
375mm is preferable minimum

Areas of exposed wall (shaded on illustrations) must be constructed as external walls with Class 'O' surface and 60 minute fire resistance within 1m from notional boundary

a. Step and stagger dimensions

b. Step and stagger dimensions with common roof plane

The relationship of step and stagger to give a common roof slope (Figure 5.12b) may be found by the following formula:

$$y \div x = \text{tangent } \theta$$

where x = dimension of stagger   y = dimension of step   $\theta$ = angle of roof pitch

For example: Assuming a roof pitch of 30° and a step of 8 brick courses (600 mm)

$$600 \div x = \text{tangent } 30°$$

$$x = 600 \div \text{tangent } 30°$$

Therefore stagger = 1040 mm

When brickwork cladding is used, dimension y should be a brick course module so that coursing can continue across the stepped area.

## 5.2.9 Specific requirements for separating walls in Scotland

In Scotland the void formed by the separating wall frames should be subdivided by cavity barriers at junctions with floors, roof and at 10 m maximum horizontal centres.

Several types of cavity barrier are permitted but 50 mm thick wire reinforced mineral wool is generally used. A non-combustible board is acceptable as an alternative and should be fastened to one leaf only to reduce sound transmission across the wall.

# 5.3 Compartment walls for buildings other than dwellings

## 5.3.1 Compartment wall construction

As there is no specific requirement for sound resistance, this type of compartment wall can be constructed as a single skin wall (Figure 5.13). The required fire resistance is achieved by multiple layers of plasterboard lining. A timber stud wall with studs at least 37 mm wide and with two 12.5 mm thick layers of gypsum plasterboard fixed with joints staggered and exposed joints taped and filled will provide 60 minutes fire resistance. (See Figure 4.24).

The wall should form a complete barrier to fire, including in the roof spaces. The complete fire barrier includes not only the wall itself, but the junctions with the roof and the external walls and any penetration of the wall permitted under the Regulations.

The compartment wall with plasterboard linings will usually provide adequate resistance to wind load on the front and rear walls. However, additional bracing can be introduced into the wall if structural calculations indicate that the safe racking resistance of plasterboard is exceeded. This can be provided by sheathing one or both faces of the wall with a wood-based board before the application of the plasterboard linings or by substituting fibre reinforced gypsum plasterboard or cement-bonded particleboard for the first layer of plasterboard (subject to appropriate racking calculations).

The junctions of the compartment wall with the roof and external walls and internal walls will be, in principle, the same as described in Section 5.2.6.

## 5.3.2 Openings

Compartment walls may contain openings for doors. The door and frame should have the appropriate fire resistance (usually half that of the wall but never less than 30 minutes) and the joint between the wall and the door frame should be pugged with mineral wool or intumescent mastic to form an equivalent barrier to fire to that of the door.

**Figure 5.13 Section through compartment wall with no acoustic requirements (non-dwelling use)**

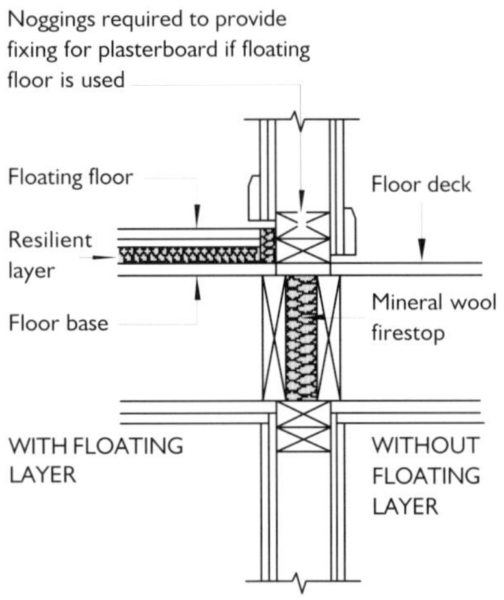

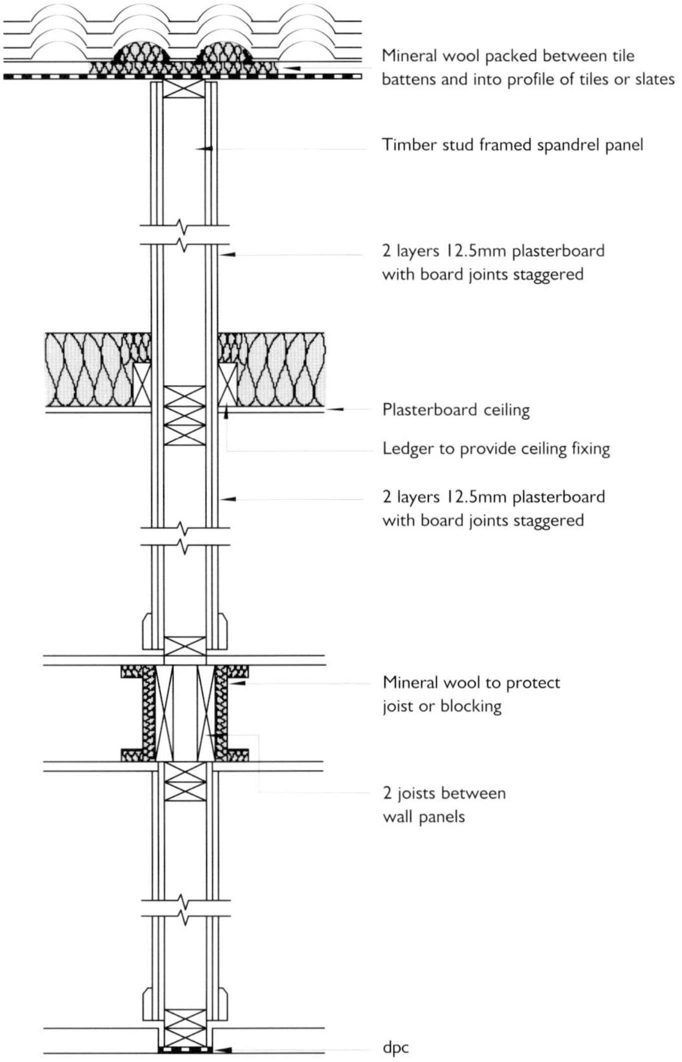

Mineral wool packed between tile battens and into profile of tiles or slates

Timber stud framed spandrel panel

2 layers 12.5mm plasterboard with board joints staggered

Plasterboard ceiling

Ledger to provide ceiling fixing

2 layers 12.5mm plasterboard with board joints staggered

Mineral wool to protect joist or blocking

2 joists between wall panels

dpc

Noggings required to provide fixing for plasterboard if floating floor is used

Floating floor

Floor deck

Resilient layer

Floor base

Mineral wool firestop

WITH FLOATING LAYER

WITHOUT FLOATING LAYER

Detail of junction of compartment wall and compartment floor. Joists parallel to wall

Section through compartment wall. Joists parallel to wall

## 5.3.3 Penetration of linings

Wall linings may be penetrated and services run in the wall, subject to the integrity of the fire resistance of the wall being maintained. Wherever possible, electrical services should be routed away from the compartment wall or should be surface mounted if positioned on it.

Electrical socket outlets or switches placed in compartment walls should not be fixed back to back and the boxes should be protected at the back by plasterboard or other material equal in performance to that used on the wall surface. Any hole cut into the wall lining should be as tight as possible around the service connection and sealed with mineral wool pugging or similar. See Chapter 10 'Services'.

Water services should not be contained within the compartment wall but may be run in specially designed service ducts within the wall thickness. See Chapter 10 for further details.

# 6 Intermediate floors

This chapter refers to intermediate floors which are a loadbearing element of structure and which are contained within a single occupancy. Party (compartment or separating) floors which separate occupancies or divide buildings into compartments are dealt with in Chapter 7.

## 6.1 Design requirements

The structural design should be carried out in accordance with the requirements of BS 5268-2. In dwellings, the live load for floors is usually taken as 1.5 kN/m$^2$ and the deflection criterion is 0.003 times span or 14 mm, whichever is the least.

In timber frame structures, the intermediate floor generally acts as a diaphragm to transmit wind loads to the wall structure. In all other respects it is similar to a timber floor in any other type of construction.

The floor is required to have fire resistance from below and this is achieved by the ceiling, the joists and the floor decking working as a composite construction. National Building Regulations differ in respect of what is allowable and should be checked for specific requirements.

The ceiling should also provide the required surface spread of flame (reaction to fire) performance. The performance of commonly used lining materials is outlined in Section 1.3.2.

Test or assessment evidence of fire resistance will be required where linings other than plasterboard are used.

Currently, there are no regulatory requirements for sound insulation in intermediate floors but National Regulations should be checked. Some designers already include mineral wool insulation to reduce sound transmission through the floor.

There are no thermal insulation requirements for intermediate floors, except when the floor projects out beyond the wall beneath, and is over an open area, such as a car port or a porch, or is over an unheated space such as a garage or where it is at the edge of an attic room adjoining the ventilated roof space.

The rules for notching and drilling joists for services are set out in BS 5268-2 and are described in Chapter 10.

The housing warranty and guarantee authorities may have specific requirements for floors between toilet areas and other rooms and for notching and drilling of joists. The latest edition of their manuals should be consulted where relevant.

In addition to meeting the Design Requirements, the successful completion and quality of the timber frame building is dependent on good on-site practice in terms of accuracy in setting out and erecting components. Guidance is given in Appendix 3 Site Supervisor's Checklist.

## 6.2 Design of intermediate floors

Platform frame construction is so described because the intermediate floors are constructed as working platforms on top of the wall panels. The upper floor wall panels are erected from this platform. The working deck can be either a temporary platform of scaffold boards or sheet material on the joists, or the final floor deck if this is of suitable material. When the floor deck is fixed after the upper wall panels, it is common practice to incorporate floor deck thickness packers beneath the wall panels so that the internal and external wall panel heights are constant. The detail of the floor-to-wall junctions varies depending upon which method is adopted. Figure 6.1 illustrates a typical floor arrangement and Figures 6.2 to 6.5 show typical details.

### Figure 6.1 Intermediate floor: Typical components

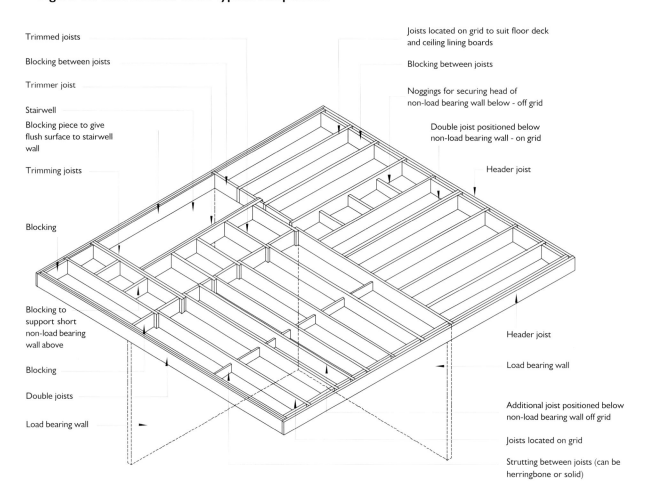

Trimmed joists

Blocking between joists

Trimmer joist

Stairwell

Blocking piece to give flush surface to stairwell wall

Trimming joists

Blocking

Blocking to support short non-load bearing wall above

Blocking

Double joists

Load bearing wall

Joists located on grid to suit floor deck and ceiling lining boards

Blocking between joists

Noggings for securing head of non-load bearing wall below - off grid

Double joist positioned below non-load bearing wall - on grid

Header joist

Header joist

Load bearing wall

Additional joist positioned below non-load bearing wall off grid

Joists located on grid

Strutting between joists (can be herringbone or solid)

Floors may be constructed using individual joists which are placed, fixed and decked on site or, if a crane is available, the floor can be of factory prefabricated panels for speed of erection; either as an open joist and deck panel or with ceiling lining included as a closed panel.

**Figure 6.2 Typical floor/ external wall junctions: Joists at right angles to wall** (Insulation not shown for clarity)

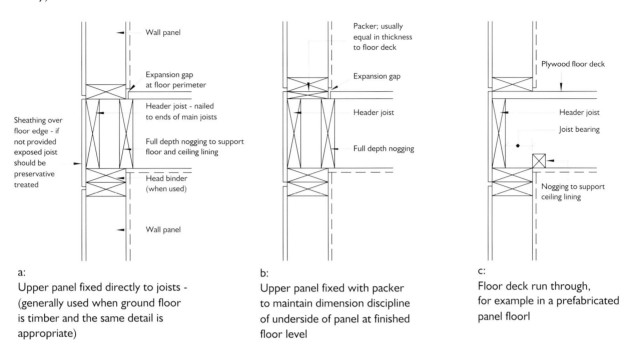

a:
Upper panel fixed directly to joists - (generally used when ground floor is timber and the same detail is appropriate)

b:
Upper panel fixed with packer to maintain dimension discipline of underside of panel at finished floor level

c:
Floor deck run through, for example in a prefabricated panel floorl

**Figure 6.3 Typical floor/ external wall junctions: Joists parallel with wall** (Insulation not shown for clarity)

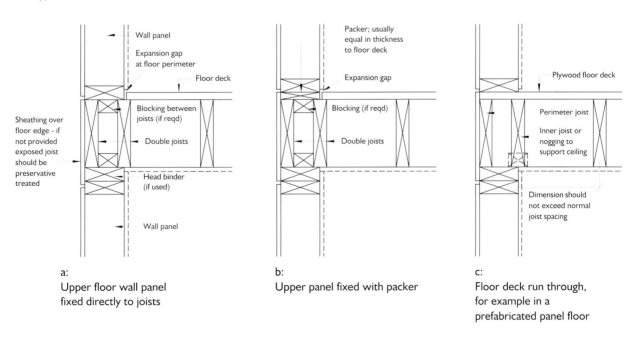

a:
Upper floor wall panel fixed directly to joists

b:
Upper panel fixed with packer

c:
Floor deck run through, for example in a prefabricated panel floor

**Figure 6.4 Typical floor/ loadbearing internal wall junction**

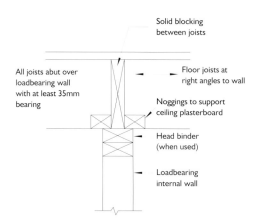

Solid blocking between joists

All joists abut over loadbearing wall with at least 35mm bearing

Floor joists at right angles to wall

Noggings to support ceiling plasterboard

Head binder (when used)

Loadbearing internal wall

**Figure 6.5 Joining joists end to end**
Note: The use of sheet types of floor deck precludes lapping joists on supports when joining them, unless the junction occurs beneath a wall to the upper storey. Joists should abut end to end and bearing should be checked. Splice plates or short lengths of plywood or OSB should be used to give additional stiffness

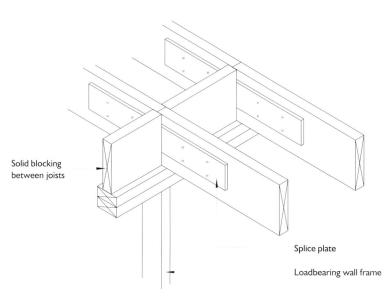

Solid blocking between joists

Splice plate

Loadbearing wall frame

## 6.3 Floor joists

Timber joist sizes can be selected from the tables in Building Regulation documents or from BS 8103-3. Joists can also be calculated in accordance with BS 5268-2. Appendix 2 gives typical weights of materials for assessment of dead loads.

The depth to breadth ratio of joists and beams should be checked to ensure that there is no risk of buckling under design load. The BS 5268-2 recommendations are given in Table 3.2. Regardless of the depth to breadth ratio of the joists, strutting between joists should be used to stiffen the floor as given in Table 3.3.

Joists are normally spaced at either 400 mm or 600 mm centres to conform with standard plasterboard and timber based board sizes. Closer centres are occasionally used when either the floor span or loading make this necessary.

When wall panels have a double top rail or a head binder and a header joist is used, floor joists can normally be set out in the most economical layout in respect of joist size and floor deck span capacity, independently of the stud positions. Trimmers or floor beams will usually require support from additional studs. When wall panels have a single head rail, ie no separate head binder is used, the joists should occur over the studs in the panels. Figure 6.6 shows the maximum recommended offset.

**Figure 6.6 Maximum offset of joists or rafters from loadbearing studs in wall frame with a single top rail**

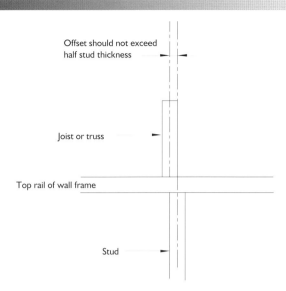

Offset should not exceed half stud thickness

Joist or truss

Top rail of wall frame

Stud

In order to maintain a constant wall height throughout the building, it is normal practice to use a constant floor depth and adjust the joist centres to compensate for varying span and load requirements. Alternatively, adjustment can be made to the joist width and/or the grade of timber used for the longer spans.

Joints in joists should only occur over loadbearing walls or beams. Joists which overlap over the wall or beam should be nailed together and not project more than 100 mm beyond the support. Joists which are butt jointed over the support should be joined mechanically to both sides of the joists using a structural wood-based board or galvanised or stainless steel proprietary nail plates. The gussets or nail plates should extend to at least three quarters of the joist depth and be nailed with at least four 3 mm minimum diameter nails into each side of the joist.

## 6.3.1 Notching and drilling

Recommendations for the allowable sizes of notches and holes in floor joists are included in BS 5268-2 and are shown in Section 10.2.

## 6.3.2 Trimmers and beams

Floor depth beams or trimmers can be fabricated by nailing or bolting floor joists together so that they act structurally as one unit. See Figure 6.7. BS 8103-3 and the TRADA *Approved Document Timber Intermediate Floors for Dwellings* include tables giving sizes/spans of trimmers, trimming joists and fixing schedules.

**Figure 6.7 Double joists used to form a floor depth beam**
Note: Multiple joists nailed together to a designed nailing pattern may avoid deep downstand beams. Joists are shown fixed with proprietary joist hangers. Alternatively a timber ledger can be nailed to the side of the double joist and the abutting joists notched over it. Ledger nailing should be calculated and notch size approved by engineer.

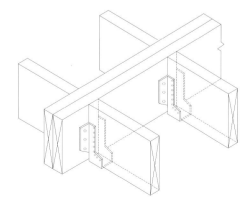

When long spans and/or larger loads have to be supported, beams of greater depth may be required. Alternatively, trimmers and beams can be of hardwood, structural timber composite or steel flitch beams. Where beams and trimmers are of greater depth than the floor thickness, both downstand and upstand arrangements can be used and they must be provided with adequate protection against fire. See Figures 6.8 and 6.9. Steel beams can be used but can be difficult to place and fix in the timber structure and will also need fire protection.

**Figure 6.8 Typical beam supports to intermediate floors**
Note: Multiple joists nailed together to a designed nailing pattern may avoid deep downstand beams. Joists are shown fixed with proprietary joist hangers. Alternatively a timber ledger can be nailed to the side of the double joist and the abutting joists notched over it. Ledger nailing should be calculated and notch size approved by engineer.

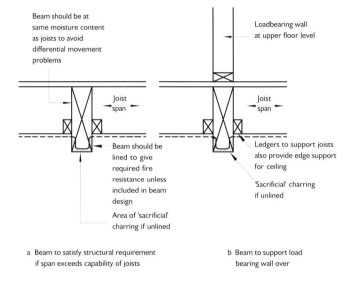

a  Beam to satisfy structural requirement if span exceeds capability of joists

b  Beam to support load bearing wall over

1  Beam set partially into floor depth

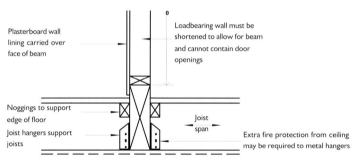

2  Upstand beam to give flush ceiling

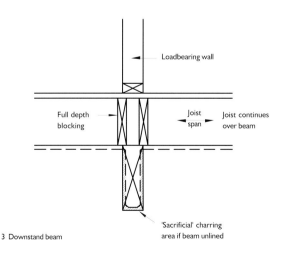

3 Downstand beam

**Figure 6.9 Alternative methods of supporting floor beams in wall framing**

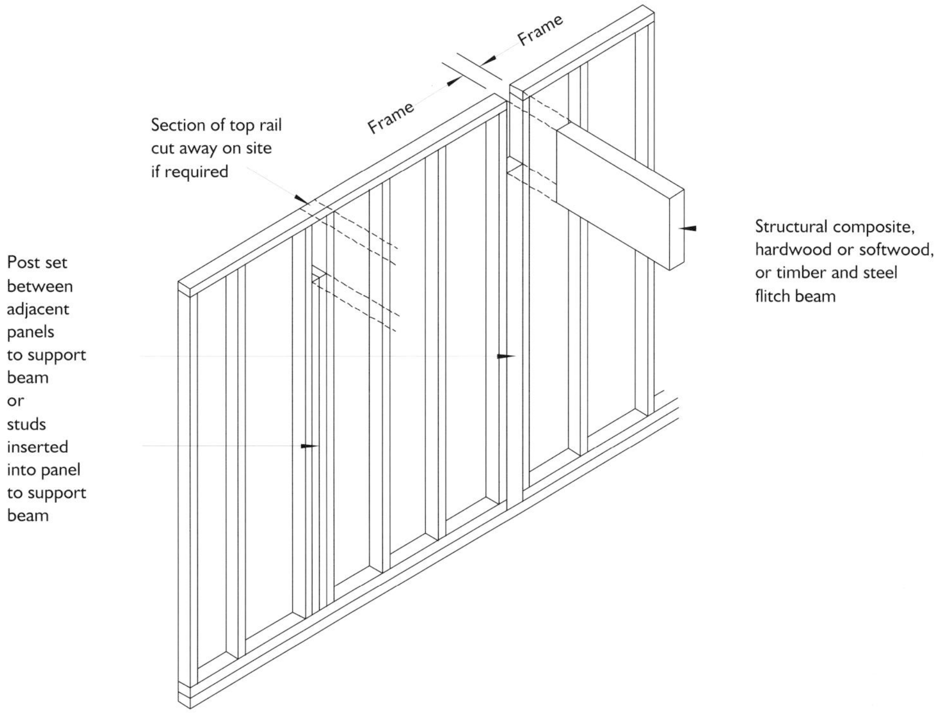

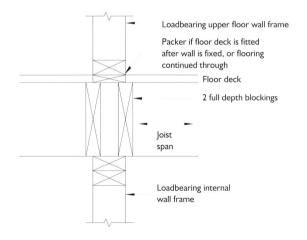

Section of top rail cut away on site if required

Frame

Frame

Frame

Post set between adjacent panels to support beam or studs inserted into panel to support beam

Structural composite, hardwood or softwood, or timber and steel flitch beam

Beams and trimmers in floor construction will require additional studs or posts in the timber wall panels to support them and transfer their load to the foundations. When small panel construction is used it is often possible to locate a panel junction beneath the beam or trimmer so that the connected studs form a post to provide support. In large panel structures or where this is not possible, additional studs or posts should be incorporated into the wall panels. Figure 6.10 illustrates typical solutions. The implications of the actual deflections of long span trimmers and beams should be considered to ensure that deflections do not impose load onto non-loadbearing wall elements and that combined joist and beam deflections are within acceptable limits.

**Figure 6.10 Typical detail where loadbearing walls are located both above and below intermediate floor**
Note: Detail shows joists at right angles to walls. Where joists are parallel, full depth blockings are replaced by two joists or a single joist and noggings to support the ceiling and floor deck

Loadbearing upper floor wall frame

Packer if floor deck is fitted after wall is fixed, or flooring continued through

Floor deck

2 full depth blockings

Joist span

Loadbearing internal wall frame

When deep beams are necessary to carry loads over long spans, these may be of solid timber or a composite structural timber beam. If solid timber is used it is important that it is dried to the appropriate moisture content to avoid differential shrinkage. It can be difficult to achieve appropriate moisture contents throughout large solid timber sections and it may be preferable to bolt together two or more thinner sections or to use a structural timber composite.

## 6.4 Supporting internal walls

The floor framing provides support for both loadbearing and non-loadbearing internal walls and transfers these loads to the supporting walls below. It also provides a head fixing for the lower wall frames. Where non-loadbearing walls occur above the floor, loads must be transferred to the walls below. See Figure 6.11. Additional joists will often be required to carry non-loadbearing walls which run parallel to the joist span. Internal walls at right angles to the joist span can normally be carried by the joists but the additional load imposed should be allowed for when selecting or calculating joist sizes. Typically the spanning capacity of the joist is reduced by 10%.

**Figure 6.11 Providing support and fixings for non-loadbearing internal walls**

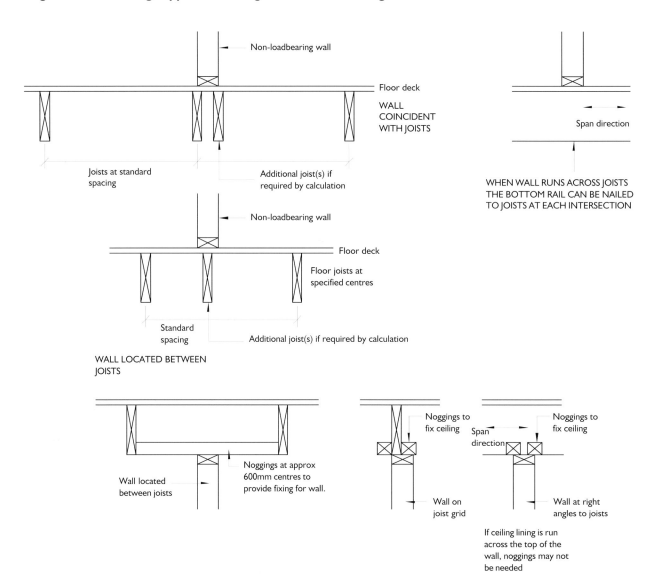

## 6.5 Fire resistance

Notional periods of fire resistance for intermediate floors can be determined by tests as defined in Regulations. Table 6.1 gives details of typical specifications.

**Table 6.1 Notional periods of fire resistance: Intermediate floors**

| Joists min breadth (mm) | Joists max spacing (mm) | Floor deck | Ceiling type |
|---|---|---|---|
| **Modified 30 minutes fire resistance** | | | |
| 37 | 600 | Any structurally suitable square edged flooring | 12.5 mm plasterboard with joints taped and filled |
| 37 | 600 | At least 15 mm t & g boarding, 15 mm t & g plywood, 15 mm t & g OSB or 15 mm t & g chipboard * | 12.5 mm plasterboard with joints taped and filled |
| **30 minutes fire resistance** | | | |
| 37 | 600 | Any structurally suitable square edged flooring | 15 mm plasterboard with joints taped and filled |
| 37 | 600 | At least 21 mm t & g boarding, 15 mm t & g plywood, 15 mm t & g OSB or 15 mm t & g chipboard * | 12.5 mm plasterboard with joints taped and filled |
| **60 minutes fire resistance** | | | |
| 37 | 600 | At least 21 mm t & g boarding, 15 mm t & g plywood, 15 mm t & g OSB or 15 mm t & g chipboard *  joints staggered, | Not less than 30 mm plasterboard (usually 19 mm plus 12.5 mm) with joints in outer layer taped and filled |

* Square edge 15 mm plywood, 15 mm OSB or 15 mm chipboard may be used provided all joints are backed by timber joists or noggings at least 37 mm in breadth

## 6.6 Floor decks

The intermediate floor deck of a timber frame structure acts as a horizontal diaphragm transmitting lateral loads through to the wall structure. Correct and secure nailing is therefore important.

Floor decks are normally of either tongued and grooved softwood, flooring grade wood chipboard, oriented strand board, plywood or, less commonly, cement bonded particleboard. Details of these decking materials and spans are given in Section 3.4.1 'Decking for suspended timber ground floors'. The material selected will depend upon the type of finish (if specified) to be laid over the deck, the sequence of construction, cost factors or personal preference.

Intermediate floors can be designed as stressed skin panels; this entails gluing and/or mechanically fixing the decking to the joists in the factory and in some instances may also incorporate a similar structural membrane beneath the joists. This technique can be useful in buildings with long span floors, such as offices or shops. However, most domestic scale floors are constructed using conventional joists and decking or with simply constructed floor panels since the structural sophistication of stressed skin panels is generally difficult to justify on economic grounds.

When the floor is prefabricated into panels for crane erection (Figure 6.12), the floor construction is generally similar to site constructed floors. It is necessary to develop a suitable detail to securely fix adjoining panels together to avoid the risk of differential deflection under differing loadings. The panels are usually prefabricated as components; 1200 mm or 2400 mm in width by either the panel's span dimension or the building's width or depth. The floor deck is fixed to the panel to provide lateral stiffness. The overall size is generally determined by the limitations of manufacture, transport or handling.

**Figure 6.12 Prefabricated floor panels for crane erection**
Note: Modular sections comprising the joists, floor deck and sometimes the ceiling lining and incorporating openings for staircases, holes and notches for services etc. Overall size and lifting method depends upon site accessibility, transport facilities and type of crane.

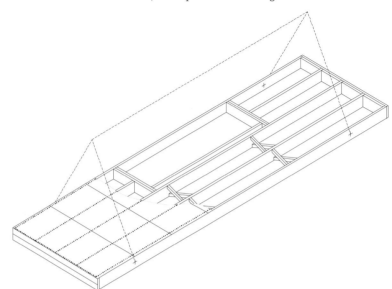

## 6.7 Ceiling linings

The ceiling lining provides a major contribution to the required fire resistance of the floor structure. The most commonly used ceiling lining is gypsum plasterboard, although other materials such as wood-based boards and timber boarding are used. Plasterboard sheets should be fixed in accordance with the manufacturer's recommendations and all edges of the sheets should be supported unless the board is at least 15 mm thick.

The Building Regulations require specific surface spread of flame (reaction to fire) classifications for ceilings which may entail treatment of timber and wood-based board materials.

When lining material other than plasterboard is used, evidence of the floor's compliance with the required periods of fire resistance is necessary. Timber board ceiling linings can satisfy these criteria, depending on thickness. Thinner timber boards can be used with a backing of plasterboard.

Downstand beams projecting below the ceiling should have the same fire resistance as the floor structure. This can be incorporated into the beam design or be obtained by lining with plasterboard or additional sacrificial timber cladding of the necessary thickness. For example, 18 mm of softwood board cladding would protect the beam for 30 minutes. A similar solution is required if it is proposed to expose the floor joists to the room below. See Figure 6.13. The method for calculating 'sacrificial' timber for achieving stability when timber is subject to fire is given in *BS 5268-4 Fire resistance of timber structures. Section 4.1 Recommendations for calculating fire resistance of timber members.*

**Figure 6.13 Exposed beams**

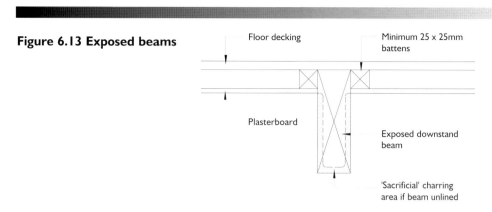

Floor decking

Minimum 25 x 25mm battens

Plasterboard

Exposed downstand beam

'Sacrificial' charring area if beam unlined

# 6.8 Cantilevered floors

The inherent stiffness and light weight of the timber frame structure makes it possible to cantilever the upper floors if required, providing this is allowed for in the structural calculations. The amount of projection will depend upon variables such as the weight and span of roof structure and wall cladding and the size and span of the floor joists.

Relatively small projections as shown in Figure 6.14 can be used to maintain the vertical plane of the elevation when claddings of different thickness are used at ground and upper floor levels. When this arrangement is required on return elevations, it is necessary to arrange the floor joists as shown in Figure 6.15 and provide a cantilevered corner joist to support the outer corner. Changing the direction of joists in this manner may affect the fixing of sheet materials and floor decking and require additional noggings between the cantilevered joists.

**Figure 6.14 Small overhangs to the upper floor**
Note: Adequate fixing between wall frames and floor construction must be provided

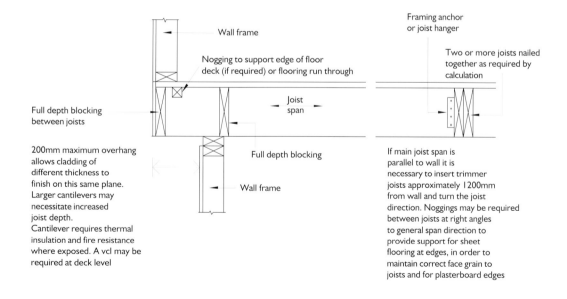

Wall frame

Nogging to support edge of floor deck (if required) or flooring run through

Framing anchor or joist hanger

Two or more joists nailed together as required by calculation

Joist span

Full depth blocking between joists

Full depth blocking

Wall frame

200mm maximum overhang allows cladding of different thickness to finish on this same plane. Larger cantilevers may necessitate increased joist depth.
Cantilever requires thermal insulation and fire resistance where exposed. A vcl may be required at deck level

If main joist span is parallel to wall it is necessary to insert trimmer joists approximately 1200mm from wall and turn the joist direction. Noggings may be required between joists at right angles to general span direction to provide support for sheet flooring at edges, in order to maintain correct face grain to joists and for plasterboard edges

**Figure 6.15 Cantilevered floor at external corner**

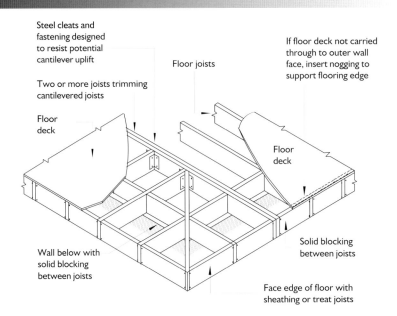

Steel cleats and fastening designed to resist potential cantilever uplift

Two or more joists trimming cantilevered joists

Floor deck

Floor joists

If floor deck not carried through to outer wall face, insert nogging to support flooring edge

Floor deck

Solid blocking between joists

Wall below with solid blocking between joists

Face edge of floor with sheathing or treat joists

Larger projections (Figure 6.16) are possible but require careful consideration at design stage to prevent overstressing of the floor structure. Fire resistance equal to that of the adjoining floor or of the supported wall (whichever is greater) will be required to the soffit of the projecting joists and exposed floors will need thermal insulation. Condensation risk should be checked using the '5 times rule' (see section 4.1.2.5) or by calculation in accordance with *BS 5250 Code of practice for control of condensation in buildings*.

**Figure 6.16 Cantilevered intermediate floor joists**
Note: Adequate fixing between wall frames and floor construction should be provided

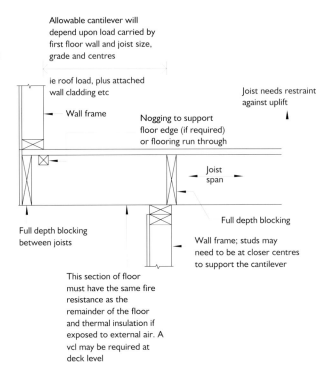

Allowable cantilever will depend upon load carried by first floor wall and joist size, grade and centres

ie roof load, plus attached wall cladding etc

Wall frame

Nogging to support floor edge (if required) or flooring run through

Joist needs restraint against uplift

Joist span

Full depth blocking

Full depth blocking between joists

Wall frame; studs may need to be at closer centres to support the cantilever

This section of floor must have the same fire resistance as the remainder of the floor and thermal insulation if exposed to external air. A vcl may be required at deck level

# 7 Party floors

## 7.1 Design requirements

'Party' floors are described in National Building Regulations as Compartment or Separating floors, depending upon the function being considered and the area of the country. See the Regulations for details. There are three types of party floor. These are:

♦ floors which separate dwellings from other dwellings and from other parts of the same building which are not used as dwellings.

♦ floors which separate different occupancies and purpose groups (excluding dwellings) within a building.

♦ floors which are required to subdivide a large building into compartments of specified size or volume for purposes of fire resistance.

Currently in Scotland, separating floors between flats less than a defined height may be of timber construction. Compartment floors are required to be of non-combustible construction.

In all cases, the party floor is required to have fire resistance from below, the required period varies depending upon the purpose group and location of the building. National Regulations vary and should be checked for specific cases.

In practice, the thickness of plasterboard ceiling required for sound resistance in flats is sufficient to enable the floor to achieve 60 minutes fire resistance. In all cases the walls supporting the floor must have the same fire resistance as is required for the floor.

The fire resistance of the party floor is obtained from the ceiling, the joists and the floor decking working as a composite construction. The ceiling should also have the required surface spread of flame (reaction to fire) performance.

Resistance to airborne and impact sound is required for floors which separate a dwelling from another dwelling or from another part of the same building above the dwelling. The floor of a dwelling over another part of the same building, including a machine or plant room, need have airborne sound resistance only. A separating floor which forms an open access balcony requires resistance to impact sound only.

Currently, sound resistance is usually achieved in a timber party floor by separating the floor deck from the 'walking surface' by floating layers, incorporating insulation within the floor and by having sufficient mass in the floor deck and the ceiling to reduce sound transmission. Current Building Regulations include prescriptive details of this type of floor. They also allow alternative constructions to be developed and tested to demonstrate that they meet the performance criteria prescribed in the regulations. Compartment floors other than those separating dwellings currently have no regulatory requirement for sound resistance, although in 'Other Residential' buildings, eg hotels, hostels etc, this is normally a design requirement. Changes to Regulations to include sound resistance requirements for such buildings have already been proposed.

There are no thermal insulation requirements for party floors, except when the floor projects out beyond the wall beneath, is over an open or unheated area (such as a car port, a porch or a garage), where the floor forms a balcony at the upper level or abuts a roof space adjacent to an attic room.

The structural design of the floor should be carried out in accordance with the requirements of BS 5268-2. In dwellings, the live load for floors is normally taken as 1.5 kN/m$^2$ and the deflection criterion is 0.003 times the span or 14 mm, whichever is the least. In timber frame structures the party floor commonly acts as a diaphragm to resist wind loads.

It is preferable to avoid running services in or through party floors whenever possible as there is a risk that the fire performance and/or sound insulation of the floor could be impaired. It will also avoid any possible future difficulty in gaining access to services when the parts of the building above and below the floor are in different occupancies. When services pass through the floor it is normal practice to form an enclosure above and below the floor, which is fire resistant and to seal the opening at the floor to maintain the fire and acoustic performance.

Further information on services in or through party floors is included in Chapter 10.

The requirement for airborne and impact sound resistance for party floors for dwellings is specific for this type of floor. Designers commonly utilise a similar floor design for buildings in other purpose groups where sound resistance is currently a user requirement.

In addition to meeting the Design Requirements, the successful completion and quality of the timber frame building is dependent on good on-site practice in terms of accuracy in setting out and erecting components. Guidance is given in Appendix 3 Site Supervisor's Checklist. Quality of workmanship is particuarly important in meeting anticipated levels of fire and acoustic performance.

## 7.2 Party floors for dwellings

Floors may be constructed using any materials and methods providing they meet the requirements of the Building Regulations for structural stability, fire resistance and sound insulation. Specified constructions are included in the supporting documents to Building Regulations. Test evidence of fire and sound resistance may be required by the building control authorities, see National Regulations for details.

## 7.2.1 Specified constructions

Current Regulations include three separate specifications for timber party floors which have been developed and used over a number of years and are accepted as providing adequate sound insulation and satisfactory fire resistance. These are described as:

♦ a ribbed floor with absorbent blanket

♦ a ribbed floor with heavy pugging

♦ a platform floor with absorbent blanket.

In neither of the ribbed floor designs can the floor deck be used to provide lateral stiffness (ie act as a diaphragm) to the timber frame structure and for this reason the platform floor is recommended for use in timber frame construction. This type of floor is also preferable in a platform frame timber structure in that it provides a working platform for the erection of the upper floors prior to the floating deck being laid. Figure 7.1 illustrates the platform floor.

Alternative floor constructions have been designed and tested and can be shown to provide adequate sound insulation. To obtain improved performance, especially for low frequency sound, the ceiling is usually de-coupled from the joists, for example with a resilient 'spring-type' bar to support the ceiling or with independent ceiling joists. Further improvements can be gained by adding more weight to the upper layers. Test evidence is normally held by the sponsors of the design.

The TRADA Technology *Report 1/2000 Acoustic performance of party walls and floors in timber framed buildings* gives details and the results from acoustic testing on 16 different floor constructions, including the 'standard floor' shown in Figure 7.1. 'Enhanced' and 'enhanced+' levels of performance well above those currently required by Regulations were achieved through increased mass, the use of proprietary resilient battens and decoupling ceilings. The tests included floors constructed using composite joists. Figure 7.2 illustrates a floor construction with separate ceiling joists which was included in the test programme.

### Figure 7.1 Platform floor with absorbent blanket

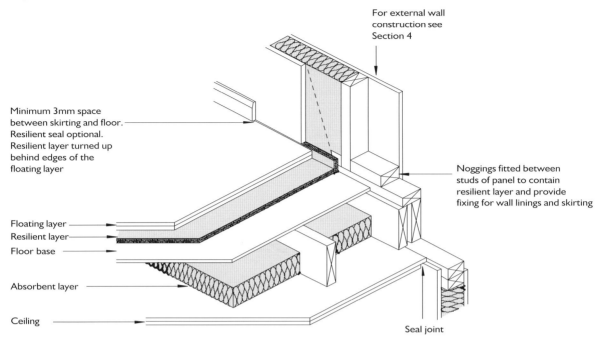

For external wall construction see Section 4

Minimum 3mm space between skirting and floor. Resilient seal optional. Resilient layer turned up behind edges of the floating layer

Noggings fitted between studs of panel to contain resilient layer and provide fixing for wall linings and skirting

Floating layer
Resilient layer
Floor base

Absorbent layer

Ceiling

Seal joint

### Floating layer:
May be 18 mm plywood to BS EN 636-2 and be one of the grades listed in BS 5268-2 or 18 mm P5 chipboard to BS EN 312-5 or P7 to BS EN 312-7 or 18 mm OSB 3 or OSB 4 to BS EN 300, with glued t and g joints, spot bonded (at approx 300 mm centres) to 19 mm plasterboard plank, or two layers of cement bonded particleboard OPC to BS EN 634-2, glued and screwed together and having a total thickness of 24 mm..
Joints between the layers of the floating layer should be staggered.

### Resilient layer:
Continuous layer of 25 mm mineral wool with a density between 60 and 100 kg/m$^3$.

### Floor base:
At least 12 mm thick wood-based board: Plywood should be to BS EN 636-2 and  be one of the grades listed in BS 5268-2. Chipboard should be P5 to BS EN 312-5 or P 7 to BS EN 312-7. OSB should be OSB 3 or OSB 4 to BS EN 300. Cement bonded particleboard should be OPC to BS EN 634-2.12 mm plywood and OSB may be used for joists spacings up to 600 mm, chipboard and cement bonded particleboards should be at least 15 mm thick to avoid damage or accidents during construction.
Information on the direction of laying wood-based boards over joists is included in Section 3.4.1.

### Absorbent layer:
At least 100 mm thick mineral wool with a density not less than 10 kg/m$^3$.

### Ceiling:
19 mm plasterboard plank plus 12.5 mm plasterboard sheets, fixed separately with joints staggered and with the joint to wall linings sealed; all joints in the outer layer should be backed by joists or noggings with nail or screw fixings to manufacturer's details. Plasterboard fixings should be :
12.5 mm board: 60 mm nails fixed as outer layer          19 mm plank: 60 mm nails fixed as the inner layer

### Floor joists:
Joists should be at 400 or 600 mm centres. (Note: Test evidence shows that joists at 600 mm centres can provide better sound insulation than joists at 400 mm centres).
Joist size, timber strength grade and spacings to be determined by calculation or from tables.

### Test results:
For detailed specification see TRADA Technology *Report 1/2000 Acoustic performance of party walls and floors in timber framed buildings*.

Sound insulation performance of tested floor

| Airborne $D_{nT,w}$ | $D_{nT,w} + C_{tr}$ | Impact $L'_{nT,w}$ | $L'_{nT,w} + C_I$ |
|---|---|---|---|
| 54 | 46 | 59 | 60 |

## Figure 7.2 Floor with ceiling supported on independent joists

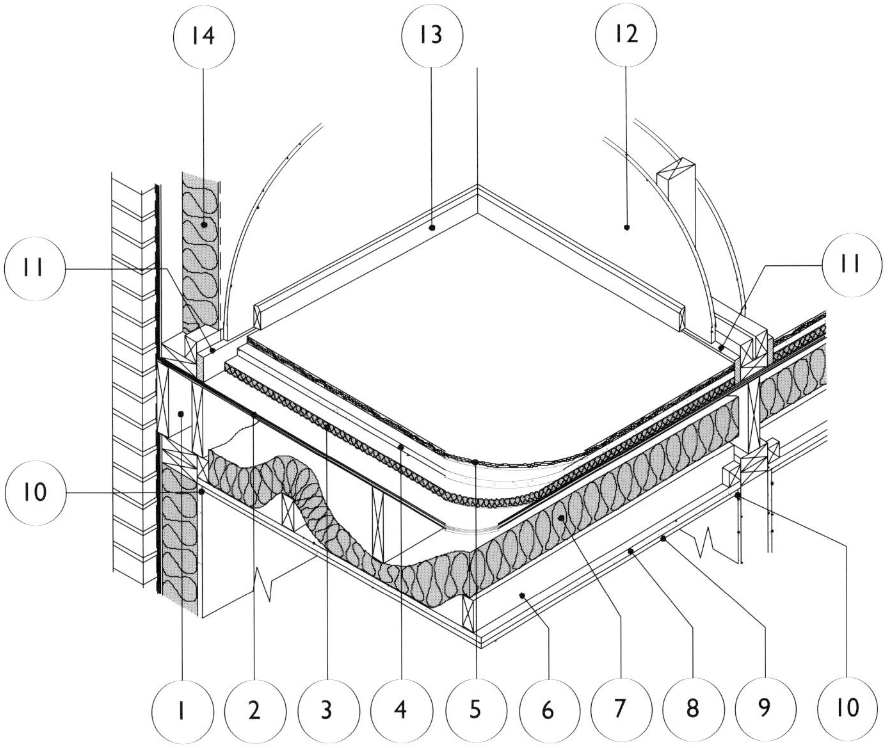

## Construction:

1       220 x 38 mm timber joist (Note: Space between joists should be filled with insulation)
2       15 mm OSB Type 3
3       25 mm glass wool slab (64 kg/m$^3$)
4       19 mm plasterboard
5       18 mm moisture resistant chipboard
6       89 x 38 mm timber ceiling joists (supported at mid-point)
7       100 mm glass wool quilt (10 kg/m$^3$)
8       19 mm plasterboard
9       12.5 mm plasterboard
10      Acoustic sealant at wall to ceiling joint with 10 mm gap between ceiling boards and wall
11      Resilient material at floor perimeter to prevent layers 4 and 5 contacting walls
12      Internal loadbearing wall
13      Skirting set 5 mm above chipboard deck to ensure there is no contact
14      External wall

## Test results:

For details see TRADA Technology *Report 1/2000 Acoustic performance of party walls and floors in timber framed buildings*.

Sound insulation performance of tested floor

| Airborne $D_{nT,w}$ | $D_{nT,w} + C_{tr}$ | Impact $L'_{nT,w}$ | $L'_{nT,w} + C_I$ |
|---|---|---|---|
| 58 | 48 | 56 | 58 |

## 7.2.2 Structure

Floor joists are normally spaced at either 400 or 600 mm centres. Test evidence has shown that floors with joists at 600 mm centres provide slightly better sound insulation. Joist sizes can be selected from tables in Building Regulation documents, from BS 8103-3 or calculated in accordance with BS 5268-2. Appendix 2 gives typical weights of materials for the assessment of dead loads.

The dead weight of party floors is greater than normal intermediate floors but this additional loading will not normally have any significant effect on the wall framing design.

Recommendations for the incorporation of trimmers and beams, depth to breadth ratios and for strutting included in Chapter 6 (Intermediate floors) are equally appropriate to party floors and should be incorporated in the specification where appropriate. Recommendations for the allowable sizes of notches and holes in joists are shown in Section 10.2.

Span tables generally make no allowance for the weight of non-loadbearing walls. Typically where the wall is parallel to the joists it requires support from one or two additional joists. When the wall is at right angles to the joists, the spanning capacity of the joist is typically reduced by 10%. Non-loadbearing walls up to a weight of 81.5 kg/m run on the upper floor may be carried by the floor base layer or by the floating layer (See Figure 7.3). When walls are supported by the floating layer, it is important that no wall fixings penetrate through the resilient layer. Supporting non-loadbearing walls on the floating floor avoids the need to cut the floor deck between walls and allows it to be laid in relatively large areas. It also reduces the risk of flanking sound transmission through the floor which might occur if the internal walls in adjoining floors were rigidly fixed to the floor structure.

Loadbearing internal walls should be constructed from the floor base.

## 7.2.3 Fire performance

The minimum 30 mm of plasterboard required to meet current sound resistance requirements for floors between dwellings is sufficient to provide 60 minutes fire resistance when correctly fixed to floor joists with a minimum width of 37 mm. The plasterboard is usually fixed in two layers, the first of 19 mm gypsum planks and the second of 12.5 mm plasterboard sheets. The board joints should be staggered and the joints in the outer layer taped and filled. Further details of the floor specification are shown in Figure 7.1.

For other floor designs, methods of determining fire resistance performance are outlined in Section 1.3.2.

All walls supporting party floors should have fire resistance equal to that required by the floor supported, eg 60 minute fire resisting floors should be supported by 60 minute fire resisting walls. This will normally be a timber stud framed wall with studs at least 37 mm wide and with two layers of 12.5 mm plasterboard to each face, see Figure 4.22.

## Figure 7.3 Supporting internal walls

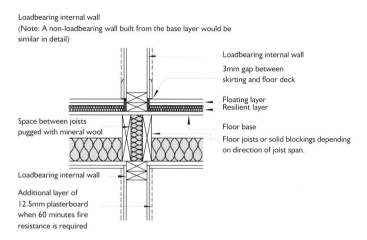

Loadbearing internal wall
(Note: A non-loadbearing wall built from the base layer would be similar in detail)

Loadbearing internal wall

3mm gap between skirting and floor deck

Floating layer
Resilient layer

Space between joists pugged with mineral wool

Floor base
Floor joists or solid blockings depending on direction of joist span.

Loadbearing internal wall

Additional layer of 12.5mm plasterboard when 60 minutes fire resistance is required

Non-loadbearing wall offset from line of floor joists

Additional joist(s)

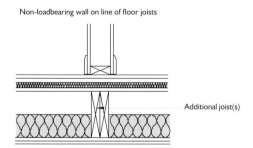

Non-loadbearing wall on line of floor joists

Additional joist(s)

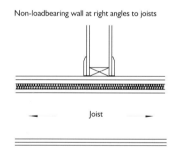

Non-loadbearing wall at right angles to joists

Joist

Alternative details at top of non-loadbearing internal walls at junction with compartment floor.

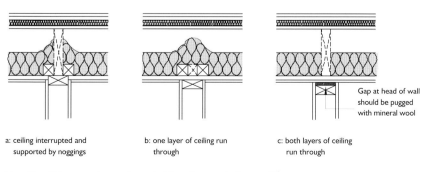

Gap at head of wall should be pugged with mineral wool

a: ceiling interrupted and supported by noggings

b: one layer of ceiling run through

c: both layers of ceiling run through

Note:  Dotted joists or noggings may be required depending upon the direction of floor joists

## 7.2.4 Sound insulation

The Building Regulations require that the floor will resist the transmission of airborne and impact sound. Building Regulations documents describe a number of specifications which are considered to provide the required performance. Currently, these include the platform floor shown in Figure 7.1 but proposals to improve acoustic performance may lead to changes in floor design. Alternative designs are included in the TRADA Technology Report 1/2000 *Acoustic performance of party walls and floors in timber framed buildings*.

It is possible to use the test method approach when using different constructions from those specified. This requires measurements to be taken in completed buildings in accordance with *BS EN ISO 140-4 Field measurements of airborne sound insulation between rooms* and *BS EN ISO 140-7 Field measurements of impact sound insulation of floors*. These tests determine the Standardized Level Difference ($D_{nT}$) for airborne sound transmission and Standardized Impact Sound Pressure Levels ($L'_{nT}$) for impact sound transmission. The Weighted Standardized Level Difference ($D_{nT,w}$) for airborne sound and the Weighted Standardized Sound Pressure Level ($L'_{nT,w}$) for impact sound is calculated in accordance with *BS EN ISO 717-1 Rating the sound insulation in buildings and of building elements Part 1 Airborne sound insulation* and *BS EN ISO 717-2 Impact sound insulation*.

Spectrum adaptation terms can be applied to the $D_{nT,w}$ and $L'_{nT,w}$ values to better indicate sound insulation performance against specific types of noise. Those relevant in this context are:

$C_{tr}$ This value is added to $D_{nT,w}$ to give an indication of airborne sound insulation against low frequency bass music and traffic noise. There is evidence that the combined value better represents the insulation against airborne noise nuisance than $D_{nT,w}$ alone. Note: $C_{tr}$ is normally a negative number, making the combined value numerically smaller.

$C_I$ There is evidence that this value added to $L'_{nT,w}$ gives a better measure of the sound insulation against the noise effects of walking than $L'_{nT,w}$ alone. Note: For timber floors, the $C_I$ value is normally positive, making the combined value numerically greater..

## 7.2.5 Floor to wall junctions

The junction between the party floor and external and party walls needs careful detailing in order not to compromise the fire and sound resistance of the construction. It is important that the floating floor deck is not in contact with the walls and it is essential to turn up the resilient layer between the edge of the floating floor and the wall and to leave skirtings at least 3 mm clear of the floor surface to avoid the possibility of flanking sound transmission.

Any air path between the floor and the wall cavity should be sealed. Where floor joists are at right angles to the wall, full depth blocking should be fixed between the joists at the edge of the floor and nailed to the rails above and below the blocking (see Figure 7.4).

Where floor joists are parallel to the wall, a joist should be provided at the edge of the floor and nailed to the wall rails above and below the joist. Where the party floor abuts a party wall the fire resistance integrity of both should be maintained at the junction (See also Chapter 5).

**Figure 7.4 a Party floor/wall junction: Platform floor: Joists parallel to wall**

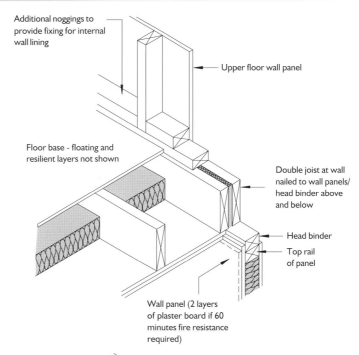

Additional noggings to provide fixing for internal wall lining

Upper floor wall panel

Floor base - floating and resilient layers not shown

Double joist at wall nailed to wall panels/ head binder above and below

Head binder

Top rail of panel

Wall panel (2 layers of plaster board if 60 minutes fire resistance required)

**Figure 7.4 b Party floor/wall junction: Platform floor: Joists at right angles to wall**

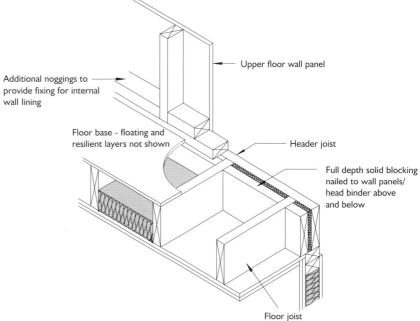

Upper floor wall panel

Additional noggings to provide fixing for internal wall lining

Floor base - floating and resilient layers not shown

Header joist

Full depth solid blocking nailed to wall panels/ head binder above and below

Floor joist

## 7.3 Compartment floors where specific sound resistance is not required

In buildings where there is no specific requirement for sound resistance, the timber compartment floor is effectively the same as a timber intermediate floor with 60 minutes fire resistance. The requirements and specification details for these are described in Chapter 6.

All walls supporting compartment floors should have periods of fire resistance equal to that required by the floor. Where the compartment floor abuts a compartment wall, the fire resistance integrity of both should be maintained at the junction.

# 8 Roofs

## 8.1 Design requirements

There are no specific differences in the roof construction of a timber framed structure compared to other types of construction. It is, however, important to ensure that any additional point loads from the roof (from purlins, hips, valleys etc) are adequately supported by additional studs or posts in the timber wall panels.

The structural design of the roof should be in accordance with BS 5268-2 and with *BS 5268-3 Code of practice for trussed rafter roofs* if trussed rafters are used, including the relevant recommendations for bracing.

In certain areas in the south of England, there is a requirement for all non-durable softwood in roofs to be treated with a suitable preservative to prevent attack by the house longhorn beetle. Details are due be included in Approved Document A to the England and Wales Regulations (Note: the requirements were originally detailed in the Approved Document to Regulation 7).

The housing warranty and guarantee authorities have specific requirements in respect of the treatment of timber in flat roof constructions and the acceptability of some types of flat roof decking. The latest editions of their manuals should be consulted.

There are no Building Regulation requirements for fire resistance for roofs, except when the roof space is used as habitable accommodation. In this case, the floor and walls should have the same fire resistance as other walls and floors in a building of a similar purpose group and number of storeys, see Figure 8.1. Specific details for achieving the required resistance are shown in Sections 8.5, 8.6 and 8.7 for 30 minutes fire resistance. Specialist advice should be obtained for fire resistance periods greater than 30 minutes.

**Figure 8.1 Fire resistance requirements for roofs containing habitable rooms**

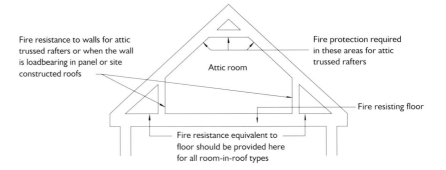

Fire resistance to walls for attic trussed rafters or when the wall is loadbearing in panel or site constructed roofs

Attic room

Fire protection required in these areas for attic trussed rafters

Fire resisting floor

Fire resistance equivalent to floor should be provided here for all room-in-roof types

Any compartment or separating walls which run through the roof space should provide the same period of fire resistance as that required beneath the roof space. The surface spread of flame (reaction to fire) requirements for the ceiling to the roof space are the same as those for ceilings to intermediate floors, see Chapter 6.

There are limitations on the type of roof covering material and supporting construction which can be used adjacent to the junction with party walls or within specified distances of the site boundary. See Section 8.9.1.

The Regulations limit the size of roof spaces for all building types except dwellings and require the installation of cavity barriers where the maximum size would be exceeded. In houses and flats of three storeys or more, the staircase enclosure should be separated from the roof space by a fire resisting ceiling or by vertical cavity barriers in the roof space.

The minimum thermal insulation requirements for roofs of buildings of different purpose groups are set out in the Building Regulations.

Pitched roofs with insulation at ceiling level or between rafters and cold flat roofs should incorporate ventilation to reduce the risk of condensation occurring. Building Regulations define the ventilation requirements. In pitched roofs with insulation at rafter level and in cold flat roofs, a vapour control layer should be included beneath the insulation. Between the insulation and the underlay or sarking, a 50 mm minimum ventilation space must be provided with vents at eaves and ridge, or at opposite sides of a flat roof. This space, combined with the thickness of the insulation can mean that the depth of the rafters is determined by thermal rather than structural requirements. The specification of breather-type underlay used in conjunction with an appropriate internal lining can obviate the need for the ventilation space between the insulation and the underlay, with ventilation provided in a counter batten space.

In addition to meeting the Design Requirements, the successful completion and quality of the timber frame building is dependent on good on-site practice in terms of accuracy in setting out and erecting components. Guidance is given in Appendix 3 Site Supervisor's Checklist.

## 8.2 Pitched roofs

Timber frame construction is normally quick to construct. To follow this process through, the roof should also be quick and simple to construct and prefabricated roof components are commonly used. These can be trussed rafters or panel roofs, although the more traditional methods of roof framing are not precluded by timber frame construction. Whichever type of roof is used, the junction details at the eaves and verge and at party walls remain the same in principle.

The roof framing should be braced to ensure the stability of the entire roof structure. This is covered for trussed rafters in BS 5268-3. Bracing is also required in other types of roof which do not themselves have sufficient stability, for example by the use of hipped ends or rigid sarking boards.

The roof structure should also provide lateral support to walls. BS 5268-3 includes requirements for lateral restraint to external and compartment walls from trussed rafter roofs. Any loads within the roof, eg from water tanks, may require additional studs in the supporting wall where the roof frame transfers these loads to the wall.

The following sections on roof framing describe the relationship between each roofing method and timber frame construction.

## 8.3 Trussed rafter roofs

Trussed rafters can be designed for symmetrical and asymmetrical roofs, monopitch roofs, roofs with sloping ceilings and as attic trusses allowing the roof space to be used to provide habitable accommodation. Manufacturer's literature will provide details of allowable spans, pitches, sizes etc. Typically these would be for roofs between 15° and 50° and spans up to 12 metres.

The structural design of trussed rafters up to 12 m span is covered by BS 5268-3 and is normally the responsibility of the manufacturer of the metal plates who licence franchised fabricators. The building designer is responsible for the overall stability of the roof and should advise the truss manufacturer of the type and weight of roof covering and of any special features to be included. Bracing design should be included by the truss manufacturer in accordance with the Code requirements, or designed by a structural engineer. In a simple rectangular roof, the roof load is shared equally by the trussed rafters which are normally spaced at 600 mm centres. When hips or valleys are introduced this can result in concentrated loads which require additional studs in the wall panels to support them. The method of constructing hips and valleys varies depending upon which system is used. Figure 8.2 shows a typical arrangement. Trussed rafters should never be modified on site without the approval of the manufacturer. They should not be birdsmouthed or cut in any other way unless this is allowed for in the initial design.

**Figure 8.2 Typical hip construction in trussed rafter roofs**

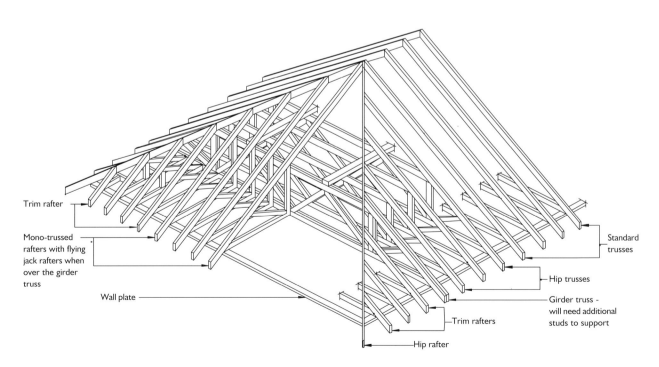

118

Trussed rafters should be fixed to wall plates by the use of proprietary truss fixing clips. Wall plates on which the trussed rafters bear should be at least 75 mm in width. See Figure 8.3.

**Figure 8.3 Fixing trussed rafters**

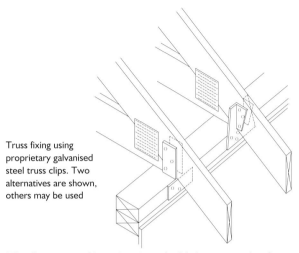

Truss fixing using proprietary galvanised steel truss clips. Two alternatives are shown, others may be used

The function of bracing is to hold the trussed rafters vertical, straight and parallel to each other at the correct centres, to provide the necessary lateral restraint and to ensure that the roof structure acts as a single rigid component. BS 5268-3 includes standard bracing details suitable for most buildings.

One alternative method of roof bracing which is commonly used in Scotland is to use timber or wood-based board sheathing (sarking) secured to the top face of the rafters.

If the details recommended in BS 5268-3 are inappropriate, an alternative bracing solution should be designed by the structural engineer. Guidance on bracing outside the Code limitations is given in TRADA Technology *GD 8 Bracing for non-domestic timber trussed rafter roofs*.

When trussed rafters are required to support water storage tanks, the trussed rafter fabricator /designer should confirm that the load can be supported and specify support member sizes. The load from the tank is normally carried by spreader beams supported on the ceiling ties, close to the node points of the truss as shown in BS 5268-3 and in Figure 8.4.

**Figure 8.4 Supports for water tanks**

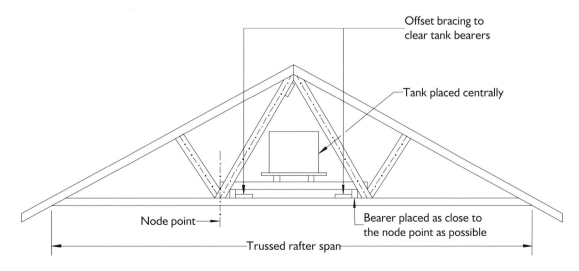

Offset bracing to clear tank bearers

Tank placed centrally

Node point

Bearer placed as close to the node point as possible

Trussed rafter span

In addition to being placed and fixed individually, trussed rafter roofs can be assembled as complete units on the ground adjacent to the building and lifted into place by crane as a complete assembly. This can have advantages on sites where crane erection is used as the roof can be built at ground level where accessibility is better, at the same time as the house shell is erected. The roof can then be lifted on to complete the dry shell in a very short timescale.

## 8.4 Roof trusses

Designs for bolted roof trusses were developed by the Timber Development Association following World War II to economise on timber. A series of Standard Design Sheets were produced by the TDA and continued by TRADA. However, these Standard Designs are no longer available since they were originally prototype-designed and cannot simply be updated to comply with modern codes and standards. TRADA Technology can undertake individual designs on a consultancy basis.

## 8.5 Attic trussed rafter roofs

There are several different types of attic truss available; Figure 8.5 illustrates two examples. In this type of truss, the central area of the roof space is kept free of obstruction allowing it to be used as habitable space. Most types of attic truss are made from heavier section timber than normal trussed rafters and may need to be crane erected. The bottom chord of the truss is effectively a floor joist and may need intermediate support. For larger roofs, the truss size may be limited by transport considerations and the truss can be manufactured in two sections to overcome this.

**Figure 8.5 a (left) Typical attic trussed rafter**

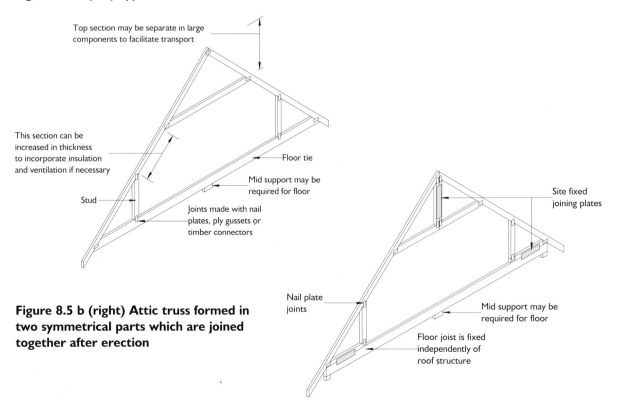

**Figure 8.5 b (right) Attic truss formed in two symmetrical parts which are joined together after erection**

**Figure 8.6 Typical roof construction with attic trussed rafters**

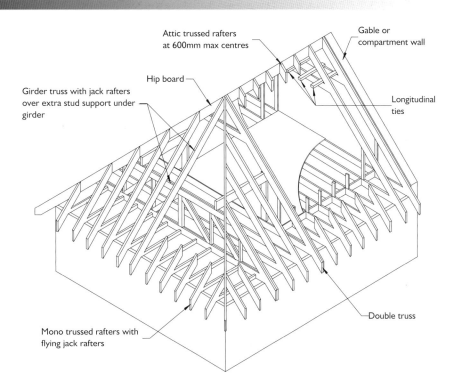

Attic trussed rafters at 600mm max centres

Gable or compartment wall

Hip board

Longitudinal ties

Girder truss with jack rafters over extra stud support under girder

Double truss

Mono trussed rafters with flying jack rafters

Attic trusses spaced at 600 mm centres can usually be supported by the timber frame walls without the need for additional studs or posts. If the centres are greater than 600 mm, for example to allow for the fitting of roof windows, it is generally necessary to provide additional stud framing in the walls to carry the point loads created. Attic trusses should not be cut or altered on site without the approval of the manufacturer. The design of the staircase opening relative to the bottom chord can be important and must be dealt with at the roof design stage.

Attic trusses have the same bracing requirements as other types of trussed rafter roof. The provision of bracing should be co-ordinated with the need to incorporate dormers or roof windows and the provision of ventilation up the pitch of the roof.

Thermal insulation may be fitted within the rafters for their full height or can follow the room profile, see Figure 8.26. The required thickness of insulation can determine the size of rafter used although it is often possible to block out the underside of the rafter to the sloping area of the ceiling to increase the insulation thickness at this critical position.

For attic trussed rafters, where all the truss members act together to form the roof and the floor structure, distortion of the metal connector plates if subjected to high temperatures is a fire performance issue. For this reason, the ceiling lining to the underside of the attic trussed rafter is required to provide more protection than the lining to a normal intermediate floor. The ceiling lining should be either 15 mm Type 1 plasterboard or 12.5 mm Type 5(F) plasterboard to *BS 1230-1 Gypsum plasterboard. Specification for plasterboard excluding materials subject to secondary operations*. Specific fire protection should be given to the other structural members of the truss by lining the habitable room surfaces (vertical walls, pitched and flat ceiling) with 15 mm Type 1 plasterboard or 12.5 mm Type 5 (F) plasterboard to BS 1230-1.

# 8.6 Panel roofs

Roof panels can be used as an alternative to attic type roof trusses to provide unobstructed roof spaces for occupation. The panels are similar in construction to timber frame wall panels and enable a weatherproof structure to be rapidly achieved on site.

TRADA developed a panel structure designed to span from eaves to ridge at pitches between 35° and 45° and at horizontal spans of 6 to 9 metres. At the lower angle, a span of approximately 9 metres is necessary to obtain adequate headroom (See Figure 8.7). Detailed structural analysis will be required for all designs.

**Figure 8.7 a Panel roof details**

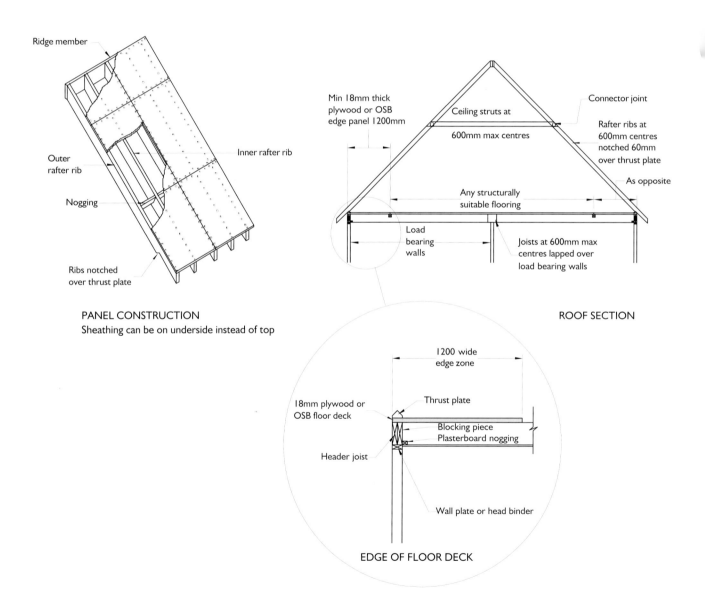

PANEL CONSTRUCTION
Sheathing can be on underside instead of top

ROOF SECTION

EDGE OF FLOOR DECK

## Figure 8.7 b Section through panel roofs

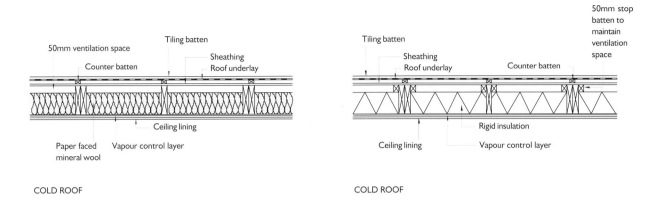

COLD ROOF

COLD ROOF

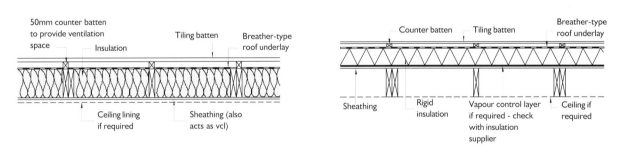

COLD ROOF

WARM ROOF

The TRADA panel design relies on four conditions which should not be varied without additional structural assessment or calculation:

♦ The floor structure acts in tension to restrain the outward force of the roof panels at the eaves. Any butt or lapped joints in the joists should be designed to withstand tension forces. A loadbearing internal wall or a beam is normally required to reduce the floor joist spans. Openings in the floor framing require special design to ensure continuity of this tension function. The staircase opening should interrupt the minimum number of floor joists and should preferably be located parallel to the joists.

♦ The ceiling strut is located where the roof collar is normally situated but, unlike the collar in a simple roof which is a tension member, the ceiling strut is in compression and therefore carries out a quite different function.

♦ The panels are sheathed to resist rafter buckling and wind (racking) forces.

♦ The resistance to horizontal thrust at the eaves relies on effective levelling and setting out of the hardwood thrust plates and on an 18 mm thick plywood perimeter deck, 1.2 m wide, accurately nailed to the floor joists.

The roof panels are designed as modular panels using standard sheet sizes but non-modular width make-up panels can be fabricated to suit specific plan dimensions where required. The panel system is most suitable for roofs with gable ends but 'T' junctions can be accommodated as shown in Figure 8.8.

**Figure 8.8 Use of panel roof in rectangular and T-shaped roof structures**

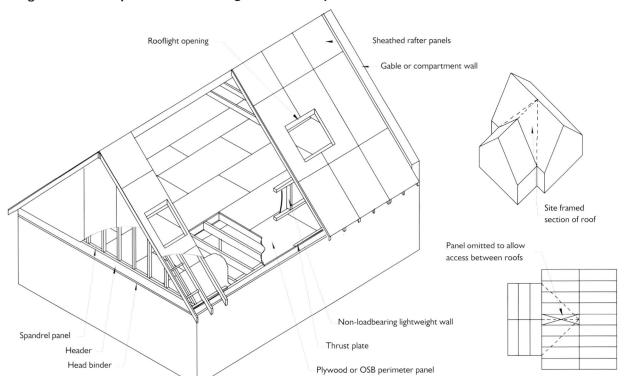

Panel sheathing may be on the underside or the top of the panels. When it is fitted on the underside, the top surface of the panel is covered with a breather type underlay to protect the insulation from the weather prior to the roof tiles or slates being fixed. The sheathing will normally also act as the vapour control layer. When the panel is sheathed on the upper face, a separate vapour control layer is normally required and should be fixed above the ceiling lining with a breather-type underlay used beneath the counter battens and tile battens. It is also possible to use a rigid insulation on top of an externally sheathed roof panel when it is desired to leave the rafters exposed internally. Figure 8.7 b illustrates all three arrangements.

The rafter size varies according to loading and span, the most common depth being 145 mm. The depth of rafter may be determined by the insulation requirements of the roof, although is often possible to block out the underside of the rafter to the sloping area of the ceiling to increase the insulation thickness.

Panels can be trimmed to permit a roof window or dormer to be incorporated. Where openings are formed for dormers, the ribs on either side of the opening are doubled. Dormer windows wider than standard panel widths require special trimming arrangements. The trimmer loads are transferred to the supporting walls and additional wall studs may be required to provide support.

Panels can be manhandled into position although if a crane is used to place wall panels this could also be used for the roof. The decision to use a crane may allow the use of wider (eg 2.4 m) roof panels.

Many other forms of panel roof, both generic and proprietary, have been developed, each of which will require specialist structural calculations to suit the characteristics of the panel design. Examples include:

♦ **stressed-skin panel roof**
These panels consist of timber rafters with a wood-based sheet material (eg plywood or OSB) on the top or bottom face or on both faces. The sheet materials are glued and mechanically fixed to the rafters to form a composite construction acting in the form of T or I-beams and the rafter size can be reduced from that for conventional spanning rafters. Other structural aspects, such as wind bracing and eaves thrust resistance are similar to those for the TRADA panel roof. Thermal insulation and condensation control detailing is also similar to the TRADA panel.

♦ **purlin panel roofs**
In this form of roof, the main structure is a purlin system with timber members running laterally across the roof pitch, supported on gable walls. Wind bracing is provided by a wood-based sheet material above or below the purlins. In this form of panel roof, eaves thrust is effectively eliminated and there is no requirement for ceiling or collar ties. At the eaves, short rafters, detailed in a similar manner to a gable ladder are used to obtain the required eaves overhang. Thermal insulation and condensation control detailing are similar to that for the TRADA panel roof.

♦ **structural insulated panel (SIPS) roofs**
In these panels, the rigid thermal insulation core and the wood-based sheet material (typically OSB or plywood) on the upper and lower face, all act together as a single structural unit. The insulation performs its normal role and also effectively acts as the 'rafters'. Structural aspects such as wind bracing and eaves thrust resistance are similar to the TRADA roof panel. These roof panel systems are usually proprietary and the supplier should be consulted for details of fixing, structural calculations and condensation control.

For panel roofs, the fire resistance to the floor can be achieved in the same way as for intermediate floors by running the floor deck right through to the eaves beneath any vertical dwarf walls forming the habitable space (see Table 6.1). If the deck cannot be run through to the eaves, the ceiling lining to the underside of the joists should be either 15 mm Type 1 plasterboard or 12.5 mm Type 5(F) plasterboard to BS 1230-1.

## 8.7 Site-constructed roofs

Unless specific provision is made in its design, a timber frame wall is not able to resist horizontal thrust from a roof. It is therefore essential that the roof structural design incorporates collars to reduce thrust on the walls. Small span roofs (up to approximately 5m span) can be constructed using simple rafters and collars as shown in Figure 8.9.

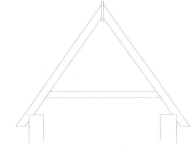

**Figure 8.9 Small span roof with simple rafters and collar**

For longer spans, purlins are required to provide support to the rafters to keep them to an economic size. Purlins should be located at mid-rafter span and be supported by struts bearing onto loadbearing internal walls with additional studs to support the point loads. This requires internal loadbearing walls at upper floor levels, with corresponding loadbearing walls below and can obviously have implications on the building's design. Purlins should be set at 90° to the roof pitch and the purlin struts notched to the purlin to provide maximum support. A strut forming a collar can be placed above the purlin to minimise deflection in the purlin and the rafters. Ceiling joists can be supported by hangers and binders or can bear upon loadbearing external and internal walls. The purlins should be connected to the timber frame gable wall or compartment wall so that the purlin loads can be safely transferred. A typical roof of this type with a span of approximately 8 metres is shown in Figure 8.10.

**Figure 8.10 Typical construction of purlin roof with strut, showing hip and valley details**

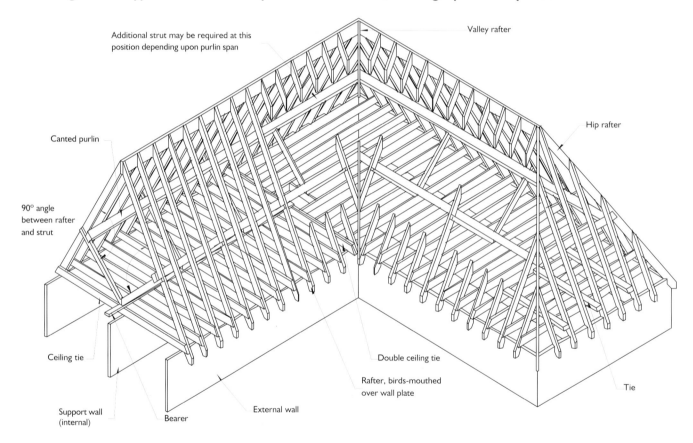

For site-constructed roofs containing a habitable space (Figure 8.11), the fire resistance to the floor can be achieved in the same way as for intermediate floors by running the floor deck right through to the eaves beneath any dwarf walls forming the habitable space. This requires accurate cutting around any struts supporting purlins. If the deck cannot be run through to the eaves, the ceiling lining to the underside of the joists should be either 15 mm Type 1 plasterboard or 12.5 mm Type 5(F) plasterboard to BS 1230-1. Specific fire protection should be given to struts which support purlins and form the vertical dwarf walls by lining such walls with 15 mm Type 1 plasterboard or 12.5 mm Type 5 (F) plasterboard to BS 1230-1.

The main disadvantage of a site constructed roof for a timber frame building is the time which is generally required to construct it. This can delay the attainment of a dry shell, which in turn delays the time that internal trades can commence. It also leaves the shell exposed to the weather for longer than when some form of prefabricated roof structure is used. Options for speeding up this form of roof construction include combining site fixed purlins with simple panel components incorporating rafters or proprietary lightweight roofing panels, or the use of prefabricated components, such as plybox beams, girder trusses or timber I-beams, together with rafter panels when crane erection is available.

**Figure 8.11 Typical details of site-built purlin and rafter roof giving habitable roof space**

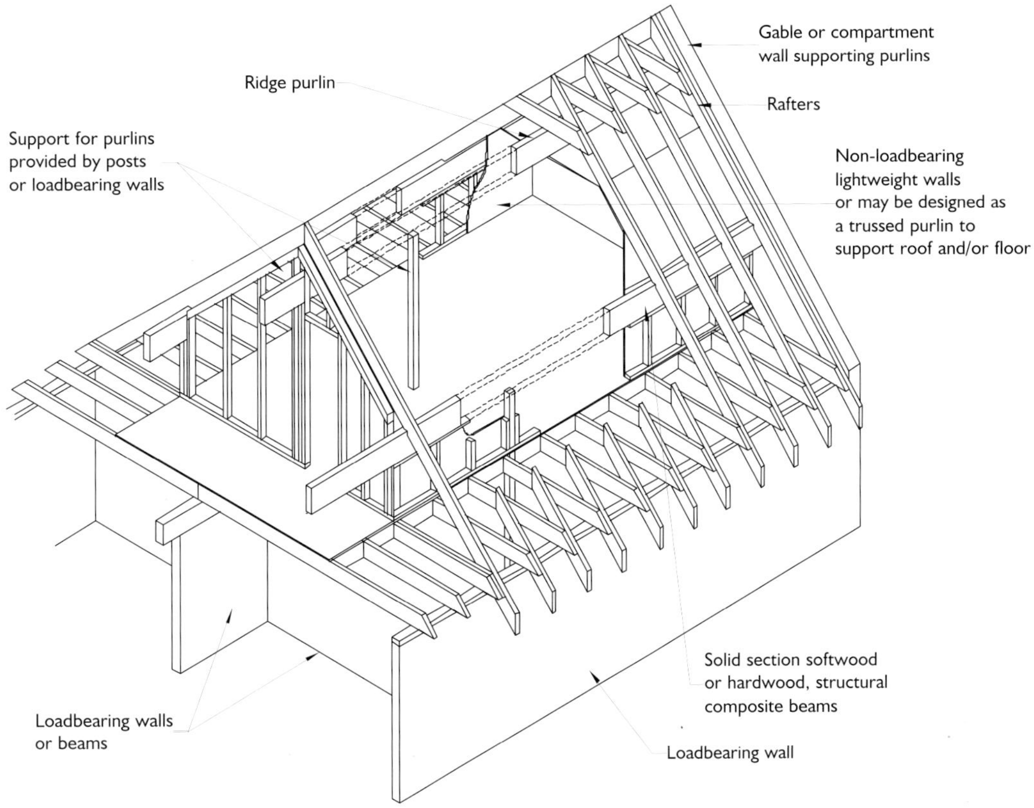

Ridge purlin

Gable or compartment wall supporting purlins

Rafters

Support for purlins provided by posts or loadbearing walls

Non-loadbearing lightweight walls or may be designed as a trussed purlin to support roof and/or floor

Loadbearing walls or beams

Solid section softwood or hardwood, structural composite beams

Loadbearing wall

## 8.8 Constructional details

### 8.8.1 Detailing at eaves

Figures 8.12 and 8.26 show typical eaves constructions. The detail will vary with the roof pitch, the projection required and the eaves soffit level, which in turn is often related to the window head level. The relevant points to consider are:

♦ Ventilation to roof space via soffit or proprietary over-eaves vents

♦ Adequate tilting to eaves tile to maintain the tile line

♦ The underlay extends into the gutter

♦ Any cavity between the cladding and the timber frame wall is closed at the top by an appropriate cavity barrier

- ◆ Roof ceiling insulation does not inhibit roof ventilation or leave gaps causing cold bridging in the ceiling edge

- ◆ Adequate precautions are taken to prevent the roof framing resting on masonry cladding as a result of differential settlement between the masonry and the timber frame wall (see Figure 9.1).

**Figure 8.12 Typical eaves construction:**

**(a) Projecting (boxed) eaves**

**b Clipped eaves**

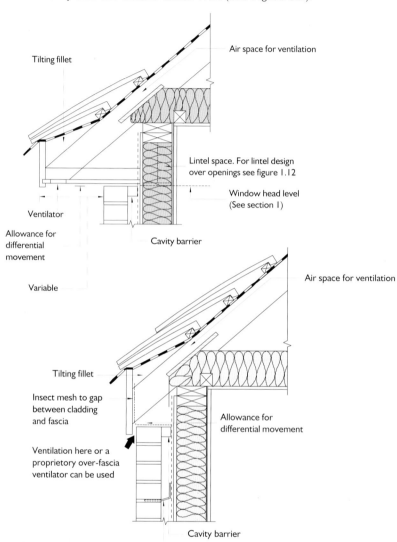

## 8.8.2 Detailing at gable walls and verge

The wall spandrel panel in the roof space can be formed using stud framing similarly to other wall panels, or roof trusses can be used to support the cladding materials (Figures 8.13 and 8.14). A barge board or projecting verge usually requires a gable ladder which necessitates a reduced height spandrel panel (Figure 8.15). When the verge is flush with the wall cladding either method may be used. The detail at the verge (and at other roof abutments) should, wherever possible, allow the roof construction to be completed independently of the wall cladding to rationalise site working so as not to delay making the building weathertight.

A stud framed spandrel panel with a breather membrane factory-fitted has the advantage that it assists in providing a weatherproof shell at an early stage of the construction. It is important to establish the final dimensions of the rafters in order to fix the panel dimensions. If trusses are used to form the gable panels, it is necessary to fix vertical battens to them to provide support for the breather membrane and brick ties or other claddings.

Except where the roof is used to provide habitable space, there is no requirement to provide internal lining or insulation to the gable end spandrels. When the roof contains accommodation, the gable-end framing should be treated as an external wall panel with the required fire resistance, thermal insulation and vapour control measures.

**Figure 8.13 a Forming verge with spandrel panel**

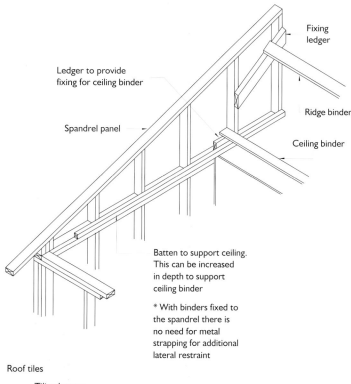

**Figure 8.13 b Typical detail at clipped verge**

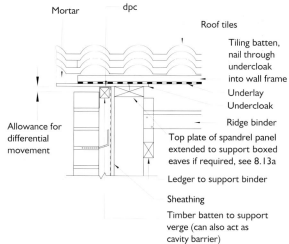

**Figure 8.14 a (left) Forming verge with trussed rafter b (right) Typical detail at verge**

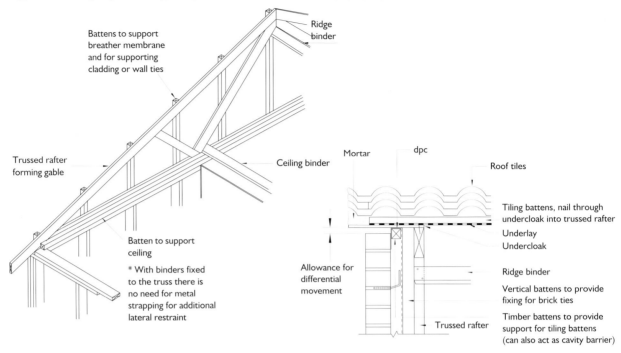

Battens to support
breather membrane
and for supporting
cladding or wall ties

Ridge
binder

Trussed rafter
forming gable

Ceiling binder

Batten to support
ceiling

* With binders fixed
to the truss there is
no need for metal
strapping for additional
lateral restraint

Mortar

dpc

Roof tiles

Tiling battens, nail through
undercloak into trussed rafter

Underlay

Undercloak

Allowance for
differential
movement

Ridge binder

Vertical battens to provide
fixing for brick ties

Trussed rafter

Timber battens to provide
support for tiling battens
(can also act as cavity barrier)

**Figure 8.15 a (left) Forming verge with gable ladder b (right) Projecting verge using gable ladder**

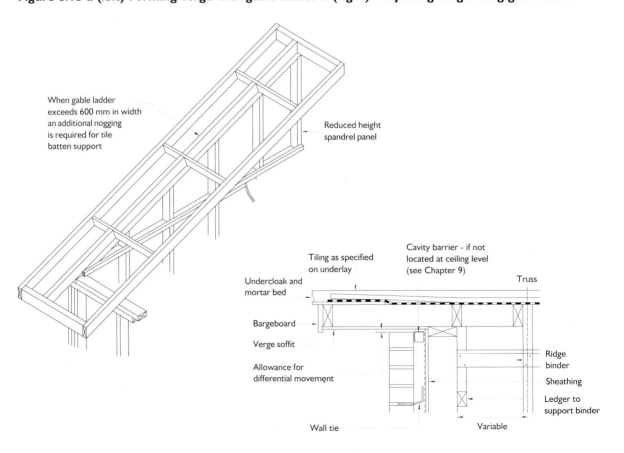

When gable ladder
exceeds 600 mm in width
an additional nogging
is required for tile
batten support

Reduced height
spandrel panel

Tiling as specified
on underlay

Cavity barrier - if not
located at ceiling level
(see Chapter 9)

Undercloak and
mortar bed

Truss

Bargeboard

Verge soffit

Allowance for
differential movement

Ridge
binder

Sheathing

Ledger to
support binder

Wall tie

Variable

130

## 8.8.3 Detailing at party walls

To maintain the fire resistance of the party wall, the continuity of the wall lining should be maintained in the roof space and the junction of the roof finish and the wall should be adequately firestopped, including the void at the eaves soffit junction.

The wall spandrel panel in the roof space can be formed using stud framing (Figure 8.16) or trussed rafters can be used to support the lining materials (Figure 8.17). If a stud framed spandrel is used, it is important to establish the final dimensions of the rafter members at an early stage in order to determine the panel dimensions. Where both components are fabricated in the same factory, it may be possible to use a trussed rafter as a template for the wall fabrication. When trussed rafters are used, it is essential to fit additional vertical battens to provide backing and fixing points for the lining board joints.

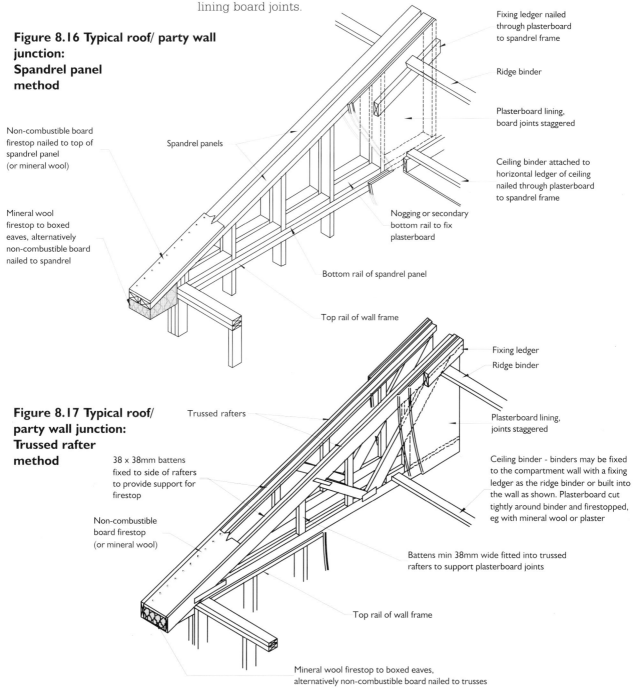

**Figure 8.16 Typical roof/ party wall junction: Spandrel panel method**

Fixing ledger nailed through plasterboard to spandrel frame

Ridge binder

Plasterboard lining, board joints staggered

Ceiling binder attached to horizontal ledger of ceiling nailed through plasterboard to spandrel frame

Non-combustible board firestop nailed to top of spandrel panel (or mineral wool)

Spandrel panels

Mineral wool firestop to boxed eaves, alternatively non-combustible board nailed to spandrel

Nogging or secondary bottom rail to fix plasterboard

Bottom rail of spandrel panel

Top rail of wall frame

**Figure 8.17 Typical roof/ party wall junction: Trussed rafter method**

Trussed rafters

Fixing ledger
Ridge binder

Plasterboard lining, joints staggered

38 x 38mm battens fixed to side of rafters to provide support for firestop

Non-combustible board firestop (or mineral wool)

Ceiling binder - binders may be fixed to the compartment wall with a fixing ledger as the ridge binder or built into the wall as shown. Plasterboard cut tightly around binder and firestopped, eg with mineral wool or plaster

Battens min 38mm wide fitted into trussed rafters to support plasterboard joints

Top rail of wall frame

Mineral wool firestop to boxed eaves, alternatively non-combustible board nailed to trusses

Where roof bracing members are fixed to the party wall, they may be nailed to the wall framing and the lining boards cut around them with solid timber blockings or mineral wool to close the joints. Alternatively, if the sequence of construction allows, the roof bracing members can be fixed to ledgers fixed after the lining is fitted and nailed through it into the wall frame. In this latter case, the linings should be moisture resistant.

It is essential that the firestop over the top of the party wall and beneath the roof finish fills the space between the two elements. Since there is likely to be some deflection of the roof structure when the tile load is applied, the use of a mineral wool firestop will allow this to occur without causing unsightly 'humping' of the roof line at the wall position. See Chapter 5 'Party walls'.

Figure 8.18 (a and b) illustrates a change in roof truss direction above a party wall with a single leaf in the roof space. Figure 8.18 (c) illustrates a change in roof direction with a full party wall in the roof space.

**Figure 8.18 a Roof/ party wall junction between roofs set at right angles to one another (single leaf in roof space)**

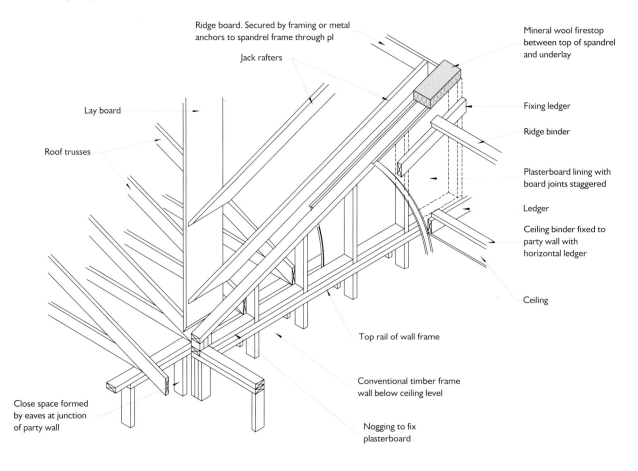

Ridge board. Secured by framing or metal anchors to spandrel frame through pl

Jack rafters

Mineral wool firestop between top of spandrel and underlay

Lay board

Fixing ledger

Ridge binder

Roof trusses

Plasterboard lining with board joints staggered

Ledger

Ceiling binder fixed to party wall with horizontal ledger

Ceiling

Top rail of wall frame

Conventional timber frame wall below ceiling level

Close space formed by eaves at junction of party wall

Nogging to fix plasterboard

**Figure 8.18 b Roof/ party wall junction between roofs set at right angles to one another: Section (single leaf in roof space)**

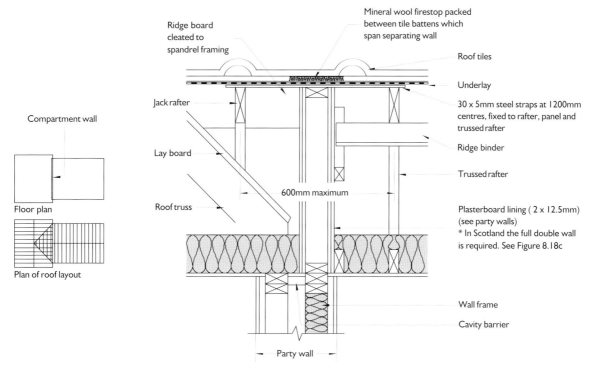

**(Figure 8.18 c Roof/ party wall junction between roofs set at right angles to one another: Trussed rafter built into party wall (full party wall in roof space)**

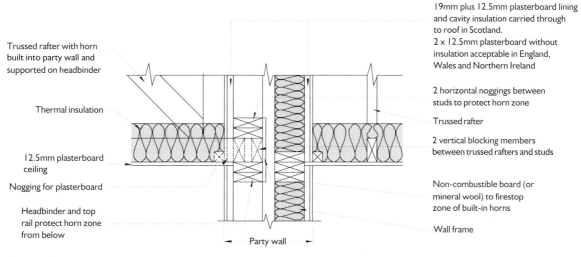

Purlins spanning between roof trusses or in site-constructed roofs are supported by gable wall and/or compartment wall frames. At compartment walls, the purlins penetrate the plasterboard lining to the wall and the plasterboard should be fitted tightly around the purlin and fire stopped with gypsum plaster, mineral wool or other suitable material, see Figure 8.19. Support for the purlin can be formed by inserting a small inclined lintel on cripple studs and transferring the purlin load in the wall, by extra studs, to the foundations. Solid blocking should be inserted to restrain the purlin to the lintel. Similar support can be provided in the gable walls.

**Figure 8.19 Junction of purlin roofs/ party wall**

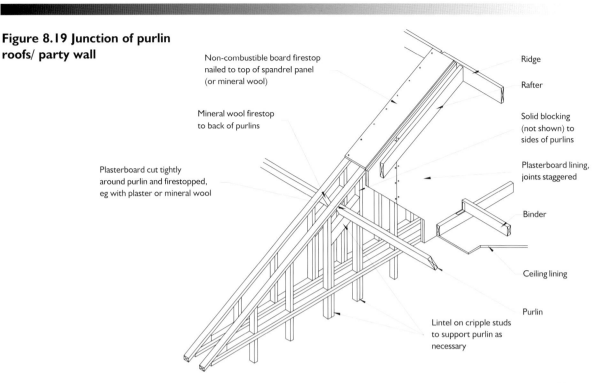

Non-combustible board firestop nailed to top of spandrel panel (or mineral wool)

Mineral wool firestop to back of purlins

Plasterboard cut tightly around purlin and firestopped, eg with plaster or mineral wool

Ridge

Rafter

Solid blocking (not shown) to sides of purlins

Plasterboard lining, joints staggered

Binder

Ceiling lining

Purlin

Lintel on cripple studs to support purlin as necessary

A panel roof at the junction with a party wall is shown in Figure 8.20.

**Figure 8.20 Junction of panel roof/ party wall**

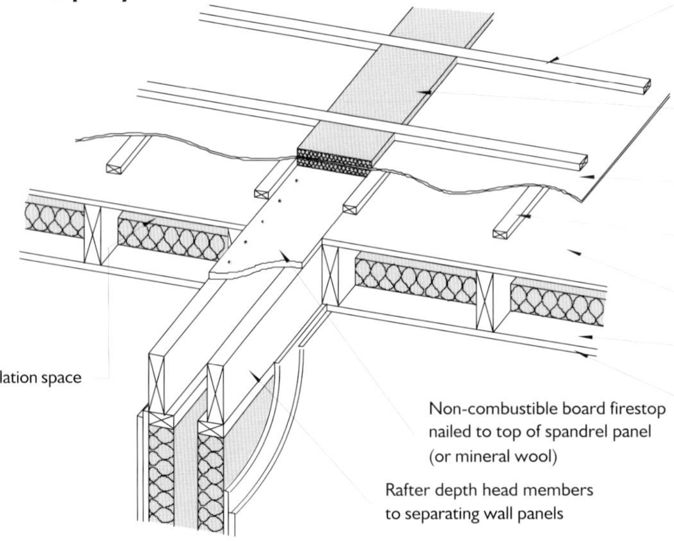

Tile battens

Mineral wool between battens and counter battens to fill space

Underlay

Counter batten at rafter positions

Sheathing (may be on underside of panel)

Vapour control layer

Ceiling

Ventilation space

Non-combustible board firestop nailed to top of spandrel panel (or mineral wool)

Rafter depth head members to separating wall panels

## 8.8.4 Detailing at abutments

Pitched roofs on lower projections adjacent to a higher wall are possible with rafters running both parallel to or at right angles to the main external wall.

When the building is brick clad, it is difficult to support brickwork over the top of the lower roof structure, unless supporting brickwork or blockwork is incorporated at the lower level, or a steel or concrete beam is incorporated within the roof depth. The problem is best overcome by adopting an attached form of wall cladding, such as timber, tiles or render above the lower roof. Figure 8.21 illustrates a typical detail.

**Figure 8.21 Roof abutment against timber frame wall**
Note: Any brickwork over abutment to be supported by steel or concrete lintel, independent of timber frame wall. Refer to lintel manufacturer for structural calculations to check suitability. Roof framing must be supported by timber construction only, avoiding mixed wall construction. Trussed rafters may require bracing, refer to BS 5268-3.

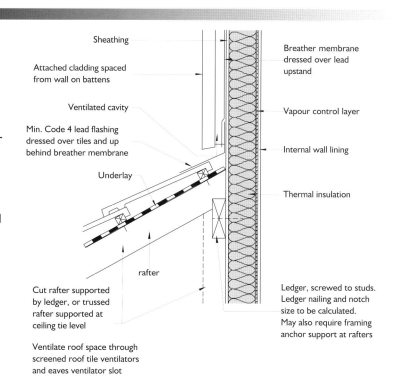

Sheathing

Attached cladding spaced from wall on battens

Ventilated cavity

Min. Code 4 lead flashing dressed over tiles and up behind breather membrane

Underlay

Breather membrane dressed over lead upstand

Vapour control layer

Internal wall lining

Thermal insulation

rafter

Cut rafter supported by ledger, or trussed rafter supported at ceiling tie level

Ledger, screwed to studs. Ledger nailing and notch size to be calculated. May also require framing anchor support at rafters

Ventilate roof space through screened roof tile ventilators and eaves ventilator slot

# 8.9 Covering for pitched roofs

## 8.9.1 External fire spread

Building Regulations control the fire exposure (radiated heat) of roofs relative to the use of the building and proximity of the roof (or part of the roof) to the site boundary. As part of this Regulation, roof coverings are currently designated by two letters; the first for fire penetration time and the second for spread of fire, derived from *BS 476-3 External fire exposure roof test*. Each condition is classified into 4 categories designated A to D.

A pitched roof with natural slate, clay or concrete tiles on timber rafters with or without underlay or timber board sarking is designated AA. Such roofs are permitted closer than 6 metres to the boundary. The extent to which other materials can be used depends upon proximity to the boundary and the cubic capacity of the building. Details are given in the Building Regulations. (Note: The BS 476 test may be replaced by a BS EN test in due course; current editions of the Building Regulations will refer.)

## 8.9.2 Tiling and slating

Clay tiles, concrete tiles, natural slates and fibre cement slates have all been used as roof finishes with timber frame structures. The one significant difference between them is the variation in weight per square metre, from about 23 kg/m$^2$ for fibre cement slates to approximately 80 kg/m$^2$ for clay plain tiles (see weights of materials in Appendix 2). This difference usually only has a significant effect in structures where upper floors cantilever out from the floor below them when the lighter types of roof cladding will be advantageous.

Tiles and slates should be used and fixed in accordance with the manufacturers recommendations and those of *BS 5534-1 Slating and tiling. Design.* Tiling battens should comply with the recommendations of BS 5534. Where battens have been treated with CCA preservative, aluminium nails should not be used; stainless steel, galvanised or sherardised nails are suitable.

Underlays on rafters may be reinforced roofing felt to *BS 747 Specification for roofing felts* or a proprietary plastic membrane. The use of an underlay with high vapour permeability will increase the safety margins against condensation within the roof space. In buildings where thermal insulation follows the pitch of rafters, high vapour permeability underlays should always be specified.

## 8.9.3 Cedar shingles

Western red cedar shingles are produced to Canadian Standards and imported into the UK; there is no relevant British Standard. Rectangular and profiled shingles are available in lengths of 400 and 450 mm and cedar shakes (which are split rather than sawn from the log) up to 600 mm.

Cedar shingles are an acceptable roof covering to many types of building although limitations relative to their use are included in Building Regulations. These limitations, which relate to the purpose group, the size of building and its relationship to the site boundary, differ in the various National Regulations. Cedar shingles are also available pre-treated to AA fire exposure rating (to BS 476-3) and subject to local approval, may be acceptable in less restrictive situations than untreated shingles. To be acceptable, the treatment should be non-leaching.

The majority of western red cedar shingles imported to the UK are treated with CCA preservative by vacuum pressure impregnation to improve their inherent natural durability. Except in severe exposure areas, no underlay should be used so as to allow a free air flow to the underside of the shingles. Where underlays are used, the shingle battens should be separated from the underlay by counterbattens to allow air movement.

Shingles are generally nailed to 38 x 19 mm battens fixed to rafters at maximum 600 mm spacing. Each shingle should be fixed with two stainless steel nails. All metal flashings and saddles should be coated with bitumen or an approved metal paint; if lead flashings are used they should be to Code 4 minimum and coated with bitumen; copper or aluminium flashings should not be used. Suppliers' advice on installation should be followed.

## 8.10 Flat roofs

The principles of flat roof design with timber frame are generally the same as with other building methods. The overriding consideration with timber frame construction is to ensure that there is equal shrinkage settlement in all the supporting walls to avoid distortion of the roof structure and weather resisting membrane. Particular care is required for the details at abutments where differential movement may occur. Spans for flat roofs are limited and will usually require intermediate internal loadbearing walls. To provide flexibility in joist selection and spacing, the use of a head binder to all wall frames is recommended, thereby avoiding the need for studs to be located directly under each joist.

Roofs should be laid to falls and due allowance made for deflection under load when calculating joists. The preferred arrangement would allow an even fall of not less than 1 in 40 which is generally sufficient to compensate for deflection.

There are three basic arrangements for the relative positions of the roof deck, the insulation and the waterproof layer which are considered practically and technically acceptable. These are described as cold deck, and two variants of the warm deck method, known as sandwich and inverted flat roofs.

## 8.10.1 Cold deck roofs

In a cold deck roof, (Figure 8.22) the insulation is placed immediately above the ceiling and therefore the temperature of the deck and the roof void is well below that of the building. This type of roof is vulnerable to condensation if moist air from the building is allowed into the roof void. It therefore relies upon the provision of a vapour control layer beneath the insulation to reduce the passage of vapour and on adequate ventilation of the voids to dissipate any vapour which penetrates into the roof. Ventilation should be unobstructed from side to side of the roof and there should be clear openings equal to a 25 mm continuous opening along both sides of the roof. There should also be a clear space of at least 50 mm between the top of the insulation and the roof deck.

**Figure 8.22 Cold deck roof**

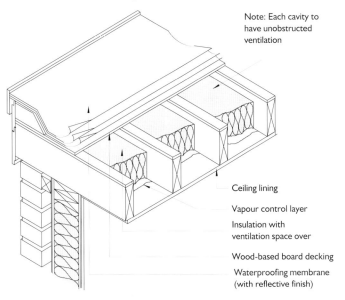

Note: Each cavity to have unobstructed ventilation

Ceiling lining

Vapour control layer

Insulation with ventilation space over

Wood-based board decking

Waterproofing membrane (with reflective finish)

The advantages of a cold deck roof are:

♦ The waterproofing membrane is directly supported by the deck and is easily repaired without damaging other parts of the construction

♦ Normal insulation materials are easily positioned.

The disadvantages are:

♦ The reliance upon ventilation, which can be difficult to achieve if solid strutting or cavity barriers are required or if the roof abuts walls or parapets; ventilators passing through the waterproof membrane increase the risk of rainwater leakage

♦ The need to place many ventilators to achieve overall ventilation without dead areas

♦ The possible difficulty in maintaining an adequate vapour control layer if services run in the roof space

♦ The possibility that if a leak occurs in the waterproof membrane the water does not necessarily appear below the leakage point due to the vcl.

Due to the difficulties of ventilation, the use of cold flat roofs should be restricted to spans up to 5 m. The Scottish Building Standards recommend that in the climatic conditions of Scotland, ventilated cold flat roofs should not be used and that warm deck and inverted roofs are the only acceptable types.

## 8.10.2 Warm deck sandwich roofs

In warm deck sandwich construction (Figure 8.23), the insulation is placed on top of the deck with a vapour control layer sandwiched between the deck and the insulation. The thermal resistance of the insulation is sufficient to ensure that the roof construction below the vcl is warm enough to be free from condensation risk.

**Figure 8.23 Warm deck roof**

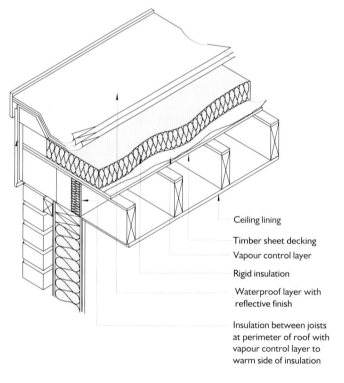

Ceiling lining

Timber sheet decking

Vapour control layer

Rigid insulation

Waterproof layer with reflective finish

Insulation between joists at perimeter of roof with vapour control layer to warm side of insulation

The main advantages of a warm deck roof are:

♦ It is relatively easy to obtain a continuous vapour control layer

♦ The waterproof layer is accessible for inspection and repair

♦ Insulation can be fixed by mechanical fastenings or bonding without penetrating the waterproof layer

♦ The structural deck is protected from temperature extremes

♦ Services are contained within the heated building envelope and do not penetrate the vapour control layer.

The disadvantages are:

♦ Any moisture which gets between the waterproof layer and the vapour control layer from leaks or during construction can be trapped, reducing thermal efficiency and possibly eventually causing deterioration of the insulation

♦ The thickness of insulation necessary to meet current thermal performance requirements increases overall depth

♦ The insulation needs to be strong enough to support the waterproof layer against roof traffic

♦ The insulation, being so close under the waterproof layer can cause extreme temperature variations in this layer. It is essential to use a solar reflective treatment or finish to reduce this as much as possible. Care is necessary in selecting the type of waterproof layer to avoid unacceptable thermal movement.

## 8.10.3 Warm deck inverted roofs

The warm deck inverted roof (Figure 8.24) places the insulation (usually with ballast on top) over the roof deck and the waterproof layer so that both are protected from extremes of temperature variation; avoiding the need for a separate vapour control layer.

**Figure 8.24 Inverted roof**

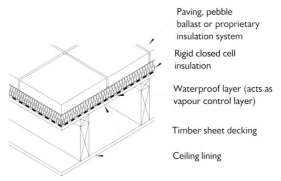

Paving, pebble ballast or proprietary insulation system

Rigid closed cell insulation

Waterproof layer (acts as vapour control layer)

Timber sheet decking

Ceiling lining

The main advantages are:

♦ The waterproof layer is protected from temperature variation

♦ The waterproof layer is protected from maintenance traffic

♦ There is no restriction on services in the warm roof void

♦ There is no risk of trapping water in the insulation.

The disadvantages are:

♦ The waterproof layer is not easily accessible, being under the ballast material and insulation

♦ The ballast increases roof weight, which in turn, may require more expensive wall and roof structures

♦ Only closed cell types of insulation can be used and the thickness may have to be increased to compensate for water percolating beneath the insulation, reducing its insulation value

♦ Increased falls may be necessary to achieve adequate drainage and provision made to avoid blockages, particularly in any gutters under the insulation.

## 8.10.4 Materials for flat roof construction

The preservative treatment of timber in cold deck flat roofs is recommended. The housing warranty and guarantee authorities have specific requirements for both cold and warm deck roofs. Where preservative treatment is used, ends of timber cut after treatment should be swabbed with suitable preservative.

♦ Flat roof decking materials may be:

♦ Plywood: to BS EN 636-2 and one of the grades listed in BS 5268-2

♦ Wood chipboard Type P5 or P7 to BS EN 312-5 and BS EN 312-7 respectively

♦ Oriented strand board OSB 3 or OSB 4 to BS EN 300

♦ Cement bonded particleboard to BS EN 634-2.

The precise specifications may vary depending whether cold or warm roof constructions are specified. General information on timber and wood-based materials is given in Appendix 1.

If square edged sheets are used, all edges should be supported on joists or noggings. All sheet materials should have gaps at roof upstands to permit movement to take place without causing distortion. Typically this should be 10 - 12 mm, but precise requirements for different materials vary and should be checked with the manufacturers or trade associations.

Details at abutments and where pipes or rainwater outlets penetrate the roof should also allow for differential movement. Figure 8.25 illustrates typical solutions.

**Figure 8.25 a Typical detail of rainwater outlet in flat roof**

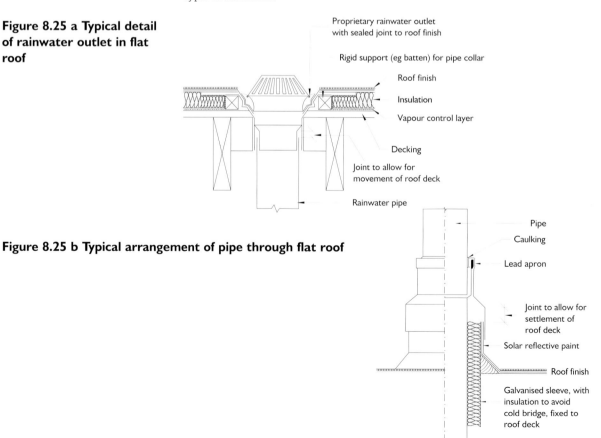

**Figure 8.25 b Typical arrangement of pipe through flat roof**

Unless manufacturers instruct otherwise, plywood sheets should be fixed with their face grain at right angles to joists. OSB sheets (tongued and grooved and square edged) should be laid with their long edges at right angles to the joists. Tongued and grooved chipboards should be fixed with their long edge at right angles to joists. Square edged chipboards are normally fixed with their long edges parallel with the joists and with the short edges supported by noggings.

Table 8.1 gives the recommended thickness of deck for warm and cold deck flat roofs. Inverted ballasted roofs have specific loading requirements depending upon the type of insulation, ballast and exposure and should therefore be assessed individually.

**TABLE 8.1 Materials for flat roof decks (access limited to repair and maintenance only)**

| Decking material | Joist centres (mm) 400 | 600 |
|---|---|---|
| | Minimum deck thickness (mm) | |
| Plywood | 12.5 | 15 |
| OSB | 11 | 15 |
| Chipboard | 18 | 22 |
| Cement bonded particleboard | 15 | 22 |

It is important that lightweight timber flat roofs are adequately restrained against uplift forces. The Regulations recommend that roofs lower than 15° pitch have vertical strapping at not more than 2 m centres at eaves.

BS 5268-2 requires lateral support when the depth to breadth ratio of the joists exceeds 6. The required bracing may be solid timber or herringbone strutting and should be spaced at intervals not exceeding 6 times the joist depth. In addition to this requirement, it is recommended that all spans in excess of 2.5 metres should incorporate bracing irrespective of the BS 5268-2 requirement as follows:

| up to 2.5 m span | none |
|---|---|
| 2.5 to 4.5 m span | one at mid span |
| over 4.5 m span | at maximum 2.5 m centres. |

Bracing should not obstruct ventilation in cold roof constructions.

# 8.11 Insulation in roofs

## 8.11.1 Ventilated pitched roofs

The U value is determined by the thickness of insulation laid at ceiling joist/rafter level. Table 8.2 shows typical values.

**TABLE 8.2 Roof U values**

| Mineral wool or cellulose fibre insulation (mm) | U value - 10% joists/rafters |
|---|---|
| 150 | 0.30 |
| 200 * | 0.20 |
| 250 * | 0.16 |
| 300 * | 0.13 |
| * U values assume insulation in two layers: the upper layer across joists/rafters | |

## 8.11.2 Room in the roof structures

Insulation is usually located at rafter level; there should be sufficient ventilation space above it (see Figure 8.26) with a breather type underlay, see section 8.12. The values of insulation are as Table 8.2. Alternatively, a warm roof can be employed, see Section 8.11.4.

**Figure 8.26 Externally sheathed panel roof eaves detail showing ventilation**

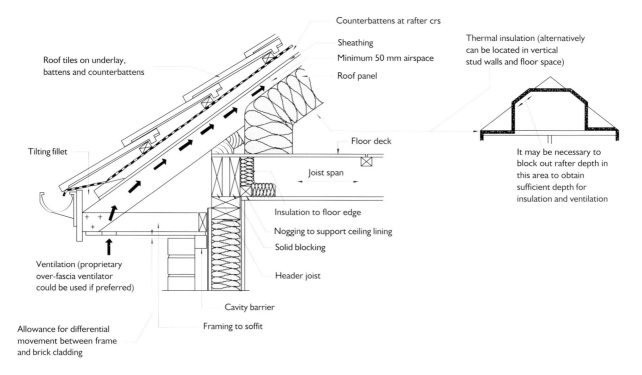

Counterbattens at rafter crs

Sheathing

Minimum 50 mm airspace

Roof panel

Roof tiles on underlay, battens and counterbattens

Thermal insulation (alternatively can be located in vertical stud walls and floor space)

Floor deck

Tilting fillet

It may be necessary to block out rafter depth in this area to obtain sufficient depth for insulation and ventilation

Joist span

Insulation to floor edge

Nogging to support ceiling lining

Solid blocking

Header joist

Ventilation (proprietary over-fascia ventilator could be used if preferred)

Cavity barrier

Framing to soffit

Allowance for differential movement between frame and brick cladding

## 8.11.3 Cold deck flat roofs

U values are as Table 8.2.

## 8.11.4 Warm deck and inverted flat roofs

The variations in thickness and type of insulation used in this form of construction make it impractical to quote typical U values, which should therefore be calculated or reference made to manufacturers' details and calculations. However, to indicate a typical example, a warm roof with 75 mm of extruded polystyrene (conductivity 0.03 W/mK) would have a U value of 0.35 $W/m^2K$. Increasing the insulation thickness to 100 mm would improve the U value to 0.25 $W/m^2K$.

Warm roofs, see Figure 8.7b, can also be used as sloping roofs where the roof encloses habitable space (ie sloping ceilings of room in the roof construction) in conjunction with tile or slate roof finishes.

# 8.12 Ventilation in roofs

*BS 5250 Code of practice for the control of condensation in buildings* sets out in detail the requirements for the ventilation of roofs of all types and pitches. It is essential to ventilate all roof spaces (with the exception of warm or inverted roofs) above the insulation if the risk of condensation is to be avoided. In standard forms of construction with roofs over 15° pitch, eaves ventilation should be provided, with openings equivalent to a continuous screened opening of not less than 10 mm on each side of the roof. For roofs of 15° pitch, or less, the ventilation openings should be equivalent to a continuous opening of not less than 25 mm on each side.

Where rooms are formed in the roof space and insulation is located between the rafters, eaves ventilation should be equivalent to a continuous opening of not less than 25 mm on each side and a clear ventilation path of at least 50 mm should normally be provided above the insulation to allow a flow of air. In these cases, and with mono pitched roofs, it is essential that high level ventilation openings are provided in addition to those at eaves level, typically equivalent to a continuous opening of 5 mm. In order to avoid the passage of fire into the roof space via windows in the lower storey, ventilation openings should not be placed in the soffit directly over window openings, especially when ceilings with 30 minutes (or more) fire resistance are required (eg a habitable roof space). An alternative location for ventilation openings is in, or over, the fascia board.

To avoid infestation by insects, ventilation openings should be protected by an insect mesh.

If it is not possible to provide ventilation space between the insulation and the roof underlay, the use of a breather type underlay may be considered with the ventilation provided in the counter batten space above the underlay. The underlay should have a maximum vapour transmission resistance value of 0.6 MNs/g.

# 9 Cladding

## 9.1 Design requirements

The main functions of the cladding on a timber frame building are to provide weather resistance and create the external appearance required by the client. Brick and blockwork cladding can contribute to the structural stability of the building; BS 5268-6 includes details of the contribution made and requirements for this.

There are Building Regulation limits on the use of combustible cladding and requirements for surface spread of flame (reaction to fire) performance for cladding adjacent to boundaries as well as rules limiting the size of 'unprotected areas' on elevations near to boundaries. Unprotected areas include windows and combustible cladding. The allowable amount varies with the distance from the boundary and height above the ground. Rules for calculation are included in national Building Regulations.

Building Regulations include requirements for cavity barriers to any cavity which occurs between the external cladding and the external face of the timber frame panel. Cavity barriers are provided to close a cavity, and to limit its area to restrict the spread of smoke or flame. Cavity barriers are required in timber frame structures if the external face of the timber frame wall panel is of combustible material. Requirements for cavity barriers vary between the National Regulations and also depend upon the purpose group of the building.

There should be a drained and vented air space behind the external cladding to all timber frame walls. To avoid infestation by insects, openings to the cavity should be protected by an insect mesh.

The housing warranty and guarantee authorities have specific requirements in respect of supporting battens and air spaces behind claddings; the latest version of their manuals should be consulted.

In addition to meeting the Design Requirements, the successful completion and quality of the timber frame building is dependent on good on-site practice in terms of accuracy in setting out and erecting components. Guidance is given in Appendix 3 Site Supervisor's Checklist.

## 9.2 Cladding materials

Materials for cladding can be subdivided into two categories; those which are built from their own foundation and which are simply tied back to the timber frame structure (brickwork, rendered and fair face blockwork, stone) and those which are fully supported by the timber frame structure (tile hanging, timber or other board and sheet materials, render on mesh etc). Whichever type of cladding is used, it is essential that it is correctly fixed to the timber frame structure, with adequate allowance for differential movement where necessary, and that weathering details are satisfactory.

## 9.3 Brick and concrete block cladding

Brickwork and blockwork should comply with *BS 5628 Use of masonry Part 1 Structural use of unreinforced masonry* and *Part 3 Materials and components, design and workmanship.*

There is a wide choice of clay and calcium silicate bricks available and all may be used providing the detailed design is appropriate. When eaves, verges and sills project sufficiently to provide the brick cladding with reasonable protection against saturation, brickwork above dpc level may be in clay bricks of durability designation FL, FN, ML or MN to *BS 3921 Specification for clay bricks* or in Class 3 calcium silicate bricks as defined in BS 187 Specification for calcium silicate (sandlime and flintlime) bricks. Where protection is limited (eg as shown in Figure 9.5b), the specification should be limited to FL or FN clay bricks or calcium silicate bricks.

Blocks should comply with the requirements of *BS 6073 Precast concrete masonry units.*

Brick or block cladding to timber frame is generally regarded as a veneered wall, defined in BS 5628 as 'a wall having a facing that is attached to the backing but not so bonded as to result in common action under load'.

Correctly detailed brick or block cladding is capable of contributing to the timber frame structure's resistance to wind loads and the current structural design code for timber frame, BS 5268-6, indicates how this contribution can be calculated. Brickwork is normally a 'half brick' thick leaf and blockwork is typically 100 mm. Each supports its own weight but is laterally restrained by the timber frame structure using wall ties specifically designed for this purpose.

A drained and vented cavity is maintained between the brickwork or blockwork and the timber frame structure to remove any water which penetrates the outer skin in extreme conditions while the venting increases the safety margin against condensation risk.

The cavity between the brick or block cladding and the outer face of the timber frame wall should be a nominal 50 mm (nominal may be taken as +/- 10 mm). Smaller cavities may be acceptable if special precautions are taken to keep cavities free from mortar droppings eg by the use of a 'draw batten'. Larger cavities may be used if special wall ties with an extended leg into the masonry are specified.

A timber frame structure is normally based upon either a 400 mm or 600 mm structural grid to make most efficient use of sheathing and lining board materials.

This grid is not compatible with the normal brick length module of 225 mm and some cutting is required unless panels and openings are specifically designed to suit brick dimensions. In practice this difference between the timber frame and brick does not cause problems to bricklayers who are accustomed to setting out brickwork to the dimensions required. Narrow sections of brickwork between openings should be kept to a minimum width of not less than 2.5 bricks (562 mm; ie 215 + 10 + 215 + 10 + 112 mm) to avoid unsightly cutting. If this is not possible it may be preferable to consider an alternative detail such as a timber cover panel between closely spaced joinery elements.

Blockwork is normally rendered and so care with the visual aspects is not paramount. Setting out to avoid difficult cutting is more a practical on-site issue.

Since brickwork or blockwork cladding is confined to face work only, attention should be given to the maximum lift permitted at any one time to avoid brickwork 'slumping' before curing. This is particularly important when constructing narrow piers.

BS 5628-3 recommends that expansion joints should be placed in brickwork and blockwork to allow lateral movement to take place; these should be:

clay bricks              10 mm wide joints at 10 - 12 m maximum centres

calcium silicate bricks   10 mm wide joints at 7.5 - 9 m maximum centres

concrete blocks          10 mm wide joints at 6 m maximum centres (if the blockwork is rendered the maximum centres should be 5 m (see Section 9.5)

When vertical expansion joints are incorporated, the brickwork or blockwork on either side of the joint should be restrained with wall ties at closer spacings than in other locations (300 mm vertical centres within 225 mm of the joint). There is a risk of vertical cracking occurring at short returns on elevations as a result of thermal movement or slight brick expansion. This is best avoided by incorporating a movement joint at the internal angle as shown in Figure 5.8.

Differential vertical movement can occur between the timber frame inner wall and the brick or block cladding as a result of shrinkage due to reduction in the moisture content of timber elements (ie rails, binders and floor and roof joists) and either the slight expansion of clay bricks or the shrinkage of blocks or calcium silicate bricks. Therefore, any material or component attached to the timber superstructure which overhangs the brick or blockwork (ie attached cladding, window sills, roof eaves and verges), or projects through the masonry (eg flues or overflow pipes) should have a clear gap beneath it and the top of the masonry cladding to allow differential movement to take place, and avoid damage to the component or to the cladding. Figure 9.1 shows the size of movement gaps to be allowed at each storey for all masonry claddings, which have been shown by experience to be satisfactory.

Further information on brick cladding is available in the Brick Development Association's *Design Note 15 Brick cladding to timber frame construction* and *Design Note 7 Brickwork durability*. Tables and guidance on setting out are included in BDA *Design Note 3 Brickwork dimensions tables*.

**Figure 9.1 Recommended minimum allowances for differential movement between timber structure and masonry claddings**

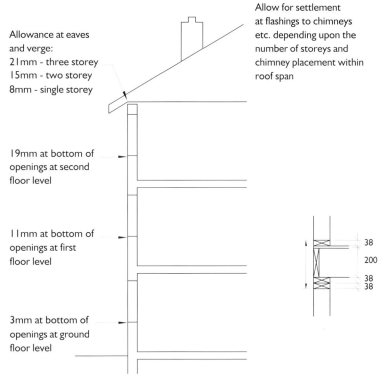

Allowance at eaves and verge:
21mm - three storey
15mm - two storey
8mm - single storey

Allow for settlement at flashings to chimneys etc. depending upon the number of storeys and chimney placement within roof span

19mm at bottom of openings at second floor level

11mm at bottom of openings at first floor level

3mm at bottom of openings at ground floor level

Note: when timber platform ground floor is used add 8mm to the differential movement allowances quoted

Note: The allowances shown are for cross sectional timber in the floor zone of conventional platform frame as shown in the detail with timber installed at 20% moisture content and drying to 10% moisture content in service.

The biggest proportion of the differential shrinkage occurs in the floor joists. The shrinkage in the rails and binders does not normally affect internal linings or the sheathing to panels. However, plasterboard lining to staircase openings of two or more storeys can be affected since it crosses the floor joist zone. A movement gap in the plasterboard with a cover strip should be specified at the floor zone.

In all cases, the movement gap allowance is for a clear gap. If compressible seals are installed in the gap, the allowance should be increased as the seal cannot be compressed to zero.

In any of the following cases, the differential movement should be re-calculated:

| Movement reduces | Movement increases |
|---|---|
| Engineered wood joists, which are manufactured at low moisture content, are used * | There is more cross-section timber in the floor zone eg deeper joists |
| Super-dried timber (at 12% moisture content) is used for joists | The in-service moisture content will be low due to constant high temperature eg in nursing homes |
| Cross-section timber is taken out of the floor zone of the wall eg storey height panels with joists hung inside (Fig 1.4) | Brickwork cladding is a type which expands over time: this can be up to 1 mm per metre height of wall. The brick supplier will have this data. |

In these cases, for solid timber and glulam * the movement calculation is as follows:

      1 Find the difference between the installed and in-service moisture content of the timber
      2 Find the total thickness of cross section timber (Y mm)
      3 Calculate dimension change X % (4% change in moisture content = 1% dimension change)
      4 Calculate allowance for movement Z = {X / 100} x Y

Allow for the calculated movement, taking account of seal compression and brick expansion.

*The formula using the 1% for 4% rule does not apply to engineered wood products, eg LVL and prefabricated I-joists. The alternative rule for % dimension change for % moisture content change should be obtained from the product manufacturer.*

The cavity between a timber frame wall and brick or block cladding should be self draining. The openings provided for drainage; open perpends (or equivalent opening area) at 1.5 m maximum centres should be kept clear of mortar (Figure 9.2). Proprietary plastic ventilators of perpend width are available. Similarly, cavities should be self draining at any horizontal cavity tray inserted over horizontal cavity barriers, over roof abutments, or over lintels above doors and windows. These provisions will also vent the wall cavity.

**Figure 9.2 Brick cladding detail at ground floor level with concrete floor slab**
See also Figure 1.13 for information on vertical dimensions and brick coursing. See Chapter 3 for ground floor specifications

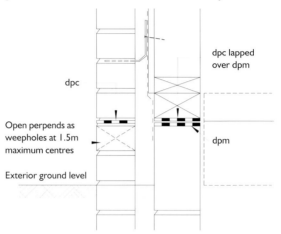

Brick coursing is usually based on a 75 mm nominal brick and bed joint dimension. A normal window or door detail in a timber frame wall requires the brickwork to course to the head of the opening so as to achieve a neat lintel detail. It is normal practice to course the brickwork to the lintel lines and to use details at the sills to adjust to the standard coursing. It is possible to arrange the full wall panel and floor joist dimensions to fit with 75 mm height coursing (see Section 1.4.2) but this can place design restrictions upon other components and is not generally necessary since experience has shown that bricklayers have no difficulty in making the small adjustments required to fit the brickwork to the structural dimensions of the timber frame.

A standard doorset requires a nominal opening height of 2100 mm which fits either 28 or 29 courses depending on the detail at the bottom of the panel. Figure 9.3 shows a typical door sill detail. The head of window openings is also normally set at 2100 mm and coursing is then arranged to fit between the heads of ground floor and upper floor openings. This can entail a small and unnoticeable variation to the bed joint.

**Figure 9.3 Brick cladding detail at door sill**

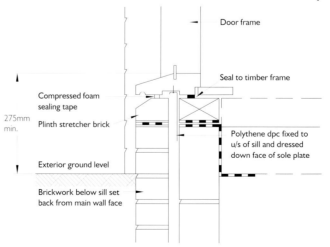

Coursing to sills is more difficult to achieve without cutting bricks, especially since openings are rarely all of one height. The recommended solution is to use a detail which permits a large construction tolerance between the window sill and the cladding. Figure 9.4 shows alternative details which satisfy this requirement. Figure 9.5 shows alternative details which can be used when the sills are dimensionally co-ordinated to the brick coursing. Figure 9.6 shows alternative ways of detailing the brickwork at window or door openings.

## Figure 9.4 Typical sill details for openings occurring off the standard brick course module

### a Brick cladding with plain tile sill
Note: In severely exposed locations, cladding bricks should be FL or FN clay bricks or calcium silicate bricks

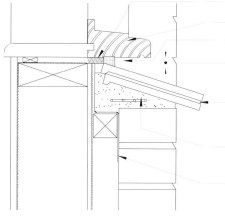

Insulation

Window fixed and sealed to timber frame wall panel

Compressed foam sealing tape

Allowance for differential movement

2 courses of plain tiles with joints staggered (overhang approx 50mm)

Bed joint reinforcement in mortar bed and into joints at reveals

500 micron polythene dpc dressed over cavity batten and under cement

### b Brick cladding with sloping brick sill
Note: Cladding and sill bricks should be FL or FN clay bricks or calcium silicate bricks

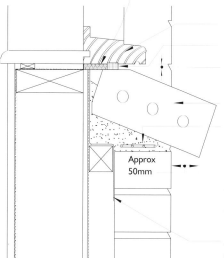

Approx 50mm

Insulation

Window fixed and sealed to timber frame wall panel

Compressed foam sealing tape

Allowance for differential movement

Squint brick or cut standard brick sill

Sills more than 1m long may need restraint by means of galvanised steel bars through perforated bricks or bed joint reinforcement in mortar below sill bricks and into joints at reveals

500 micron polythene dpc dressed over cavity batten and under cement

## Figure 9.5 Typical details for openings occurring on brick course module

### a Brick cladding with special profile brick sill

Sill bricks should be FL or FN clay bricks or calcium silicate bricks

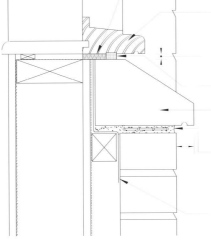

Insulation

Window fixed and sealed to timber frame wall panel

Allowance for differential movement

Compressed foam sealing tape

Special profile brick sill

Bed reinforcement in joint below sill bricks and into joints in reveals when dpc is incorporated in joint below

500 micron polythene dpc dressed over cavity batten, behind sill, under cement

### b Plinth stretcher brick sill

Cladding and sill bricks should be FL or FN clay bricks or calcium silicate bricks

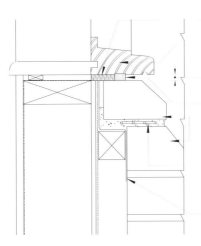

Insulation

Window fixed and sealed to timber frame wall panel

Allowance for differential movement

Compressed foam sealing tape

Plinth stretcher bricks

Bed joint reinforcement in joint below sill bricks and into joints in reveals when dpc is incorporated into joint below

500 micron polythene dpc dressed over cavity batten, behind sill, under cement

### c Precast concrete sill

Cladding bricks may be ML, MN, FL or FN clay bricks or calcium silicate bricks

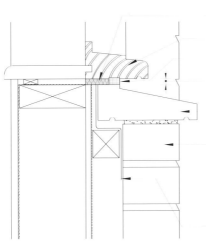

Insulation

Window fixed and sealed to timber frame wall panel

Compressed foam sealing tape

Allowance for differential movement

Precast concrete sill

Course of bricks below sill can be either a split course or a brick on edge course to allow for some variation in coursing relative to the window opening

500 micron polythene dpc dressed over cavity batten, behind sill, under cement

**Figure 9.6 Typical window detailing to brick cladding**
See Section 9.9 for details of
window location and fixings

**a Brickwork flush with
window opening**

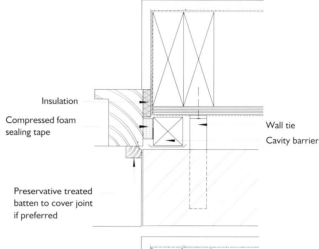

Insulation

Compressed foam
sealing tape

Wall tie

Cavity barrier

Preservative treated
batten to cover joint
if preferred

**b Brickwork projected over
window/panel joint**

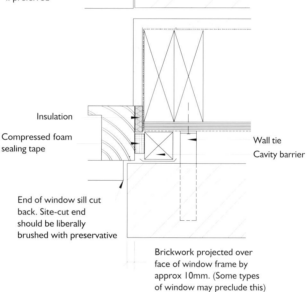

Insulation

Compressed foam
sealing tape

Wall tie

Cavity barrier

End of window sill cut
back. Site-cut end
should be liberally
brushed with preservative

Brickwork projected over
face of window frame by
approx 10mm. (Some types
of window may preclude this)

Brick cladding is tied to the timber frame wall by flexible wall ties which are embedded into the masonry wall and nailed to the timber frame at stud positions. It is important to ensure that the ties are nailed to solid frame members and not to the sheathing material alone.

The 'standard' concrete block is three bricks high (215 mm) by two bricks long (440 mm) by 100 mm wide. It is intended to course with brickwork but, as it is normally rendered, inaccurate coursing or irregular cutting does not result in visual problems. Blockwork is tied to the timber frame in the same way as for brickwork.

There is no British Standard covering wall ties specifically for use in masonry clad timber frame construction. A British Standard Draft for Development *DD 140 Wall ties Part 2 Recommendations for the design of wall ties* was published in 1987. It relates only to brick ties and is based upon Building Research Establishment studies with the design loads modified to suit the safety factors given in BS 5628-1. The major manufacturers of wall ties have had their products tested to DD140 and this should be a requirement for specification. Ties and their nail fixings should be of stainless steel, the size and gauge of fixings should meet the recommendations of the wall tie manufacturer and nail substitution should be permitted only with the approval of the manufacturer or the structural engineer.

Wall ties for brick or block cladding should normally be fixed at a minimum density of 4.4 ties per square metre.

To satisfy this requirement, ties should be on stud centres horizontally and at a vertical spacing of 375 mm (5 brick courses) when the timber frame studs are at 600 mm centres and at 525 mm vertical centres (7 brick courses) when studs are at 400 mm centres (Figure 9.7). In exposed locations the tie spacing may need to be reduced and should be calculated in accordance with BS 5628-6. Housing warranty and guarantee authorities may accept ties at 450 mm vertically when studs are at 600 mm centres but in such cases, the brickwork may not be taken into account as a contributor to wind resistance.

**Figure 9.7 Location of wall ties in brickwork cladding**

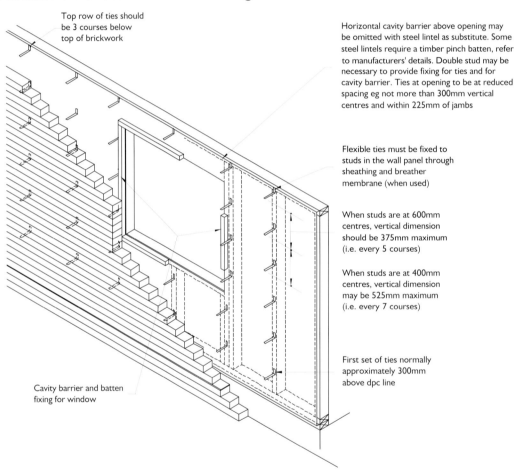

Top row of ties should be 3 courses below top of brickwork

Horizontal cavity barrier above opening may be omitted with steel lintel as substitute. Some steel lintels require a timber pinch batten, refer to manufacturers' details. Double stud may be necessary to provide fixing for ties and for cavity barrier. Ties at opening to be at reduced spacing eg not more than 300mm vertical centres and within 225mm of jambs

Flexible ties must be fixed to studs in the wall panel through sheathing and breather membrane (when used)

When studs are at 600mm centres, vertical dimension should be 375mm maximum (i.e. every 5 courses)

When studs are at 400mm centres, vertical dimension may be 525mm maximum (i.e. every 7 courses)

First set of ties normally approximately 300mm above dpc line

Cavity barrier and batten fixing for window

The top of brickwork cladding needs restraint and the top row of ties should be located three courses below the top of the cladding. At sloping verges, ties should be located within 225 mm of the top of the brickwork at every fourth course down the slope. Ties should be fixed at the sides of window and door openings spaced at not more than 300 mm vertical centres and within 225 mm of the jambs. This spacing is also required at either side of vertical expansion joints. Closer vertical spacing may be specified in exposed locations.

Wall ties for concrete blockwork are normally specified horizontally at stud centres (either 400 or 600 mm) and vertically at 450 mm (2 block courses) for both stud centre options. Blockwork should be tied one course down at the top to provide restraint. Ties at the side of openings and at either side of vertical expansion joints should be at every block (215 mm vertically) and within 250 mm of the opening or joint.

Lintels supporting brick or block cladding over openings should be structurally independent of the timber frame. (Loads over openings in the timber frame wall panel are carried independently by timber lintels.) Figure 9.8 shows a typical lintel arrangement. Where cavity tray lintels are used, they should not be fixed to the timber frame, but restrained back to the timber frame at stud centres by clips designed to permit vertical movement.

There are a number of proprietary lintels available, designed specifically for use with brick or block cladding and timber frame walls. Proprietary lintels should have independent certification and reference should be made to the manufacturer's recommendations regarding maximum span, end bearing, loading characteristics and requirements for dpcs.

When the brick or block cladding is continued over openings located immediately under the eaves it may be preferable to use a steel angle (Figure 9.9) which is shallower than a proprietary lintel to enable the masonry above the lintel to be tied back to the timber frame panel.

**Figure 9.8 Window head detail with brick cladding using a proprietary steel lintel**

**Figure 9.9 Window head detail with brickwork supported on a galvanized mild steel angle**
This detail is useful when brickwork occurs over an opening immediately below the eaves or a change of cladding where the use of a proprietary lintel may not allow space for brick ties

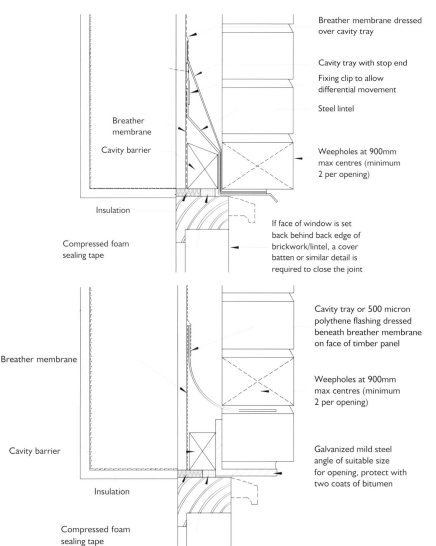

Breather membrane dressed over cavity tray

Cavity tray with stop end

Fixing clip to allow differential movement

Steel lintel

Weepholes at 900mm max centres (minimum 2 per opening)

Breather membrane

Cavity barrier

Insulation

Compressed foam sealing tape

If face of window is set back behind back edge of brickwork/lintel, a cover batten or similar detail is required to close the joint

Cavity tray or 500 micron polythene flashing dressed beneath breather membrane on face of timber panel

Weepholes at 900mm max centres (minimum 2 per opening)

Breather membrane

Cavity barrier

Insulation

Compressed foam sealing tape

Galvanized mild steel angle of suitable size for opening, protect with two coats of bitumen

## 9.4 Tile or slate cladding

Vertical tile hanging using concrete or clay tiles or natural or fibre cement slates can all provide a long life, low maintenance cladding to timber frame structures. Mathematical tiles can provide a cladding similar in appearance to brickwork but are not commonly used.

Tiles (including mathematical tiles) or slates are fixed to horizontal preservative-treated timber battens which are nailed to the studs in the timber frame wall. (Figures 9.10 - 9.12). In severely exposed conditions, the use of vertical counter battens fixed between the horizontal battens and the breather membrane is recommended to permit more efficient drainage of any water which might be driven through the tile joints. Vertical and horizontal battens should be fixed to the studs in the timber frame wall panel. When CCA treated battens are used, aluminium nails should not be used to fix the cladding. Site-cut ends of preservative-treated battens should be liberally brushed with additional preservative to maintain protection.

**Figure 9.10 Typical construction: Tile hanging**

**Figure 9.11 Typical construction: Slate hanging**

**Figure 9.12 Typical construction: Mathematical tiling**

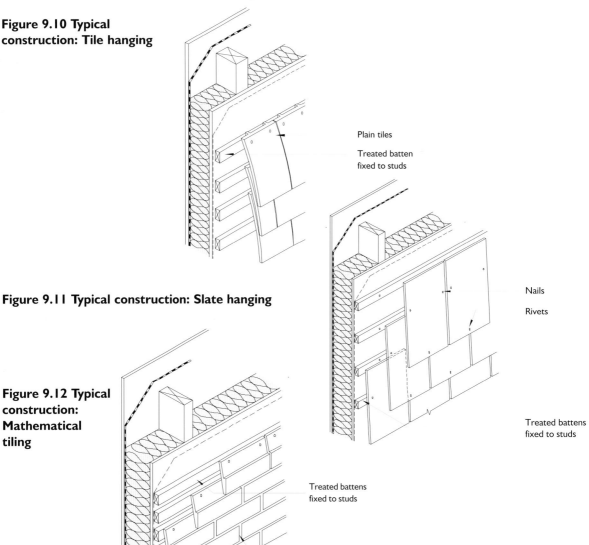

Plain tiles

Treated batten fixed to studs

Nails

Rivets

Treated battens fixed to studs

Treated battens fixed to studs

Tile joints pointed with mortar

The cavity behind the cladding should be closed off by cavity barriers and firestops as required by Building Regulations. (See section 9.1 and Figure 9.13).

**Figure 9.13 Typical detail of lightweight cladding at party wall**

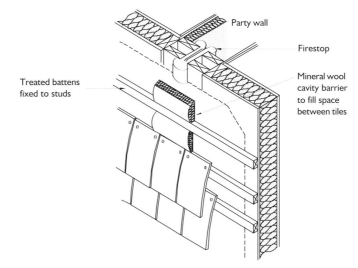

The final appearance of hung tiles and slates relies on the details at junctions with other elements. Many producers or suppliers can provide recommended details for their products. A typical detail at window openings is shown in Figure 9.14. Typical details of junctions with brick and block cladding are shown in Section 9.8; window location and fixings are shown in Section 9.9.

**Figure 9.14 Typical window detail for tile cladding**

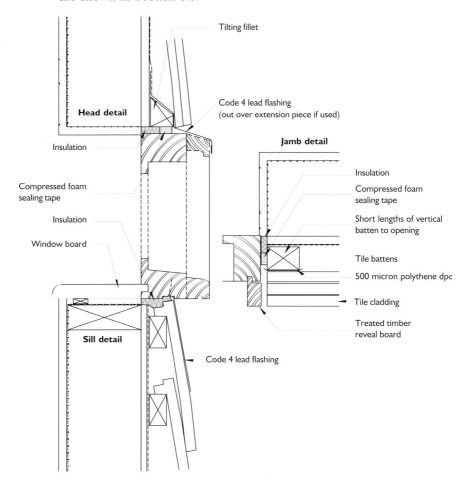

## 9.5 Cement render cladding

Cement render can be used as a finish on brick or blockwork cladding to timber frame, or it can be applied direct to metal lathing fixed to preservative treated battens on the face of the sheathing (Figure 9.15).

**Figure 9.15 Typical construction: Cement render on lathing cladding**

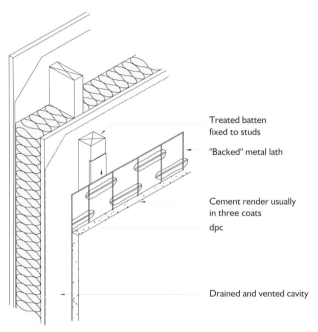

Treated batten fixed to studs

"Backed" metal lath

Cement render usually in three coats

dpc

Drained and vented cavity

When render is used in conjunction with a skin of masonry, the details are similar to those used for facing brickwork and the render details are the same as for cavity blockwork construction. This type of construction results in deeper reveals to door and window openings than would normally be possible with render applied to metal lathing. Further information on rendered blockwork is available from the British Cement Association.

Cement render can be applied to stainless steel lathing fixed to preservative-treated vertical battens. Site-cut ends of preservative-treated battens should be liberally brushed with additional preservative to maintain protection. The battens are fixed to the studs in the wall panels in order to maintain a cavity between the back face of the render and the sheathing. The cavity allows any water which penetrates the render to drain out and also vents to increase the safety margin against condensation risk. The cavity should incorporate cavity barriers and firestops at the positions required by the Building Regulations.

Metal lathing is available with a layer of building paper incorporated. When used on a timber frame wall this assists in containing the render behind the mesh but should not replace the breather membrane applied to the sheathing. The metal lathing should be fixed to the battens in accordance with the manufacturer's instructions. The manufacturers of the metal lathing usually also produce the necessary trim sections for internal and external corners and edges. When lathing with a building paper backing is used, the cavity should be at least 25 mm. When unbacked laths are used the cavity should be at least 50 mm.

The render materials can be site mixed or proprietary pre-mixed render can be used which usually requires only the addition of water. Detailed information on render mixes is included in BS 5262 Code of practice for *external renderings* and also in the British Cement Association publication *Appearance matters 2: External rendering*.

Render on stainless steel lathing is normally three coat work with a total thickness of at least 16 mm. When rendering extends over more than one storey, provision should be made for movement in the timber frame structure by the inclusion of horizontal movement joints in the render at the floor zone as well as the supporting vertical battens. Similarly, vertical movement joints should be included to avoid shrinkage cracks occurring in the width of the cladding. BS 5262 recommends that no single panel should exceed 5 metres in length or height (effectively storey height in timber frame for horizontal joints). Figures 9.16 to 9.20 illustrate typical cement render details.

Proprietary render or textured cement finishes can also be applied to fibre cement or cement-bonded particleboard cladding boards which are fixed to battens on the face of the timber frame panel. Subject to the appropriate allowance for differential movement being made, joints between the cladding boards can be covered with scrim tape and a flush joint achieved. The board or render manufacturers' details and recommendations should be followed.

**Figure 9.16 Typical window detail with cement render on lath**

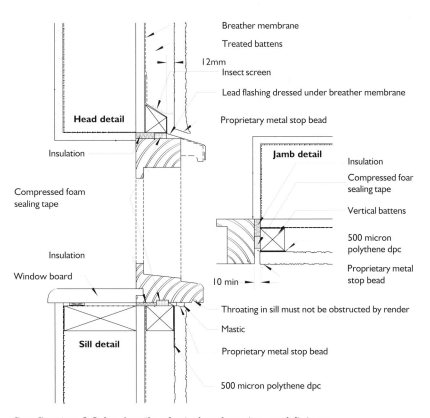

See Section 9.9 for details of window location and fixings

**Figure 9.17 Typical horizontal movement joints with cement render on lath**

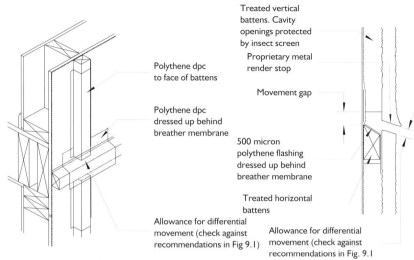

Polythene dpc to face of battens

Polythene dpc dressed up behind breather membrane

Allowance for differential movement (check against recommendations in Fig 9.1)

When cement render finishes pass across the intermediate floor zone, a movement joint should be placed at approximately mid-joist depth

Treated vertical battens. Cavity openings protected by insect screen

Proprietary metal render stop

Movement gap

500 micron polythene flashing dressed up behind breather membrane

Treated horizontal battens

Allowance for differential movement (check against recommendations in Fig. 9.1

**Figure 9.18 Typical base detail with cement render on lath**

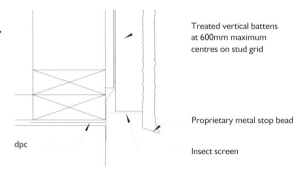

Treated vertical battens at 600mm maximum centres on stud grid

Proprietary metal stop bead

Insect screen

dpc

**Figure 9.19 Typical movement joints in cement render on lath**
Note: illustrations show typical types of galvanized mild steel or stainless steel proprietary beads and trims. Other sections from other manufacturers are equally suitable. Manufacturers' literature should be consulted.

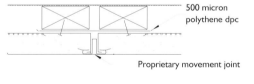

500 micron polythene dpc

Proprietary movement joint

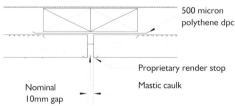

500 micron polythene dpc

Proprietary render stop

Mastic caulk

Nominal 10mm gap

**Figure 9.20 Typical external corner joint in cement render on lath**

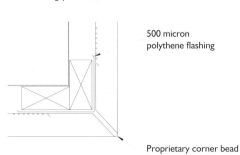

500 micron polythene flashing

Proprietary corner bead

## 9.6 Timber cladding

All timber cladding should be designed as a 'rainscreen' in principle. This assumes that the cladding will always be subject to some penetration of rainwater. The secondary weather protection provided by the breather membrane, dpcs, flashings and vented cavity disperses this to outside. Timber cladding can be used to achieve a variety of patterns, textures and colours on buildings, either as conventional boarding or open-jointed. Boards can be used vertically, horizontally or diagonally and by the use of different widths, profiles and jointing, an almost unlimited variety of surface effects can be achieved.

Although some standard profiles for cladding are available, special profiles can generally be machined if a reasonable quantity is required. However, if special profiles are to be machined it is important that designers understand the principles of weatherproofing and allow for possible moisture movement in the wood. The practicality of manufacture in terms of available sizes, lengths in the species chosen and the limitations of machining should be discussed with a supplier. The method of erection and fixing of the cladding should also be considered.

The design of timber cladding and materials selection is covered in detail in the TRADA Technology publication, *External timber cladding*.

### 9.6.1 Support battens

Cladding boards are normally fixed to preservative-treated softwood battens nailed to the timber frame studs. Site-cut ends of preservative-treated battens should be liberally brushed with additional preservative to maintain protection. The thickness of horizontal battens will depend on the nail penetration required but the width should never be less than 38 mm to avoid the risk of splitting when nailed. Vertical battens should coincide with studs behind and the thickness should be a minimum of 19 mm. Horizontal battens should be spaced at maximum 600 mm vertical centres and be 19 mm minimum thickness. If horizontal battens are not supported by sheathing they will need to be sufficiently stiff for nailing as well as providing sufficient nail retention; a minimum thickness of 25 mm is recommended.

The battens provide a cavity for the drainage of any water which may penetrate the cladding and also allow ventilation to the back face of the cladding, allowing any moisture to evaporate. With horizontal boards the vertical battens create this cavity, see Figure 9.22, but when vertical boarding is used and the battens run horizontally, space for drainage and ventilation must be provided. Profiles that have a flat back face therefore require vertical counter battens behind the horizontal battens for this purpose, see Figure 9.23.

With a 'board on board' system the gaps between the inner boards provide sufficient space for drainage and ventilation, and it is unnecessary to provide counter battens, see Figure 9.24. The tops of the horizontal battens should be sloped to the outside to shed any water that accumulates in the cavity.

Boards should be end-jointed over battens.

## 9.6.2 Board profiles

The suitability of particular profiles for specific layouts is discussed below and illustrated in Figure 9.21 (opposite). The thickness of tongued and grooved boards should not be less than 22 mm and rebated boards not less than 16 mm. The thin edge of feather edged boards should never be less than 8 mm. Square cut boards may be a minimum of 16 mm thickness, depending upon species.

A maximum board width of 150 mm is generally recommended to avoid problems of movement and distortion, although tongued and grooved boards are better limited to 100 mm in width because any distortion will be increased on wider boards, making it difficult to engage the tongues. Tongued and grooved boards should be installed tongue up in horizontal and diagonal configuration. The groove should be minimum 12 mm deep and there should be 2 mm clearance above the tongue when installed to allow for possible expansion. Overlapped or open-jointed boards are more tolerant of any moisture-induced movement and should always be used if boards are to be used undried ('green'). Overlaps should be a minimum of 15 mm.

### Horizontal boards

Tongued & grooved, rebated, open jointed and traditional weatherboards are all suitable for horizontal cladding, see Figure 9.22 (below).

An open-jointed rain screen design is particularly suitable for undried wood, which is liable to shrink and possibly distort after installation. With open jointed boards, water penetration will be greater than for the other profiles and the secondary weather protection should take account of this. Chamfering the top and bottom edges of the board will help shed water to the outside.

**Figure 9.22 Typical construction: Horizontal weatherboarding on vertical battens**

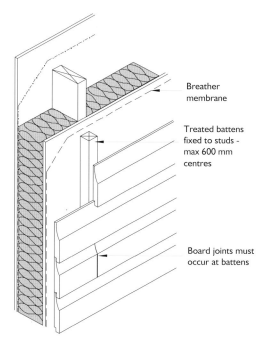

Breather membrane

Treated battens fixed to studs - max 600 mm centres

Board joints must occur at battens

**Figure 9.21 Examples of timber cladding profiles**

Vertical & Diagonal Boarding

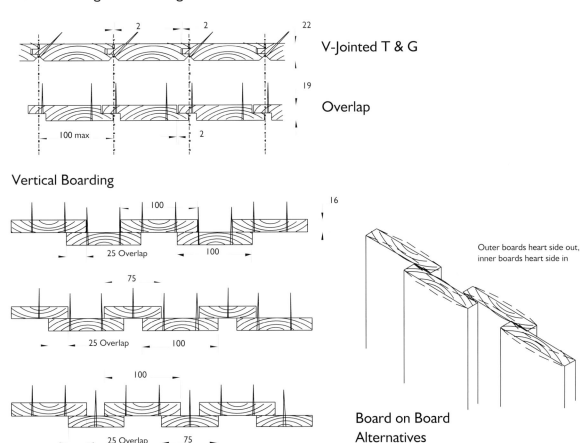

V-Jointed T & G

Overlap

Vertical Boarding

Board on Board
Alternatives

Outer boards heart side out,
inner boards heart side in

Horizontal Boarding

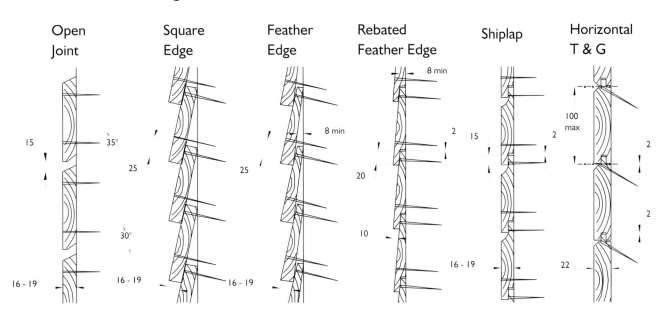

Open Joint

Square Edge

Feather Edge

Rebated Feather Edge

Shiplap

Horizontal T & G

## Diagonal boards

A shiplap profile is most appropriate for this application as the curved shoulder will effectively channel water away from the upstand, providing it is sufficiently large. Simple overlapping boards, board-on-board or open-jointed boards are not suitable as they will let significant water through by capillary action or wind pressure. Capillary action may cause water to be drawn up the face of the tongues of t & g boards which can result in sustained wetting of the joint. If the support battens are vertical, the boards span further than if they were horizontal and a thicker board may be required. Alternatively the battens can be fixed diagonally at right angles to the boarding when the span is the same as for horizontal boarding. In either case, a drained and vented cavity is provided without the need for counterbattens.

## Vertical boards

Tongued and grooved or overlapped boards are suitable for vertical use. To provide sufficient ventilation and drainage behind the boards, horizontal battens should be mounted on vertical counterbattens to provide a minimum 15 mm ventilation space, see Figure 9.23.

An alternative is to use a 'board-on-board' arrangement. An inner layer of square-edged boards is fixed to horizontal battens with gaps between and an outer layer of square-edged boards is then fixed to overlap the inner layer, see Figure 9.24. The size of inner and outer boards can be varied to provide a wide variety of pattern and shadow effects. The outer boards should overlap sufficiently, typically 25 mm, to allow for moisture movement in the boards.

Open-jointed boards are occasionally used as a vertical rain-screen, but there will be more penetration of rain into the cavity than with open-jointed horizontal boards and the secondary weatherproofing of breather membrane and flashings should take account of this.

**Figure 9.23 Typical construction: Vertical tongued and grooved boarding on horizontal battens and vertical counterbattens**

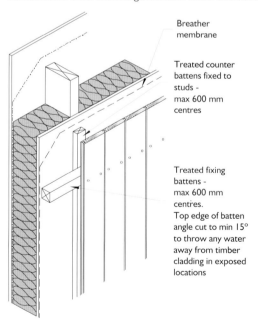

Breather membrane

Treated counter battens fixed to studs - max 600 mm centres

Treated fixing battens - max 600 mm centres. Top edge of batten angle cut to min 15° to throw any water away from timber cladding in exposed locations

162

**Figure 9.24 Typical
construction: Board-on-
board cladding**

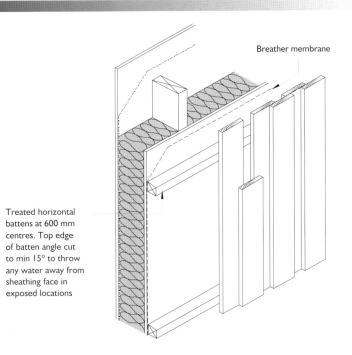

Breather membrane

Treated horizontal
battens at 600 mm
centres. Top edge
of batten angle cut
to min 15° to throw
any water away from
sheathing face in
exposed locations

## Cedar shingles

For a general description of cedar shingles, see Section 8.9.3. Shingles
are usually applied in a single course, with a double layer at the base,
nailed to battens normally spaced at 150 mm minimum centres (190 mm
maximum for 400 mm shingles) on counter battens fixed to studs, see
Figure 9.25. Joints between shingles should be staggered, usually with a
5 mm gap between. Fixing nails should be stainless steel and each
shingle should be fixed with two nails. Ferrous metal nails should not be
used with Western red cedar. Since most shingles imported to the UK are
pre-treated with CCA, aluminium nails should also be avoided. Corners
can be formed by 'lacing shingles with nails driven near the butts to
tighten and hold the lapped corners. Alternatively, vertical boards can be
inserted behind to form stopped ends for the shingles. Metal flashings,
suitably protected, should be used at corners exposed to severe weather.

**Figure 9.25 Typical
construction: Cedar shingles**

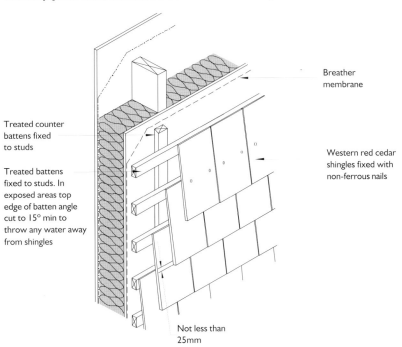

Breather
membrane

Treated counter
battens fixed
to studs

Treated battens
fixed to studs. In
exposed areas top
edge of batten angle
cut to 15° min to
throw any water away
from shingles

Western red cedar
shingles fixed with
non-ferrous nails

Not less than
25mm

## 9.6.3 Durability

Although the primary means of ensuring durability is in the correct design and detailing of cladding, any timber rated less than 'moderately durable'under BS EN 350-2: 1994 should be treated with preservative. The sapwood of all timbers should be excluded or should be treated with preservative.

*BS 1186-3 Timber for and workmanship in joinery. Specification for wood trim and its fixing* lists timbers and their requirement for treatment. The only effective methods of applying preservative is either by immersion or pressure and double vacuum methods; the latter being the more effective.

If the timber is to be left unfinished, water-borne copper chromium arsenic (CCA) should always be used. This will leave a greenish tinge to the wood which will only fade with time. If the cladding is to be finished with a protective coat of paint or stain, organic solvent preservative or the waterborne mixed-emulsion types now available may be specified. An alternative is to use boron salts, but this is only rated as suitable for a 30 year life, even when protected by a surface coating.

Detailed specifications for the preservative treatment of timber cladding are provided in *BS 5589 Code of practice for the preservation of timber.* None of the approved methods of application permit brushing or spraying, except on limited areas of freshly exposed timber resulting from on-site cutting or drilling.

Timber treated with water-borne preservatives must be redried after treatment.

## 9.6.4 Species

The timbers commonly used for cladding in the UK are softwoods such as European redwood or European whitewood. Both require treatment (redwood being easier to treat than whitewood) and a protective finish is recommended. They are similar in appearance except that redwood generally has fewer but larger knots and is more resinous. Western hemlock is occasionally used because of the straight-grain and few knots but also requires treatment.

Other common softwood species for cladding are Douglas fir, and European larch which are both rated moderately durable, or Western red cedar which is rated durable. These woods can be left untreated if the sapwood is excluded. (Note: UK grown Douglas fir is rated non-durable and will require treatment. UK western red cedar is generally rated moderately durable but may still be used without treatment.) They will all weather to a natural grey if left unfinished, but Western red cedar tends to have a more lustrous appearance. Western red cedar is a low density timber and if cladding is likely to be subject to impact or scoring, Douglas fir or European larch are more robust and would be more suitable.

Hardwoods are generally denser and more robust than softwoods and European oak or iroko are often used for this reason. Both can be left unfinished and will weather to a natural grey. Other hardwoods used for cladding include African mahogany, balau, jarrah, opepe, sapele, teak and sweet chestnut.

## 9.6.5 Quality

The designer should specify the required quality of the finished cladding and should ensure that this is brought to the attention of the supplier, to allow him to select from the most appropriate commercial grade.

*BS 1186 Timber for and workmanship in joinery Part 2 Specification for workmanship* and *Part 3 Specification for wood trim and its fixing* may be used to provide a basic specification for the quality of material. Four classes of timber are defined for wood trim:

♦ Class CSH for trim made from `clear' grades of softwood and hardwood

♦ Class 1 for high quality or specialised trim

♦ Class 2 and Class 3 for general purpose trim

Classes 1, 2 and 3 are obtainable in commercially available softwood and hardwood. Class 3 is normally accepted as a serviceable quality for most cladding applications. Where European softwoods such as redwood, whitewood or larch, are required to achieve a higher visual quality, Class 2 can be specified. Class 1 will require special selection and will be more costly; it is therefore only appropriate if large knots are not visually acceptable. Softwoods such as Douglas fir, Western red cedar and hemlock can be supplied to Class 1 or even CSH grade, although this is not normally used for external cladding because of the high cost.

Further selection can be made on site as each board is cut to length. Local unacceptable defects can be cut out and with care, economic use of the boards can be achieved. If the boards are required to be of standard lengths to match the spacing of supports, or to give a designed joint pattern, more careful selection may be required from the supplier.

## 9.6.6 Moisture content

The best way of minimising any problems of movement is to ensure that the moisture content of the boards when erected is as close as possible to the likely 'in use' moisture content. BS 1186-3 recommends a moisture content of 13-19% for external trim. TRADA recommends that cladding is installed at 16% as typical of the likely average level in use.

The moisture content of timber boarding on any one face of a building is likely to show a seasonal variation of about 6 – 8% which will cause some swelling and shrinkage in the wood. Timbers described as having 'large' movement properties are not recommended for use as cladding. Information on the properties of selected timber species is given in the TRADA Wood Information Sheet *Timbers: their properties and uses.*

## 9.6.7 Fixings

Cladding boards are commonly fixed with lost-head annular ring shank nails, but with Western red cedar, roundhead nails are preferable because of the softness of the wood. Special care is also required not to overdrive, particularly if nail guns are used.

Stainless steel nails are recommended, particularly for woods containing tannin, such as Western red cedar, Douglas fir or European oak. While hot dipped galvanised nails can be used, driving the nail can damage the coating and any corrosion may result in staining of the wood. Stainless steel nails should always be used if the wood is to be left unfinished.

Plain shank nails should be 2.5 times and annular ring shank nails 2 times the cladding board thickness. Nails should be driven flush with the surface of the board, but if an opaque paint finish is to be used the nail can be punched below the surface and the holes stopped with a filler.

Hardwood cladding is usually fixed with screws and the boards should always be pre-drilled. It is preferable if the hole is larger than the shank of the screw, to allow for possible shrinkage of the board. The heads of the screws, whether countersunk or roundhead, will provide adequate retention to the battens. If undried wood is to be used with double fixings larger holes will be necessary to allow for possible shrinkage. In this case it may be necessary  to add stainless steel washers under the screw heads.

Boards 100 mm wide or above will require double nailing. Nails are best positioned at quarter points in the board width, between any tongues or rebates, to minimise the amount of shrinkage between the fixings. With board-on-board types, the fixing of the outer board should be between the inner boards and not through them.  Similarly with any horizontal overlap detail, the fixing of the outer board should clear the board underneath, only clamping the top of the lower board in place. 'Secret' fixing with single nails is not recommended for t & g boards because of the risk of the tongue splitting. Where boards are butt jointed, the junction should always occur over battens and nails should be at least 15 mm from the ends of the boards. This may require wider or additional fixing battens behind.

## 9.6.8 Detailing

Corners and junctions with doors and windows require careful detailing to ensure durability, reduce water leakage and give a satisfactory appearance. To ensure a consistent appearance, either the spacing and size of windows should relate to the board dimensions and layout, or the board dimension should be designed to relate to the pattern of openings. Figures 9.26 and 9.27 show examples of corner detailing and Figures 9.28 – 9.30 show detailing around windows.

Space should be provided at the end of any boards to allow for drying out and for future maintenance of any finish. This is important where the boards butt to each other and where the boarding abuts other materials either horizontally or vertically. It is good practice to splay cut the ends of vertical boards at joints to assist in shedding water away from the end grain to the outside.

It is advisable to stop cladding at least 150 mm (200 mm preferred) above ground level or above any other horizontal projection, to avoid excessive wetting due to splashing off the horizontal surface below, see Figure 9.31.

If the boards are to be finished, sharp edges or arrises should be avoided since these tend to induce early failure of finishes. A chamfered or "pencil-round" radius is recommended if the board is to be planed or profiled.

**Figure 9.26 Typical corner details: Horizontal boarding**

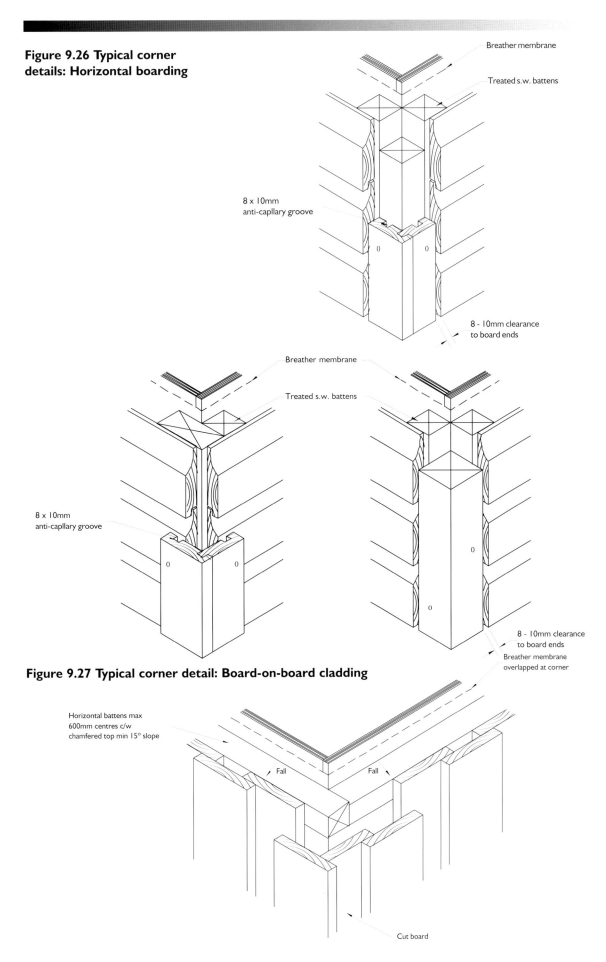

Breather membrane

Treated s.w. battens

8 x 10mm anti-capllary groove

8 - 10mm clearance to board ends

Breather membrane

Treated s.w. battens

8 x 10mm anti-capllary groove

8 - 10mm clearance to board ends

Breather membrane overlapped at corner

**Figure 9.27 Typical corner detail: Board-on-board cladding**

Horizontal battens max 600mm centres c/w chamfered top min 15° slope

Fall

Fall

Cut board

**Figure 9.28 Typical detail of window in horizontal boarding** (Insulation not shown for clarity)
See Section 9.9 for window location and fixings

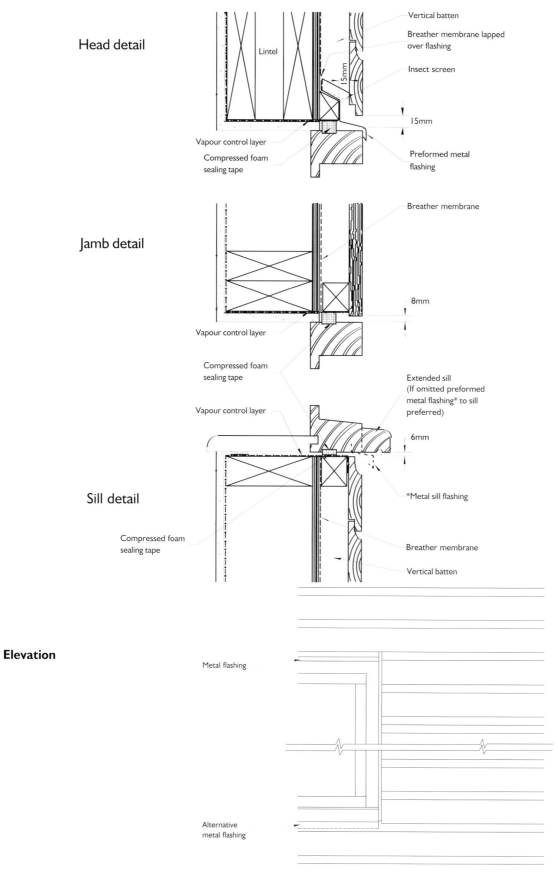

Head detail

Vertical batten

Breather membrane lapped over flashing

Insect screen

Lintel

15mm

15mm

Vapour control layer

Compressed foam sealing tape

Preformed metal flashing

Jamb detail

Breather membrane

Vapour control layer

8mm

Compressed foam sealing tape

Vapour control layer

Extended sill (If omitted preformed metal flashing* to sill preferred)

6mm

*Metal sill flashing

Sill detail

Compressed foam sealing tape

Breather membrane

Vertical batten

**Elevation**

Metal flashing

Alternative metal flashing

**Figure 9.29 Typical detail of window in vertical boarding** (Insulation not shown for clarity)
See Section 9.9  for window location and fixings

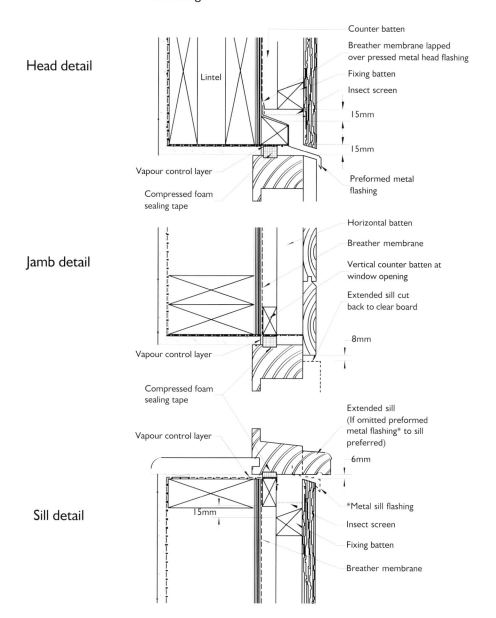

Head detail

Counter batten

Breather membrane lapped over pressed metal head flashing

Fixing batten

Insect screen

15mm

15mm

Lintel

Vapour control layer

Compressed foam sealing tape

Preformed metal flashing

Jamb detail

Horizontal batten

Breather membrane

Vertical counter batten at window opening

Extended sill cut back to clear board

8mm

Vapour control layer

Compressed foam sealing tape

Extended sill
(If omitted preformed metal flashing* to sill preferred)

6mm

Vapour control layer

Sill detail

15mm

*Metal sill flashing

Insect screen

Fixing batten

Breather membrane

**Figure 9.30 Typical detail of window in board-on-board cladding** (Insulation not shown for clarity)
See Section 9.9 for window location and fixings

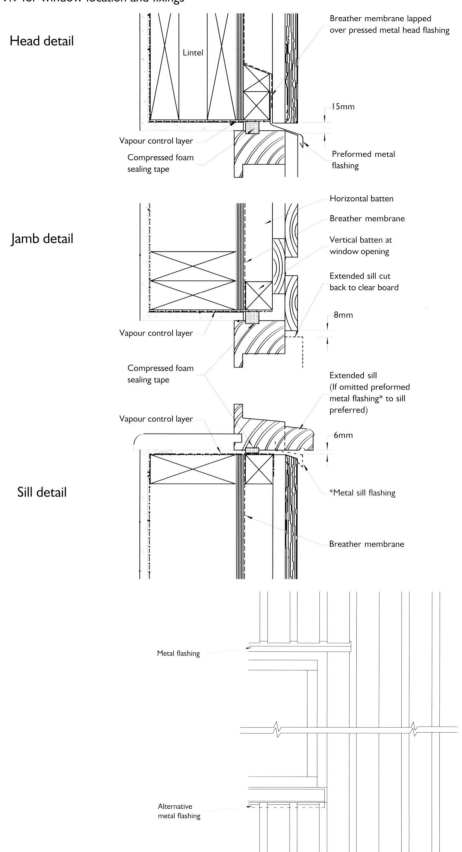

Head detail

Breather membrane lapped
over pressed metal head flashing

Lintel

15mm

Vapour control layer

Compressed foam
sealing tape

Preformed metal
flashing

Jamb detail

Horizontal batten

Breather membrane

Vertical batten at
window opening

Extended sill cut
back to clear board

8mm

Vapour control layer

Compressed foam
sealing tape

Extended sill
(If omitted preformed
metal flashing* to sill
preferred)

Vapour control layer

6mm

Sill detail

*Metal sill flashing

Breather membrane

**Elevation**

Metal flashing

Alternative
metal flashing

**Figure 9.31 Base details for timber cladding** (Insulation not shown for clarity)

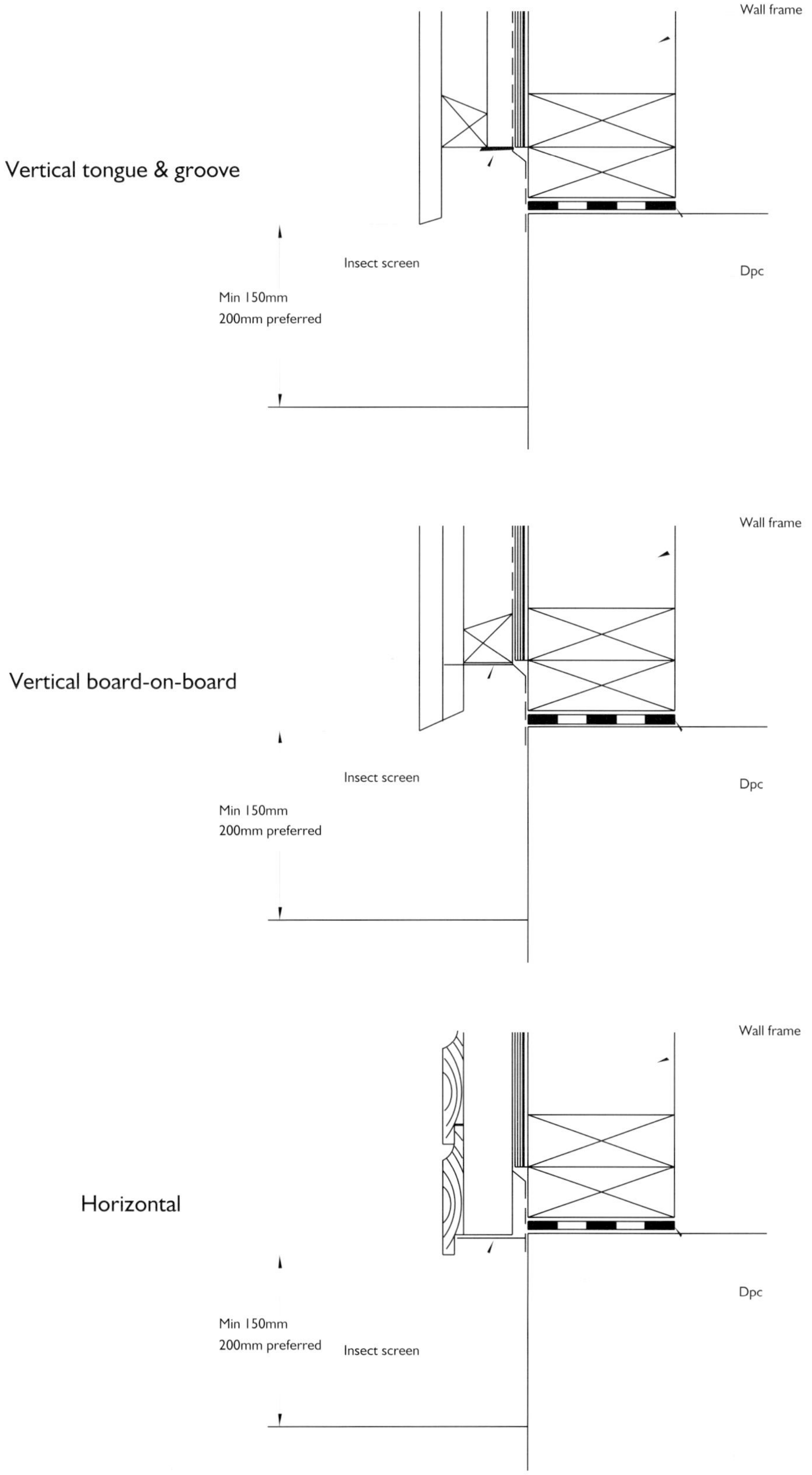

Vertical tongue & groove

Wall frame

Insect screen

Min 150mm
200mm preferred

Dpc

Vertical board-on-board

Wall frame

Insect screen

Min 150mm
200mm preferred

Dpc

Horizontal

Wall frame

Min 150mm
200mm preferred    Insect screen

Dpc

Figure 9.31
Base details for timber cladding

### 9.6.9 Finishes

Timber boarding can be either left unfinished (depending on species) or finished with microporous stains or paints.

Exterior stain finishes, whether translucent or opaque, do not rely upon a surface film to provide protection and are the most appropriate choice where a finish is required. Details may be found in the TRADA Wood Information Sheet *Finishes for exterior timber*. The first coat of finish should be applied to the face, back and edges of boards before fixing. This will avoid the exposure of any untreated surfaces should slight withdrawal of overlaps or tongues occur, as well as providing additional protection to the concealed faces of the board, which cannot be repainted in the future. Although applying stains to sawn rather than planed surfaces will take up more stain initially, far longer periods between recoating can be expected (possibly up to three times as long).

Varnishes or oil based paints are not recommended because they are too inflexible and will crack if there is any movement of the timber. They are also vapour resistant so that any moisture that penetrates will be held in the wood behind the surface film.

### 9.6.10 Fire performance

Timber and wood-based materials may be used for cladding providing that they satisfy the external fire spread requirements of the Building Regulations, either inherently or by appropriate treatment. It should be noted that some of these treatments require a surface coating to provide protection to the impregnated salts in the wood.

### 9.6.11 Wood-based board materials

Plywood panels or other wood-based boards are occasionally used as cladding. This requires careful detailing and specification which is beyond the scope of this book. Specialist advice should be sought.

# 9.7 Cavity barriers

Requirements for cavity barriers differ between National Building Regulations. The most recent edition of the Regulations should always be checked.

Cavity barriers in timber frame can be of the following materials:

Rigid type:

♦ preservative-treated timber battens; minimum size 38 mm x cavity dimension

♦ calcium silicate, cement-based or gypsum-based boards, at least 12.5 mm thick.

Flexible type:

♦ wire reinforced mineral wool blanket at least 50 mm thick

♦ polythene sleeved mineral wool or mineral wool slab, in either case under compression when installed in the cavity.

A combination of a rigid type with a flexible facing is sometimes used, eg a timber batten with mineral wool fixed to the outer face. Figures 9.32 and 9.33 illustrate typical external wall cavity barrier details.

**Figure 9.32 Vertical cavity barriers in external walls (a, right)** Note: not required in all buildings in all areas. Check relevant Building Regulations

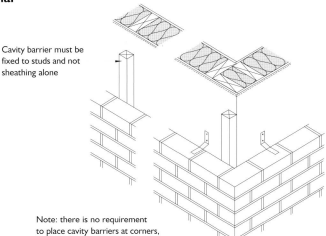

Cavity barrier must be fixed to studs and not sheathing alone

Note: there is no requirement to place cavity barriers at corners, it is however often convenient to do so

**(b) at party wall**

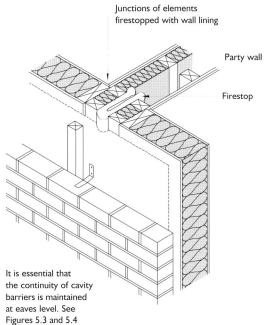

Junctions of elements firestopped with wall lining

Party wall

Firestop

It is essential that the continuity of cavity barriers is maintained at eaves level. See Figures 5.3 and 5.4

**Figure 9.33 Cavity barrier in external wall at intermediate or compartment floor level**

Polythene dpc over timber cavity barrier tucked beneath breather membrane or polythene sleeved mineral wool tacked to face of breather membrane

Joint between horizontal and vertical cavity barriers must be tightly butted and the horizontal dpc lapped over the vertical dpc

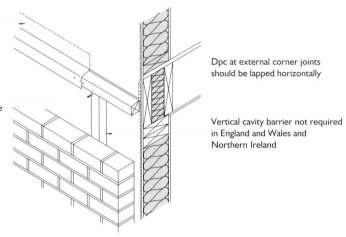

Dpc at external corner joints should be lapped horizontally

Vertical cavity barrier not required in England and Wales and Northern Ireland

## 9.8 Junctions between heavy- and lightweight claddings

Heavy claddings such as brickwork or blockwork are constructed from the foundations and tied back to the timber frame structure with flexible ties to allow for differential movement between the timber structure and the cladding. Lightweight claddings such as timber, render or tile hanging are fixed directly to and supported by the timber frame wall structure.

Vertical junctions should allow for differential movement and limit water penetration between the two claddings. A typical detail is shown in Figure 9.34.

**Figure 9.34 Typical detail of vertical junction between heavyweight and lightweight claddings**
Note: Breather membrane, dpcs etc not shown for clarity

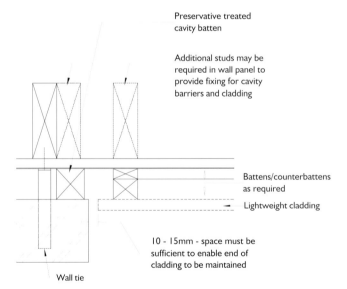

Preservative treated cavity batten

Additional studs may be required in wall panel to provide fixing for cavity barriers and cladding

Battens/counterbattens as required

Lightweight cladding

10 - 15mm - space must be sufficient to enable end of cladding to be maintained

Wall tie

Horizontal junctions can be of two basic types; those where the upper (thinner, lightweight) cladding is fixed to the wall panel and either flashed over or flared out over the thicker cladding below, and those where the upper wall panels are projected to allow the claddings to be in the same plane or project beyond the lower level cladding. (Figure 9.35) See Section 6.7 for the structural implications of this arrangement.

**Figure 9.35 Typical detail at junction of lightweight and heavyweight claddings using an overhanging platform floor**

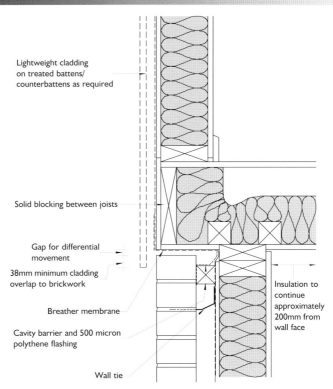

Lightweight cladding on treated battens/counterbattens as required

Solid blocking between joists

Gap for differential movement

38mm minimum cladding overlap to brickwork

Breather membrane

Cavity barrier and 500 micron polythene flashing

Wall tie

Insulation to continue approximately 200mm from wall face

The upper cladding can be flashed over the cladding below using a tiled sill, preformed brick or precast concrete sill. Typical details are shown in Figure 9.36. This method can be used with all types of lightweight cladding. It is important that allowance is made for differential movement between upper and lower claddings and that the cavity to the brick cladding is closed to satisfy the requirements of the Building Regulations. When cladding occurs over window and door openings, the soffit cavity should be closed with either 38 mm thick timber or a fire resistant board material to prevent fire penetration to the floor above. Draining and venting to the cavity above the window (above the cavity barrier) can be via small openings in the cladding, similar to the open perpends above brick openings, outside the breather membrane in the batten space.

**Figure 9.36 Typical details of lightweight cladding over heavyweight cladding using a tile or brick sill**

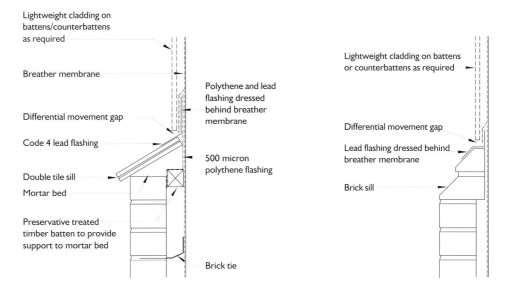

Lightweight cladding on battens/counterbattens as required

Breather membrane

Differential movement gap

Code 4 lead flashing

Double tile sill

Mortar bed

Preservative treated timber batten to provide support to mortar bed

Polythene and lead flashing dressed behind breather membrane

500 micron polythene flashing

Brick tie

Lightweight cladding on battens or counterbattens as required

Differential movement gap

Lead flashing dressed behind breather membrane

Brick sill

## 9.9 Location and fixing of external joinery

Joinery components should be detailed so that they are fixed to the timber frame structure. This enables them to be fitted in the factory or, at an early stage after the timber structure is erected on site, enabling the structure to be secure and weathertight as early as possible.

Sealing to the timber cavity barrier is recommended rather than sealing to the external cladding. It avoids the problem of differential movement stressing the sealed joint and also keeps the seal protected from the direct weather and UV light which can cause deterioration. The seal can be gun-applied mastic although a pre-compressed impregnated foam tape or strip is preferable as it is vapour permeable and can accommodate any movement of the timber that may occur. Because of the risk of cold bridging at the edge of the joinery frame, the joint should be filled with mineral wool or blown polyurethane foam.

Fitting joinery in the factory allows the wall panels to be fabricated accurately around the door and window components. This makes it relatively easy to make a consistent joint between the panel and the door or window frame. Care is required to prevent damage to projecting joinery components during transport and erection.

Fixing joinery on site makes it necessary to detail the interface joint carefully in order to achieve a well sealed joint and avoid cold bridging. A 10 mm fitting tolerance between the size of the opening and the size of the joinery component provides a joint that can contain both insulation and the weather seal to avoid cold bridging and air leakage.

# 10 Services

## 10.1 Design requirements

The installation of electrical, telecommunications, plumbing, heating and ventilation services in timber framed construction can be achieved quickly and efficiently, using the spaces formed in the framing to locate cables, pipes and ducts. Installation in floor and roof framing is no different from other types of construction. In all loadbearing elements, care is required in maintaining fire resistance and in party walls and party floors, additional attention should be paid to maintaining sound insulation. Services are currently precluded from timber separating and compartment elements in Scotland and Northern Ireland.

Services can be installed into panels in the factory, thereby reducing work on site to making the necessary connections from panel to panel and connecting to the supply. Some systems of construction follow this method though it is more common for services installation work to be done on site, commencing as soon as the timber frame shell is weathertight.

Mains wiring should be kept away from telephone, alarm, aerial or data cabling to avoid interference. When electrical cables are surrounded by, or adjacent to, insulation this increases the risk of their overheating and cables may need to be de-rated to compensate. Alternatively electrical wiring may be run in plastic conduit. Pvc sheathed cabling should not be placed in contact with expanded polystyrene because plasticiser migration will make the pvc brittle. Electrical services should be installed in accordance with *BS 7671 Requirements for electrical installations, IEE Wiring Regulations*.

Solid fuel, oil and gas heating appliances can all be installed in timber frame structures. There are Building Regulation limitations on the proximity of timber members to chimneys, flues and hearths. Flues and chimneys passing through compartment floors should be in enclosures with fire resistance of at least half that required for the floor and should be of non-combustible construction and maintain the required distance from any combustible materials.

The general requirements in respect of appliances and fittings are dealt with in detail in National Building Regulations and by the service industries and are applicable to all forms of construction. This chapter deals only with specific requirements for timber frame construction. The housing warranty and guarantee authorities have their own requirements in respect of services installation; the latest version of their manuals should be consulted.

A TRADA Technology report, Timber frame walls and floors: Fire resistance of service penetrations gives the results of tests on electric box fittings, pipes and light fittings in timber frame walls and floors.

All services connections details should be confirmed with the appropriate service industry before installation.

In addition to meeting the Design Requirements, the successful completion and quality of the timber frame building is dependent on good on-site practice in terms of accuracy in setting out and erecting components. Guidance is given in Appendix 3 Site Supervisors' Checklist.

## 10.2 Cutting framing members

Services in walls and floors may run parallel with the timber framing members or across them. Running services parallel with the framing is obviously easier, and services, wherever possible, should be set out with this in mind. Where running at right angles, care is necessary when cutting, notching or drilling.

The rules for notching and drilling joists are set out in BS 5268-2 and shown in Figure 10.1. Any deviation from these rules should be calculated in accordance with BS 5268-2.

**Figure 10.1 Notching and drilling of floor joists**
Note: Notches may be at the top or bottom of the joist, but not both at the same end. If notches are limited to the area between 0.1 and 0.2 of span, the maximum notch depth may be increased to 0.15 x joist depth

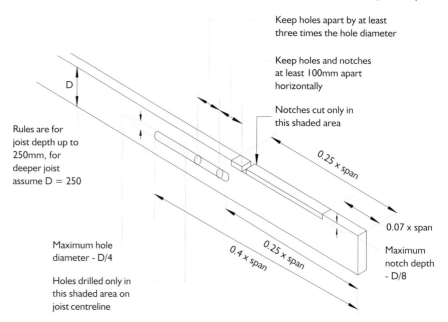

Keep holes apart by at least three times the hole diameter

Keep holes and notches at least 100mm apart horizontally

Notches cut only in this shaded area

D

Rules are for joist depth up to 250mm, for deeper joist assume D = 250

0.25 x span

0.07 x span

Maximum hole diameter - D/4

Holes drilled only in this shaded area on joist centreline

0.4 x span

0.25 x span

Maximum notch depth - D/8

Stud frames should not normally be notched; services should be run in holes drilled on the centre line of the stud. The hole diameter should not exceed 25% of the stud depth and should be placed in the areas shown in Figure 10.2.

**Figure 10.2 Drilling holes in studs**

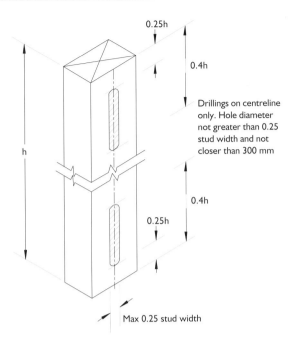

0.25h

0.4h

Drillings on centreline only. Hole diameter not greater than 0.25 stud width and not closer than 300 mm

h

0.4h

0.25h

Max 0.25 stud width

A hole within these rules in a stud which is at least 89 mm deep will generally ensure that pipes or cables are clear of the 40 or 50 mm long nails normally used to fix 12.5 or 2 x 12.5 mm plasterboard linings respectively. If other board thickness/nail length combinations are specified, the risk of damage to the services should be checked. Where there is risk to services from nails or screws used to fix lining or flooring boards, proprietary steel protection plates should be fixed to bridge the notch and protect the services. If holes or notches larger than 25% of stud depth are necessary, double studs may be needed at these positions to offset the effect of cutting away the cross sectional area. Where such holes or notches occur in loadbearing walls, the modified members should be checked by calculation.

Roof rafters and purlins, trusses, trussed rafters or bracing should never be notched or cut away without the relevant calculations being checked or approval obtained from the structural engineer or specialist component supplier.

When drilling or notching is carried out by the electrician or plumber as part of their installation work, it is essential that they are aware of the above limitations.

## 10.3 Fixing services to timber framed walls

Lightly loaded fixings can be made to the plasterboard lining with proprietary fixing devices. There are a number of different types available, made of light gauge metal or polypropylene, see Figure 10.3.

### Figure 10.3 Proprietary fixings for use with plasterboard linings

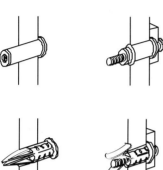

The flexible sleeve which grips the outer surface by expanding, can regain its shape when the screw is unscrewed, so the fixing can be removed and used again.

Plastic plug which springs out after passing through the hole; the board thickness is critical

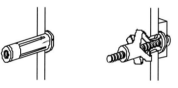

Plastic or metal anchor type, operating by setting tool or by screw tightening. The socket is formed on both sides of the face board, allowing the screw to be removed and replaced in the same fixing

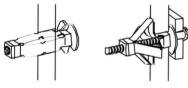

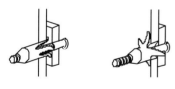

Spreading type; the legs spread out after passing through the hole

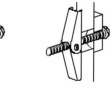

Spring toggle; can only be used once. If the screw is removed, the remaining toggle or flange on the other side of the board is released and will fall down inside the cavity

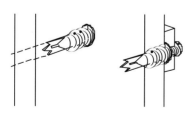

Plastic or metal self-drilling plug allowing the fixing screw to be removed and replaced. The plug can also be removed and the hole filled if no longer required.

Fixings vary in respect of the thickness of material they can be fixed into, in strength and in cost. Those which have a screw or bolt supplied as part of the fixing usually have a limitation on the maximum thickness of material through which they can fix. There are two basic types; those where the fixing screw can be removed and replaced in the captive socket and those which can only be used once and have to be replaced once the fixing screw is removed. Fixings to take greater loads should be made by screwing directly into studs or noggings.

When services are concentrated on external walls, the internal lining can be battened away from the wall studs to form a service zone on the warm side and avoid perforating the vapour control layer; see Figure 10.4. A similar solution can be used in timber frame structures where the sheathing is fixed on the internal face of the studding. The service zone void should be sealed at its perimeter to avoid convection air currents and can if required, be filled with insulation to increase the thermal performance of the wall. Filling this space will also be helpful in reducing the perception of 'hollowness' if the wall is tapped. A similar service zone can be used at a compartment or separating wall if required and would normally be accepted in Scotland and Northern Ireland.

**Figure 10.4 Detail of wall with services zone inside the vapour control layer**

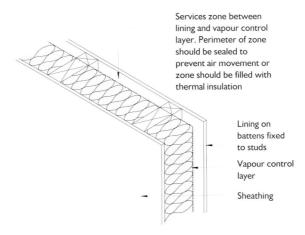

Services zone between lining and vapour control layer. Perimeter of zone should be sealed to prevent air movement or zone should be filled with thermal insulation

Lining on battens fixed to studs

Vapour control layer

Sheathing

## 10.4 Drainage and plumbing installation

Soil and vent pipes should be set out so that they do not interfere with wall and floor framing members and should, where possible, relate to the spacings between floor joists to avoid unnecessary cutting and trimming. The flashing junction of a soil or vent pipe should allow for differential movement between the pipe and the structure, see Figure 9.1.

Soil and vent pipes passing through habitable rooms should be encased by timber framing lined with a minimum of 25 mm of plasterboard or other equally dense material. The pipe should be wrapped for its full height in a layer of insulation, secured with plastic tape or wire. Soil and vent pipes within floors should be similarly wrapped. Mineral wool pugging should be fitted to fill the framed zone around soil pipes passing through timber floors to improve, where necessary, the resistance to flanking sound transmission.

To avoid the possibility of condensation occurring on the pipes and the risk of hidden leakage, water service pipework preferably should not be located within external wall panels. This may be acceptable where the pipes are near the inner face of the wall (condensation) and do not include any joints (hidden leakage). If in the wall near the surface, pipes must be protected against damage from plasterboard nails or future DIY work.

Pipe drops preferably should be run on the internal face of the wall lining or in services ducts formed on the warm side of the vapour control layer by blocking out a section of the wall lining. When locating ducts it is necessary to consider the detail at the floor junction to avoid cutting floor joists or headers.

Plumbing can be located within internal walls but again joints are best avoided in the enclosed part; if this is not possible, access must be provided at joint locations. Pipes should be protected against the risk of damage from plasterboard nailing.

When service pipes are run on wall surfaces, the clips should be screwed to the stud framework through the lining boards. Where this is not possible, noggings should be fixed between studs to provide fixings or appropriate cavity fixings should be used.

Pipe ducts should have suitable access panels provided adjacent to joints or bends in the pipework and this is a requirement of many water authorities. Access panels should not reduce the fire resistance of loadbearing walls.

Water storage tanks in roof spaces should be fully supported by sheet material on bearers. The precise design of this will depend upon the type of roof construction; see Chapter 8 'Roofs'.

Noggings should normally be incorporated into plasterboard lined wall panels to provide fixings for items such as sanitary fittings and radiators. It is often possible to obtain some fixings from the vertical studs and provide noggings for the remaining fixings. An alternative solution is to locate the structural sheathing on the inner stud face or to use a wall lining board such as cement-bonded particleboard or fibre reinforced plasterboard which will provide sufficient support. Heavy items, such as wall-hung boilers, may still require additional studs to provide the necessary support.

Plumbing services should not be run within party walls since any future need to gain access to them is likely to damage the fire and acoustic performance. If services location in compartment walls is essential, a service duct incorporating the necessary fire resistance and acoustic requirements can be incorporated in the wall design. Figure 10.5 illustrates a typical service duct.

**Figure 10.5 Typical detail of full height service duct in a party wall**
Note: Service ducts should not be located back-to-back in adjacent buildings

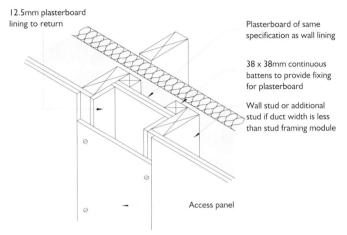

12.5mm plasterboard lining to return

Plasterboard of same specification as wall lining

38 x 38mm continuous battens to provide fixing for plasterboard

Wall stud or additional stud if duct width is less than stud framing module

Access panel

In platform-type party floors, it is possible to locate limited runs of pipework to supply the upper level, above the floor base and within the resilient layer thickness. In resilient batten-type floors, pipes can normally be run in the batten zone. In each case, suitable access should be provided to the pipes. However, since any leakage would not be easily noticeable, it is recommended that pipework should be located above the finished floor wherever possible.

When services pass through the party floor, it is normal practice to form an enclosure above and below the floor which is fire resistant and to seal the joint at the floor to maintain the fire and acoustic performance of the floor (See Figure 10.6). The walls of the enclosure should be of a board material with the required flame spread (reaction to fire) resistance (currently Class O) internal surface and weighing at least 15 kg/m$^2$ (eg 19 mm plasterboard), fixed to a suitable timber framework. The enclosure should be lined with mineral wool at least 25 mm thick or the pipework or duct wrapped in 25 mm mineral wool. The duct lining board should stop 3 mm clear of the floor surface and the gap sealed with an acoustic sealant. The ceiling junction should be sealed with tape and/or filled with a gypsum based compound. When the service duct abuts a loadbearing or party wall, the full lining specification of the wall should continue behind the duct.

The duct may have access panels but these should not open into bedroom or circulation spaces and should have the same fire resistance as the duct lining. The access panel should be made of plywood or similar wood-based board with a plasterboard internal lining or made of cement bonded particleboard or mineral fibre board of suitable thickness. The panel should be tight fitting and be fixed with cups and screws.

Soil or vent pipes passing through the floor within the duct should be set out to avoid unnecessary cutting and trimming of the joists. The opening through the floor should be sealed with either an approved proprietary sealant which has been tested to show the appropriate fire resistance or by mineral wool. Maximum pipe sizes are given in Building Regulations.

**Figure 10.6 Enclosure for pipes penetrating party floors**
Note: Party wall/ party floor junction shown: detail is similar at external and internal loadbearing walls.
Detail at compartment floor without floating layer is otherwise similar

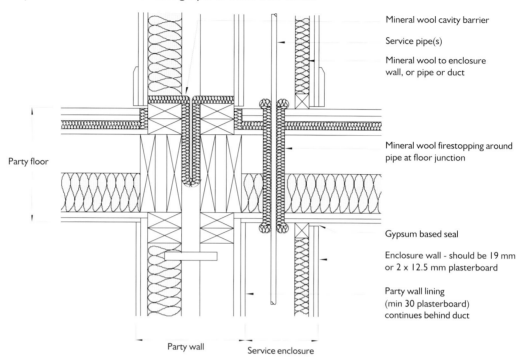

Mineral wool cavity barrier

Service pipe(s)

Mineral wool to enclosure
wall, or pipe or duct

Mineral wool firestopping around
pipe at floor junction

Gypsum based seal

Enclosure wall - should be 19 mm
or 2 x 12.5 mm plasterboard

Party wall lining
(min 30 plasterboard)
continues behind duct

Party floor

Party wall

Service enclosure

## 10.5 Electrical installation

Wiring can be located in the floor, roof or wall voids in timber frame construction, unless precluded in National Building Regulations. By preplanning, it is usually possible to use the space between intermediate floor joists for the main distribution, with vertical drops between studs to socket outlets and switches in the storey below and short rises to socket outlets in the storey above. For disabled use, all socket outlets should be at least 450 mm above floor level and light switches not higher than 1200 mm. The de-rating of electrical cables surrounded by or located against insulation referred to in Section 10.1 should be noted.

When standard plasterboard is used for wall linings, boxes for outlets and switches are usually fixed to horizontal timber noggings placed between studs as shown in Figure 10.7.

**Figure 10.7 Electrical socket
box fixing: external and
internal walls only**

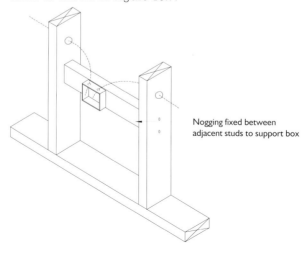

Nogging fixed between
adjacent studs to support box

Proprietary plastic switch and socket boxes are available which clip directly to the plasterboard and thus eliminate the need for backing noggings. More robust types of wall lining can accept metal box fixings. When wiring is installed in external walls which incorporate a vapour control layer, it is essential that the hole in the vcl is as small as possible with minimum gaps around the box fitting. It is good practice to seal the holes in the vcl, either by self adhesive tape or by sealing the vcl to the switch or socket box with a mastic.

Wherever possible, placing electrical fittings in compartment walls should be avoided. When this cannot be avoided in compartment walls, penetrations by cables or sockets should be adequately fire stopped and sealed for acoustic reasons and no outlets should be fixed back to back. See Figure 10.8. Electricity, telephone or television cables serving more than one occupancy should not be run through party walls or floors.

In platform-type party floors, it is possible to locate cables to supply the upper level above the floor base and within the resilient layer thickness and to locate cables to serve ceiling mounted light fittings to the lower level within the joist zone. It may be necessary to derate the cables to avoid overheating if they are within or adjacent to insulation material. Holes for electrical connections to lighting points should be firestopped using a gypsum based compound or mineral wool at the ceiling rose position.

**Figure 10.8 Electrical socket outlet in party wall**
Note: Duct extended to full height or closed off above and below outlet with 19 mm plasterboard and penetration for cable fire stopped with plaster or mineral wool

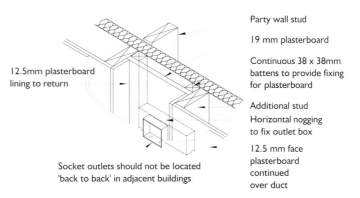

12.5mm plasterboard lining to return

Socket outlets should not be located 'back to back' in adjacent buildings

Party wall stud

19 mm plasterboard

Continuous 38 x 38mm battens to provide fixing for plasterboard

Additional stud
Horizontal nogging to fix outlet box

12.5 mm face plasterboard continued over duct

## 10.5.1 Electricity meter boxes

The standard meter box is primarily designed for use in a masonry cavity wall. These are suitable for brick clad timber frame walls but with thinner cladding, provision should be made for a sub-frame around the box. The meter box should not be cut into the timber wall panel thickness unless structural calculations allow this. Figure 10.9 shows a typical installation in brick cladding.

**Figure 10.9 Electricity meter installation in brick cladding**

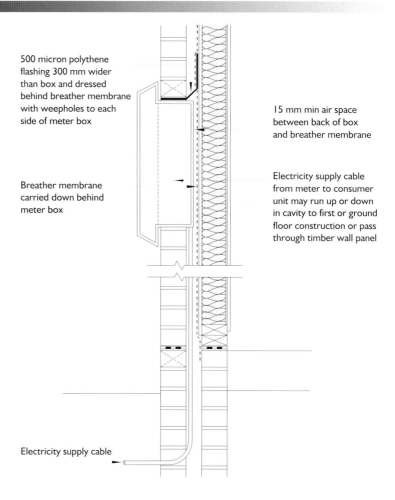

500 micron polythene flashing 300 mm wider than box and dressed behind breather membrane with weepholes to each side of meter box

Breather membrane carried down behind meter box

15 mm min air space between back of box and breather membrane

Electricity supply cable from meter to consumer unit may run up or down in cavity to first or ground floor construction or pass through timber wall panel

Electricity supply cable

## 10.6 Gas installations

Domestic installations should be in accordance with *BS 6400 Specification for installation of domestic gas meters* and *BS 6891 Specification for installation of low pressure gas pipework up to 28 mm (RI) in domestic premises*. Requirements for installations in other building types should be agreed with the gas supplier.

The Institution of Gas Engineers publishes specific guidance on the installation of gas services in timber frame structures in IGE/UP/7. The information included here is intended only to give basic information in respect of the timber frame detailing.

If a duct is used to install gas supply pipes into the meter, the enclosure should be ventilated to outside at high and low level at each floor level and the internal walls of the duct should be insulated with mineral wool.

### 10.6.1 Gas meter boxes

The standard built-in meter box, primarily intended for use in brick or block external walls with a 50 mm cavity, can be fitted in a brick clad timber frame wall where the cavity and brickwork thickness is 150 mm or more. When the cladding thickness is less than 150 mm, it is necessary to include a subframe around the meter box to achieve an acceptable arrangement. The meter box should not be cut into the timber wall panel thickness unless structural calculations allow for this.

Other designs of meter boxes are available, for example a box designed for surface mounting on existing walls could be used, although such boxes protrude further than built-in boxes. A semi-concealed type can be used partially buried in the ground, close to an outside wall.

There are three possible locations for the gas installation pipe from the meter. One of these conceals the pipe in the wall of the building (Figure 10.10a). To satisfy the requirements of the gas safety regulations and prevent gas entering the cavity, it is essential to seal the area of the wall containing the pipe from the remainder of the wall void (Figure 10.11). The installation pipe can also be run through the external wall from the rear of the meter box (Figure 10.10b). In both these cases a special rear spigot is required. Where this passes through the vapour control layer, the joint should be sealed with tape and the plasterboard joint sealed with a mastic sealant. The third location keeps the installation pipes to and from the meter box on the external face of the wall and enters the building at ground floor level (Figure 10.10c).

**Figure 10.10 a Concealed gas installation pipe entry**

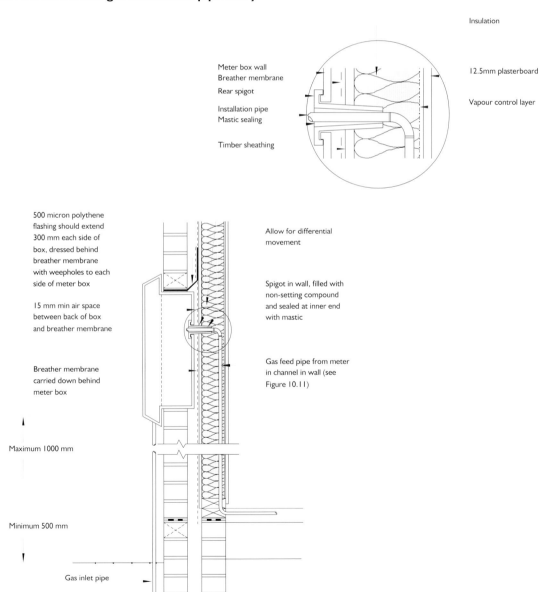

Insulation

Meter box wall
Breather membrane

Rear spigot

Installation pipe
Mastic sealing

Timber sheathing

12.5mm plasterboard

Vapour control layer

500 micron polythene flashing should extend 300 mm each side of box, dressed behind breather membrane with weepholes to each side of meter box

15 mm min air space between back of box and breather membrane

Breather membrane carried down behind meter box

Maximum 1000 mm

Minimum 500 mm

Gas inlet pipe

Allow for differential movement

Spigot in wall, filled with non-setting compound and sealed at inner end with mastic

Gas feed pipe from meter in channel in wall (see Figure 10.11)

**Figure 10.10 b Gas installation pipe entry with exposed internal pipework**

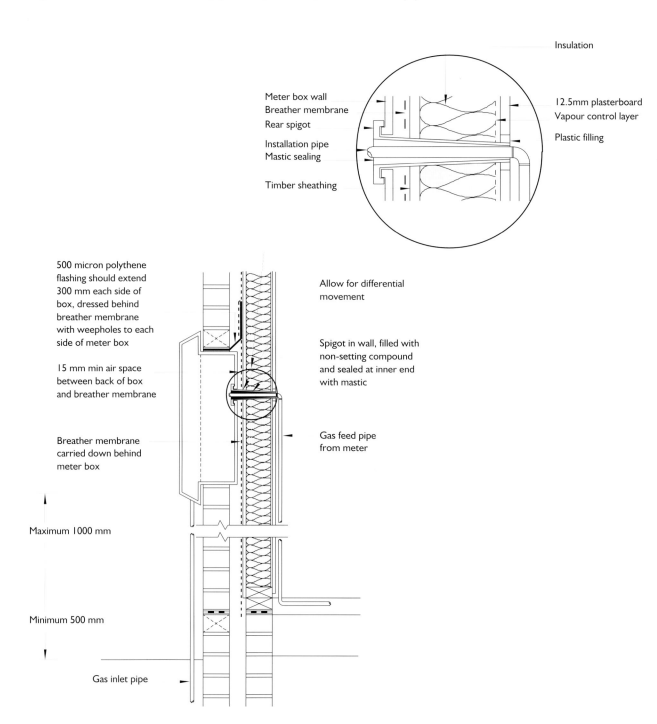

Insulation

Meter box wall
Breather membrane
Rear spigot

12.5mm plasterboard
Vapour control layer

Installation pipe
Mastic sealing

Plastic filling

Timber sheathing

500 micron polythene
flashing should extend
300 mm each side of
box, dressed behind
breather membrane
with weepholes to each
side of meter box

Allow for differential
movement

15 mm min air space
between back of box
and breather membrane

Spigot in wall, filled with
non-setting compound
and sealed at inner end
with mastic

Breather membrane
carried down behind
meter box

Gas feed pipe
from meter

Maximum 1000 mm

Minimum 500 mm

Gas inlet pipe

**Figure 10.10 c Gas installation pipe entry with pipes on external face**

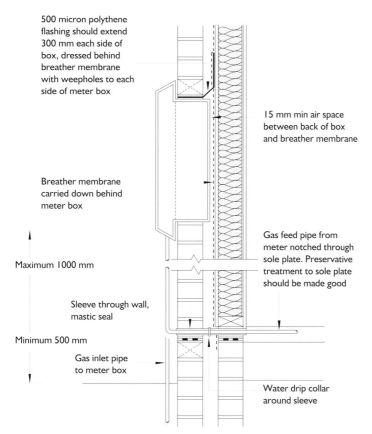

500 micron polythene flashing should extend 300 mm each side of box, dressed behind breather membrane with weepholes to each side of meter box

15 mm min air space between back of box and breather membrane

Breather membrane carried down behind meter box

Gas feed pipe from meter notched through sole plate. Preservative treatment to sole plate should be made good

Maximum 1000 mm

Sleeve through wall, mastic seal

Minimum 500 mm

Gas inlet pipe to meter box

Water drip collar around sleeve

**Figure 10.11 Gas service pipe in external wall**
Note: Illustration shows riser to an appliance fixing point. Similar storey height duct may be used to provide a gas service duct to the upper floor

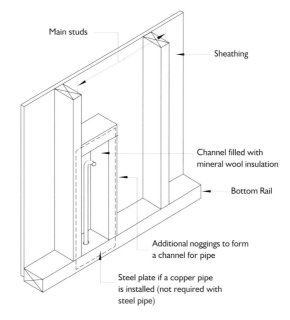

Main studs

Sheathing

Channel filled with mineral wool insulation

Bottom Rail

Additional noggings to form a channel for pipe

Steel plate if a copper pipe is installed (not required with steel pipe)

## 10.6.2 Gas installation pipework

Installation pipework within the building should be surface fixed or laid within vented suspended floors, ducts or cupboards. Installing pipework between joists at intermediate floor levels will require special detailing to provide ventilation in conjunction with adequate thermal, acoustic and fire performance,

Pipes rising from ground floor slabs adjacent to walls should be positioned so that adequate space is allowed for the installation of the wall lining and the skirting board. When it is essential to run gas installation pipes in the timber frame wall cavities, the following recommendations are made by the Institution of Gas Engineers:

♦ pipes should not be located in compartment or separating walls

♦ the pipe runs should be kept to a minimum and run within purpose designed channels as shown in Figure 10.11

♦ the channels should be filled with mineral wool insulation and be lined with a vapour control layer and plasterboard to the same standard as the remainder of the wall

♦ the pipe run cannot contain compression fittings

♦ in external walls, the pipe should be secured to the stud on the warm side of the insulation to minimise the risk of condensation occurring on the pipework

♦ where copper pipes are used, they should be enclosed behind a 1 mm steel or equivalent metal plate.
Alternatively steel pipes can be used without further protection.

♦ provision should be made for any shrinkage movement of the timber frame structure

♦ pipework shall be secured to a stud using purpose-designed fixings.

## 10.6.3 Gas appliance installation

Most gas appliances can be installed on or adjacent to a timber frame wall. There are Building Regulation requirements relating to the proximity of gas appliances to combustible materials. However, most appliances have been exempted from the relevant Regulation since they have satisfied the fire hazard and limiting temperature clauses of *BS 5258 Safety of gas appliances* and *BS 5386 Specifications for gas burning appliances*. The appliance manufacturer's instructions should be consulted to establish whether a particular appliance is suitable for mounting on a timber frame wall and if any special requirements for fire protection are recommended.

When an appliance is not suitable for direct mounting on a timber frame wall, it should be separated from the wall structure by a 75 mm air gap or by 25 mm of non-combustible material. The latter is usually achieved by adding a 12.5 mm thickness of non-combustible board to the plasterboard lining of the wall.

Wall mounted boilers should be fixed to the stud framework of the wall or to noggings securely fixed between studs at an appropriate height. To simplify boiler installation, a preformed mounting frame (Figure 10.12) can be made for the boiler and the balanced flue, with noggings placed to provide the necessary fixings. This can then be fitted at the appropriate height in the timber frame panel.

Lightweight boilers may be fixed by locating the fixing screws on one side of the appliance into studs and using suitable cavity fixings for the remainder. The appliance manufacturer's advice should be sought if this method is proposed.

**Figure 10.12 Purpose-designed panel for wall-hung appliances (eg boilers)**
(Insulation not shown for clarity)

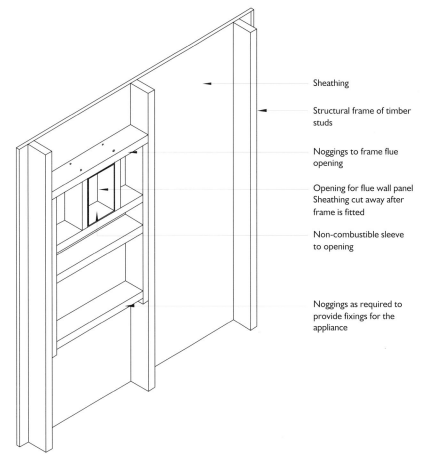

Sheathing

Structural frame of timber studs

Noggings to frame flue opening

Opening for flue wall panel Sheathing cut away after frame is fitted

Non-combustible sleeve to opening

Noggings as required to provide fixings for the appliance

## 10.6.4 Flues for gas appliances with a rated output of up to 60 kW

Open flues routed through a dwelling to the roof are commonly used and installation in timber frame is no different from other types of construction. The allowable distances between combustible materials and flues are shown in Figure 10.13.

**Figure 10.13 Separation of combustible material from flues for gas burning appliances with a rated output up to 60kW**

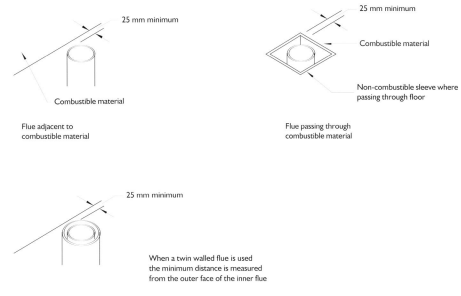

25 mm minimum

Combustible material

Flue adjacent to combustible material

25 mm minimum

Combustible material

Non-combustible sleeve where passing through floor

Flue passing through combustible material

25 mm minimum

When a twin walled flue is used the minimum distance is measured from the outer face of the inner flue

Where the pipe passes through timber walls, floors or ceilings it should be at least 25 mm from any combustible material or encased in a non-combustible sleeve with a 25 mm air space between the sleeve and flue. In Northern Ireland, the sleeve should extend so that no combustible material is closer than 50 mm to the flue and open flues should also be encased in non-combustible material in an internal space unless the space is accessible or in the room where the appliance is situated. In Scotland, open flues should be protected to prevent damage and danger to building users. This is good practice in all areas and is recommended. Where flues pass through a party wall or floor, the flue should be cased with non-combustible material with at least half the fire resistance needed by the wall or floor.

The flashing junction of an open flue with the roof finish should allow for initial differential movement between the flue and the structure. The allowances should be based on the information in Figure 9.1.

The requirements for location and height of terminals are given in the Institution of Gas Engineers recommendations IGE/UP/7.

Although open flues can be installed to pass through the external wall, this is not common practice and is best avoided wherever possible since it is difficult to achieve satisfactory weathering details. A balanced flue provides a better solution, and is also technically preferable, since it incorporates provision for combustion air direct from outside.

In any installation using open flues, it is essential for the efficiency and safety of the installation that an adequate supply of combustion air is provided. Timber framed buildings are generally more airtight than most other types of construction and it is therefore recommended that the full provision for combustion air for appliances should be provided for by design and no reliance is placed on air leakage through the timber structure. Figure 10.14 illustrates a typical air brick installation. A balanced flue does not need additional provision of combustion air.

**Figure 10.14 Air brick in brick clad timber frame wall**

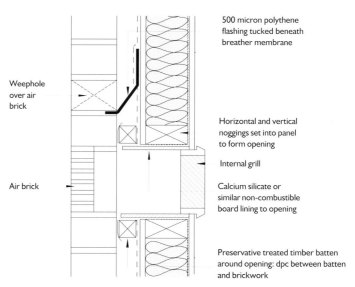

500 micron polythene flashing tucked beneath breather membrane

Weephole over air brick

Horizontal and vertical noggings set into panel to form opening

Internal grill

Air brick

Calcium silicate or similar non-combustible board lining to opening

Preservative treated timber batten around opening: dpc between batten and brickwork

A balanced flue boiler, with its terminal duct passing through the timber framed wall, requires careful detailing and installation. The outlet passing through the wall should be surrounded by a sleeve of non-combustible material, such as metal or non-combustible board, with a gap of not less than 25 mm between the flue assembly and the combustible material. The gap should be sealed to prevent excessive air penetration with an internal lining of non-combustible board or by packing the inner side with mineral wool. Some types of balanced flue boilers incorporate a seal between the appliance backplate and the internal wall lining, obviating the need for an additional seal. Figures 10.15 and 10.16 show typical arrangements.

**Figure 10.15 Balanced flue boiler installation in brick clad timber frame wall**

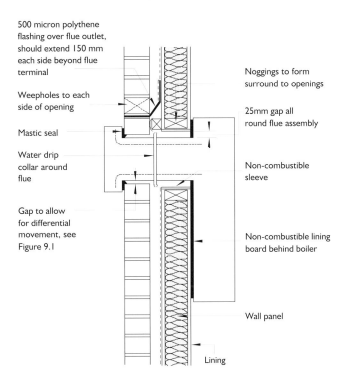

500 micron polythene flashing over flue outlet, should extend 150 mm each side beyond flue terminal

Weepholes to each side of opening

Mastic seal

Water drip collar around flue

Gap to allow for differential movement, see Figure 9.1

Noggings to form surround to openings

25mm gap all round flue assembly

Non-combustible sleeve

Non-combustible lining board behind boiler

Wall panel

Lining

**Figure 10.16 Balanced flue terminal in timber clad wall**

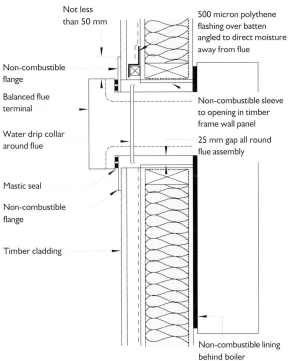

Not less than 50 mm

Non-combustible flange

Balanced flue terminal

Water drip collar around flue

Mastic seal

Non-combustible flange

Timber cladding

500 micron polythene flashing over batten angled to direct moisture away from flue

Non-combustible sleeve to opening in timber frame wall panel

25 mm gap all round flue assembly

Non-combustible lining behind boiler

When masonry cladding is used, provision should be made for differential movement between the cladding and the timber frame wall which supports the boiler and flue. A gap at the bottom edge of the flue will satisfy this requirement and will normally be covered by the flue terminal flange. The dimensions given for differential movement at window openings (See Figure 9.1) are appropriate. The terminal flange should be sealed to prevent rain penetration. In order to minimise the risk of water passing across the wall cavity to the sheathing, a drip collar should be fitted around the flue. This may be incorporated by the manufacturer or can be added on site. A length of wire wrapped around the flue or a bead of mastic applied to the casing will suffice. If wire is used, this should be of a type that will not cause corrosion of the steel flue.

If the external wall cladding is of combustible material, a metal or other non-combustible face plate should be used to maintain the terminal in position and protect the cladding (Figure 10.16). This plate should extend at least 50 mm beyond the edge of the flue terminal flange and a greater projection may be advisable to avoid damage to painted claddings. The flue terminal manufacturer's advice should be sought.

There are limitations on the location of balanced flue terminals relative to other parts of the building such as windows, balconies and rain water gutters. These are the same for all types of construction. Details are included in *BS 5440-2 Installation and maintenance of flues and ventilation for gas appliances of rated input not exceeding 70 kW net (1st 2nd and 3rd family gases). Part 2 Specification for installation and maintenance of ventilation for gas appliances* and are also available from the Institution of Gas Engineers.

## 10.7 Chimneys and flues for solid fuel and oil appliances with a rated output up to 45 kW

This section deals with chimneys with refractory cement flue liners encased in non-combustible material such as brickwork or blockwork.

It is essential for the efficiency and safety of the installation, that an adequate supply of combustion air is provided. Timber frame structures are generally more airtight than most other types of construction and it is therefore recommended that the full provision for combustion air for appliances should be provided by design and no reliance placed on air leakage through the structure.

The range of appliances and proprietary chimney systems presently available is such that manufacturers' recommendations should be sought and considered in relation to the information given in this section.

The main points to consider, regardless of whether traditional or proprietary systems are used, are:

◆ the effect on the structural stability of the timber frame

◆ the effect of differential movement, caused by timber shrinkage, between the frame and the chimney and/or by thermal movement of the chimney in use

◆ the integrity of the fire resistance of the timber frame when penetrated by the chimney breast or stack

◆ the proximity of combustible materials (timber frames, sheathing, and floor decks) to the flue and fire recess

♦ the maintenance of the sound insulation of compartment and separating walls when chimneys are recessed into these walls

♦ the maintenance of sound insulation of compartment and separating floors when chimneys pass through

♦ the provision of an adequate supply of combustion air for the appliance or fire.

The relevant distances between combustible material and chimneys and flues are shown in Figure 10.17. Flue pipes should only be used to connect an appliance to the chimney and should not pass through any roof space without a chimney surround.

Guidance on additional provisions for oil burning appliances, such as the positioning of outlets from flues and the direction of flues, is given in National Building Regulations.

**Figure 10.17 Separation of combustible material from flues for solid fuel burning appliances with a rated output up to 45kW**
Note: A flue pipe should only be used to connect an appliance to a chimney and should not pass through any roof space

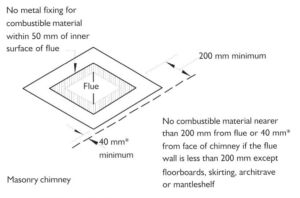

No metal fixing for combustible material within 50 mm of inner surface of flue

Flue

200 mm minimum

40 mm* minimum

No combustible material nearer than 200 mm from flue or 40 mm* from face of chimney if the flue wall is less than 200 mm except floorboards, skirting, architrave or mantleshelf

Masonry chimney

* England, Wales and Northern Ireland only.
  In Scotland, joists etc should be at least
  200 mm from the inner surface of the flue

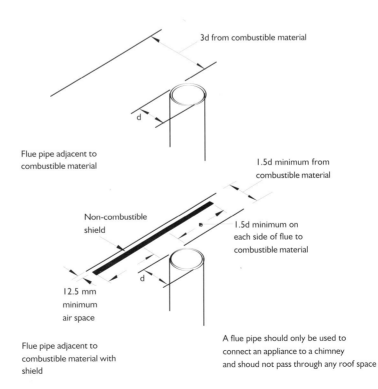

3d from combustible material

d

Flue pipe adjacent to combustible material

1.5d minimum from combustible material

Non-combustible shield

1.5d minimum on each side of flue to combustible material

d

12.5 mm minimum air space

Flue pipe adjacent to combustible material with shield

A flue pipe should only be used to connect an appliance to a chimney and shoud not pass through any roof space

No combustible materials may be located beneath a hearth unless there is an air space of at least 50 mm between the material and the underside of the hearth, or a distance of 250 mm between the material and the top of the hearth. If the hearth is at least 125 mm thick, combustible material (timber) may be used to support the edge.

## 10.7.1 Chimneys in external walls

A fireplace recess and chimney may be built inside the room after the internal linings have been fixed (Figure 10.18). This is the simplest form of construction since it has no effect on the timber frame external wall elements. As the floor and roof members are framed and trimmed around the chimney stack, there are no problems arising from differential movement between the timber frame and the chimney stack, except at roof level. At this point, allowance should be made for timber movement when detailing the flashing between the chimney and the roof finish, see Figure 9.1.

**Figure 10.18 Internal chimney**

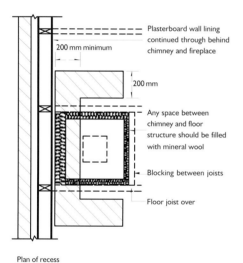

Plan of recess

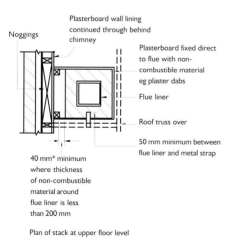

Plan of stack at upper floor level

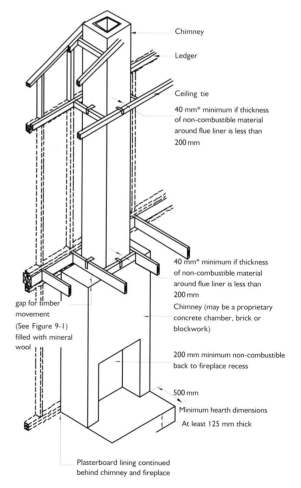

* Note. In Scotland, joists and timber wall framing should be at least 200 mm from the internal surface of the flue

Alternatively, the fireplace recess and chimney can be located on the outside of the timber frame external wall panels. The fireplace is simply projected towards the outside of the building through a preformed aperture in the timber frame wall panel. (See Figure 10.19) This method is less efficient in conserving heat than an internal chimney, but it avoids the need to trim special openings through floors and roofs. It also has less effect on the sequence of erection since the chimney can be built as part of the cladding operation when brick or block claddings are used.

## Figure 10.19 External fireplace recess and chimney

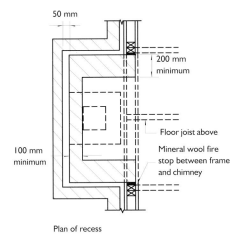

Plan of recess

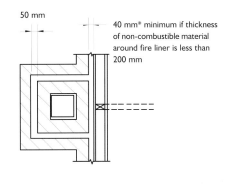

Plan of chimney at upper floor level

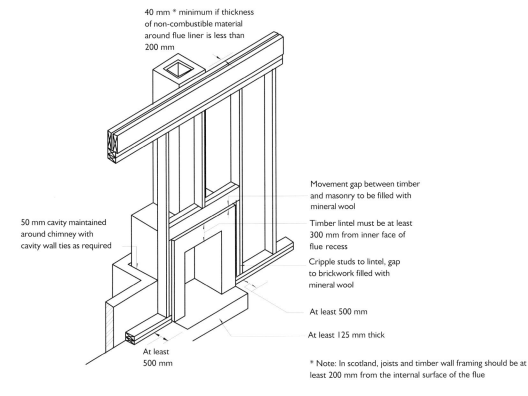

## 10.7.2 Chimneys in party walls

Fireplace recesses and chimneys may be placed on party walls but the details are complex and should be avoided wherever possible, particularly at changes of level between dwellings. One method is similar to that previously described for external walls where the fireplace recess and chimney are built after the wall has been lined and, consequently, do not interfere with the acoustic and fire performance of the wall. This would entail offsetting fireplaces and chimneys in adjoining buildings as back-to-back fireplace recesses, with timber frame walls passing between them, are not recommended.

The second method, shown in Figure 10.20, allows the fireplace recess and chimney to be placed partially within the party wall itself. It is essential to ensure that the junctions between the timber frame panels and the fireplace recess/chimney are effectively sealed against both sound transmission and fire penetration and allow for possible differential movement between the timber frame and the chimney stack. It is important to obtain Building Regulation clearance for this type of installation at an early stage since it entails alteration to the specified construction of the party wall details prescribed in the regulations.

**Figure 10.20 Chimneys recessed into party walls**

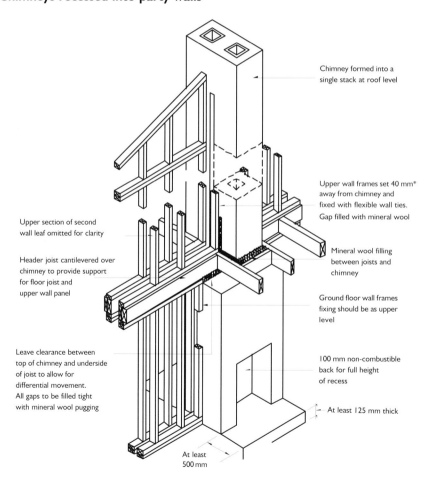

Chimney formed into a single stack at roof level

Upper wall frames set 40 mm* away from chimney and fixed with flexible wall ties. Gap filled with mineral wool

Upper section of second wall leaf omitted for clarity

Header joist cantilevered over chimney to provide support for floor joist and upper wall panel

Mineral wool filling between joists and chimney

Ground floor wall frames fixing should be as upper level

Leave clearance between top of chimney and underside of joist to allow for differential movement. All gaps to be filled tight with mineral wool pugging

100 mm non-combustible back for full height of recess

At least 125 mm thick

At least 500 mm

* Note: In Scotland, joists and timber wall framing should be at least 200 mm from internal surface of the flue

**Figure 10.20 Chimneys recessed into party walls - continued**

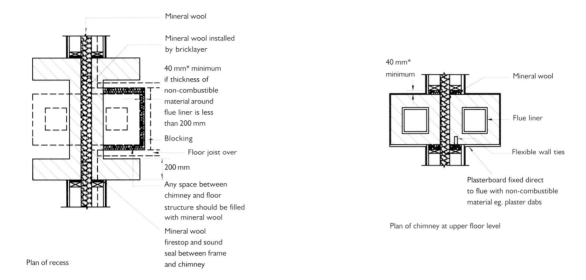

Plan of recess

Mineral wool

Mineral wool installed
by bricklayer

40 mm* minimum
if thickness of
non-combustible
material around
flue liner is less
than 200 mm

Blocking

Floor joist over

200 mm

Any space between
chimney and floor
structure should be filled
with mineral wool

Mineral wool
firestop and sound
seal between frame
and chimney

40 mm*
minimum

Mineral wool

Flue liner

Flexible wall ties

Plasterboard fixed direct
to flue with non-combustible
material eg. plaster dabs

Plan of chimney at upper floor level

## 10.7.3 Chimneys in internal walls

The general framing principles of incorporating chimney breasts and stacks into external and party walls are equally applicable when incorporating them into internal walls.

## 10.7.4 Chimneys through party floors

In order to maintain the required sound insulation performance of party floors, the designer should, where possible, avoid chimneys passing through them.

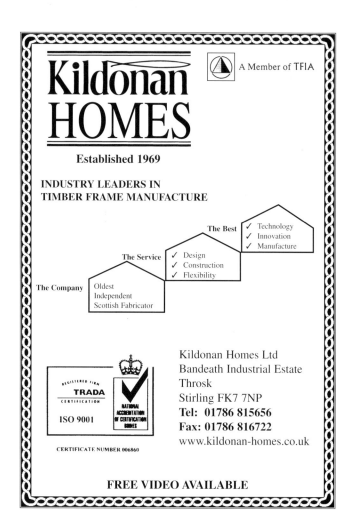

# EFFECTIVE PROTECTION FOR TIMBER FRAME COMPONENTS

The environmental credentials of using timber in construction are undisputed; so why don't we use wood to build all our homes and buildings? Timber is a natural material and therefore subject to degradation by the elements and nature. The perception that wood will decay and be attacked by insects leading to structural failure is often exaggerated but does hold some truth. The use of effective preservative treatments helps to ensure that wood can be specified and used with confidence. It is this confidence, that will help ensure the sustained growth of the timber frame industry that relies on our most sustainable construction material.

Arch Timber Protection (formerly Hickson Timber Products Ltd) pioneered the development of organic water-based preservatives during the 1990's and Vacsol® AQUA treatment is now widely available to protect timber frame and roofing timbers used in the UK and overseas.

Vacsol® AQUA

- Environmentally advanced water-based wood preservative
- Protects against fungal and insect attack, including termites
- 60 years anticipated service life for Hazard Classes 1 & 2 (timber frame)
- Ideal for applications where there is a low to medium risk of fungal decay or insect attack. e.g. timber frame components, roof timbers, internal flooring.

TO SPECIFY VACSOL® AQUA TREATED TIMBER
The following wording is recommended

*The timber as detailed...(insert quantity, dimensions, species and its end use/description of component)... is to be vacuum/pressure treated with Vacsol® AQUA preservative to comply with Arch Timber Protection treatment code HVA1 (timber frame).*

*Following treatment, any areas of timber revealed by cross cuts, holes, notches etc. shall be brushed with Vacsele AQUA or other approved end grain preserver.*

Useful documents relating to Vacsol® AQUA treatment are available on request:

The Vacsol® AQUA treated timber and plywood Code of Practice 30, provides full details on the properties of Vacsol® AQUA treated timber.

The Vacsol® AQUA treated timber Safety Data Sheet SD 601 provides information on the handling of treated timber.

The Arch Timber Protection Specifiers Guide also provides detailed specification information for all preservative, fire retardant and protective coatings products.

For copies of the above documents or details on the availability of Vacsol® AQUA treatment, contact the Arch Timber Protection Advisory Service on Freephone 0800 833402.

# Timber Frame Specialists

## DESIGN & MANUFACTURE

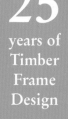

## Complement design with efficiency

Established in 1996 Warm-Wood Homes is one of the most innovative manufacturers of specialised Timber-Frame structures in the domestic and commercial sector.

The principal partners, and major shareholders, have considerable experience in Timber-Frame and Timber supplies, having had personal involvement in thousands of Timber construction projects in the UK and world wide.

Warm-Wood has the knowledge and skills to provide a professional and flexible service that meets the needs of today's customers from developers, contractors and the self-build market.

Warm-Wood Homes can undertake the complete process from feasibility study to construction, working closely with the client to ensure the best Timber-Frame and environmental solution are achieved.

Today's Timber-Frame construction is an established, effective modern building method that offers tremendous advantages and flexibility to the designer, builder and final occupier.

Every Warm-Wood structure is pre-engineered providing complete construction details, including full structural calculations supporting the frame design. Independent "NHBC certification" of the frame design is provided for all domestic developments. Internal environmental engineering design can be provided to ensure maximum lifestyle benefits from this exciting method of construction.

Warm Wood Homes benefits from senior design staff with over 25 years of design experience specifically with Timber-Frame Technology and pre-engineered Timber structures.

Warm-Wood Homes are pleased to convert any existing designs to Timber-Frame construction working closely with the client and the chosen building designer. Alternatively you can choose from our range of exciting standard Timber house types specifically designed to to complement the beauty in wood and natural materials and the demands of modern living.

Warm-Wood offers a choice of Timber Frame construction concepts including standard 90/140mm insulated frame construction and specifically designed 'Eco-housing', with breathable wall systems. Most independent designs can be converted to our "Eco house" system, ensuring energy costs of the completed project are kept to the bare minimum.

Choosing any Timber-Frame package from Warm-Wood will ensures savings in labour time and construction costs together with complementary energy efficient design.

Warm-Wood Homes, environmental policy ensures all frames are strictly manufactured using machine stress graded softwoods from renewable forestation sources.

# For everything you will ever need in timber

The **Finnforest** Corporation is one of the world's most respected timber suppliers, whose philosophy is to offer the highest level of service and product range possible. This is especially useful when specifying as you know all your timber based products can be sourced from one company.

Softwood, Hardwood, MDF profiles, flooring and sheet materials form the core of the **Finnforest** business, but we offer a complete range of high technology LVL products in Kerto Laminated Veneer Lumber beams. These are strong, dimensionally precise laminated beams specifically for use in advanced engineering and construction applications including new buildings, renovation and repair and the manufacturing of prefabricated components. We offer two very individual product types - Kerto Q is cross bonded for extra lateral bending strength, whilst Kerto S, with its longitudinal grains on all veneers, is perfect for long structural beams. The product is usually supplied in straight beams but can be cut to shape as required for your specific project.

For more information on how **Finnforest** can help you

# call 01375 856 855

# finnforest

# Osmose®

# MARTIN

## An experienced UK company specialising in Automated Timber Assembly Systems

### TIMBER FRAMES

A FULL RANGE OF MODULAR DESIGNED ASSEMBLY MACHINES STARTING WITH BASIC BENCH JIGS UP TO FULLY COMPUTERISED SYSTEMS.

### ROOF TRUSSES

A CHOICE OF MACHINES FROM SIMPLE SPLICING PRESSES TO CAD/CAM LINKING AND LASER PROJECTION TECHNOLOGY PROVIDING FULLY AUTOMATED TRUSS PRESSES.

### PALLETS

SIMPLE MANUAL NAILING JIGS WITH ACCESS TO NAILING BOTH SIDES OF A PALLET, UP TO FULLY PROGRAMMABLE NAILING MACHINES WITH QUICK CHANGEOVER TIMES.

## W I L L I A M   H E N R Y   M A R T I N   L T D

Allfield Court, Condover, Shrewsbury, Shropshire, United Kingdom SY5 7AP  Tel: 00 44 (0) 1 743 874 550  Fax: 00 44 (0) 1 743 874 650

# CONQUER YOUR INSULATION NEEDS!

Insulating a timber frame house can be a complicated business, especially when you have to go to various manufacturers to meet your insulation needs.

That's why you should talk to Owens Corning Alcopor – because we don't specialise in JUST one kind of insulation or system.

Our range and expert knowledge extends from glass and rock mineral wool to cellular plastics and construction membranes. So you can be confident that our recommendations really do offer you the best solution for the whole house and not just for one element of it.

We can even advise you on other aspects of insulation such as Building Regulations and what they mean to you.

So for the best technical advice or further information call free on *0800* **627465** (*0800* **OCPINK**)

or visit us at **www.owenscorningalcopor.co.u**

The colour Pink is a registered trade mark of Owens Corning. The PINK PANTHER and associated marks and characters TM&© 2001 United Artists Corporation.

TM&© 2001 U.A. Corp

# C L S

## C is for CANADIAN
## L is for LUMBER
## S is for STANDARDS

The staple of housebuilding in North America and now an industry standard for timber frame construction in the UK, but –

### not all CLS sold is Canadian!

Adopted by others to meet the demand created by the **original!**

**For quality assurance, specify lumber grade marked by an accredited Canadian grading agency**

- The size – 38 x 63, 89, 140, 184, 235, 285
- Strength Class allocation of grades and species and design values - in BS 5268 : Part 2
- Span tables - in BS 8103 : Part 3
- Two moisture contents to choose from:
    - Maximum 15% - for those sensitive areas!
    - Maximum 19% - a more general specification
- Planed all round with eased edges for smooth operations! No undersize permitted.
- Visual and machine grades available
- Precision-end-trimmed studs available
- Finger jointed studs – utilising the resource
- Produced under the rigorous surveillance of the grading agencies to the exacting requirements of the Canadian Lumber Standards Accreditation Board

### Also available for your timber frame projects:

- Kiln-dried and graded timber to BS 4978 and customary UK dimensions.
- Other Canadian specialities - for joinery, exterior cladding, interior fittings, decoration, flooring and roofing - including Douglas fir, western red cedar, yellow cedar, eastern white cedar, eastern white /Quebec yellow pine, western hemlock, hardwoods, shingles and shakes..........**and PLYWOOD**

## Canadian Plywood

*Over **50** years of proven service as a structural panel and used **worldwide**, with CLS lumber, for the construction of **homes.***

- Exterior glue bond – all Canadian plywood!
- Douglas fir (DFP); softwood (CSP); poplar
- Design values in BS 5268 : Part 2
- New design values for sanded grades
- Manufactured under the rigorous quality control regime of the Canadian Plywood Association – **(certified testing agency recognised around the world)**
- Thicknesses of regular grades of CANPLY exterior plywood range from **9.5**mm to **28.5**mm.
- Highly impact resistant and continues to perform even when wet
- Available with patented tongue and groove edge profiles for floor decking and roof sarking – 'EASY T&G'

**See separate advert also**

### And, not forgetting the environment

*Certification in Canada's forests is on the rise. November 1, 2000 - about 22.5 million hectares of forest land across the country, representing an annual allowable cut of more than 34 million m³, have been certified - about 19% of Canada's annual harvest.*

*By the end of 2001 the list of companies with successful certification will be longer and the total area of forest under certified management systems will be much larger. Employing a number of systems, including CSA, FSC and ISO, this growth will continue into the future. For details -* **www.sfms.com/decade.htm**

## Advert Sponsored by:

 **Canadian Lumbermen's Association**

 **CANPLY** CANADIAN PLYWOOD ASSOCIATION

 **CFLA** COAST FOREST & LUMBER ASSOCIATION

 **MLB** **Maritime Lumber Bureau**

 **WEB** **Quebec Wood Export Bureau**

**Canada Wood UK ● PO Box 1 ● FARNBOROUGH Hants ● GU14 6WE Tel: 01252 522545 ● Fax: 01252 522546 e-mail: canadawooduk@aol.com**

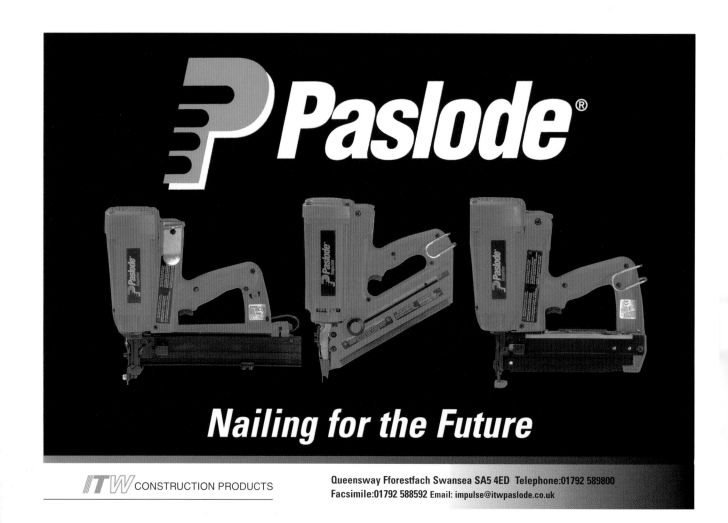

# Think Proctors for roofs, walls and floors...

## Roofshield

**Benefits of using Roofshield:**

- Reduced risk of condensation.
- No requirements for eaves and ridge or tile ventilation into loft space.
- Independent research.
- Full BBA certification.
- A warmer roofspace.
- Increased efficiency of insulation.
- Easy to install (laid the same as a traditional underlay).
- Easier supervision on site.
- Simpler specifications.
- Highest vapour permeability of any underlay.

- May be used as temporary waterproofing underlay.
- Enables contact with other materials without risk of water penetration.
- U.V. stabilised with maximum five month exposure period.
- Clean, easy to handle, rot proof with excellent nail tear resistance.

## Frameshield 100

**Benefits of using Frameshield 100:**

- Conforms to BS 4016.
- BBA Certification.
- Water Resistant.
- High Vapour Permeability.
- Clean and Easy to Handle.
- Excellent Nail Tear and Tensile Strengths.
- Range of Colours Available on Application.
- Printing Facility.

**NOW available in your company's corporate colours and can be printed onto.**

## Profloor Dynamic Batten

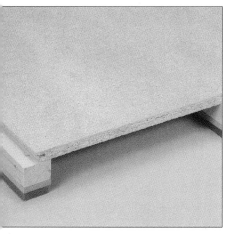

**Benefits of using Profloor Dynamic Batten**

- For both new build and refurbishment.
- Significantly reduces impact and airborne noise pollution in multi level dwellings.
- Versatile, suitable for most domestic flooring applications.
- Easy and fast to install to wooden joisted or concrete floors (pre-cast or in situ) with no 'wet trades' involved.
- Use of floors immediately after installation.
- BBA Certification..

- Will last the lifetime of the floor.
- Non load bearing partition walls can be erected on the finished acoustic floor where a double batten run has been positioned beneath the wall.
- Services can be run in the void created by Dynamic Batten and access gained by siting a hatch.

**proctor**
GROUP LTD

# Appendix I Timber and wood-based materials

## AI.I Structural timber

### AI.I.I Sizes

Sizes for structural timber are given in BS EN 336 *Structural timber – Coniferous and poplar – Sizes – Permissible deviations*. This includes a National Annex which details sizes customary in the UK.

The sizes are quoted as Target sizes at a moisture content of 20%. The cross sectional dimensions (thickness and width) are assumed to increase by 0.25% for every 1.0% increase in moisture content above 20% up to 30%, and to decrease by 0.25% for every 1% decrease in moisture content below 20%.

Two Tolerance Classes are recognised for deviations in thickness and width from the target sizes. Tolerance Class 1 is usually applied to sawn sections and Tolerance Class 2 to machined (processed) sections. The Tolerance Class should be quoted when specifying section sizes; the class references are abbreviated to T1 and T2.

**Table AI.I Tolerance classes for structural timber sizes**

| Thicknesses and widths: | Tolerance Class I (TI) | Tolerance Class 2 (T2) |
|---|---|---|
| up to and including 100 mm | + 3 / -1 mm | + 1 / - 1 mm |
| over 100 mm | + 4 / -2 mm | + 1.5 / - 1.5 mm |

Softwood 'machined on the width' may also be used in timber frame construction. This process used to be known as 'regularising'. These target sizes for softwood and hardwoods are shown in Table A1.2.

The customary lengths of softwood are shown in Table A1.3

**Table AI.2 Target sizes for timber machined on the width**

| Thickness (TI) mm | Width (T2) mm | | | | | | | | | |
|---|---|---|---|---|---|---|---|---|---|---|
| | 72 | 97 | 120 | 145 | 170 | 195 | 220 | 245 | 270 | 295 |
| 22 | | ✔ | ✔ | ✔ | ✔ | ✔ | ✔ | | | |
| 25 | ✔ | ✔ | ✔ | ✔ | ✔ | ✔ | ✔ | | | |
| 38 | ✔ | ✔ | ✔ | ✔ | ✔ | ✔ | ✔ | | | |
| 47 | ✔ | ✔ | ✔ | ✔ | ✔ | ✔ | ✔ | ✔ | | ✔ |
| 63 | | ✔ | ✔ | ✔ | ✔ | ✔ | ✔ | | | |
| 75 | | ✔ | ✔ | ✔ | ✔ | ✔ | ✔ | ✔ | ✔ | ✔ |
| 100 | | ✔ | | ✔ | | ✔ | ✔ | ✔ | | ✔ |
| 150 | | | | ✔ | | ✔ | | | | ✔ |

**Table A1.3 Softwood lengths**

| Length m | | | | | | | |
|---|---|---|---|---|---|---|---|
| 1.80 | 2.10 | 3.00 | 4.20 | 5.10 | 6.00 | 7.20 | |
| | 2.40 | 3.30 | 4.50 | 5.40 | 6.30 | | |
| | 2.70 | 3.60 | 4.80 | 5.70 | 6.60 | | |
| | | 3.90 | | | 6.90 | | |

Note that lengths of 5.70 m and over may not be readily available without finger jointing.

Negative length deviations are not permitted.

The majority of timber frame construction uses softwood surfaced to the sizes shown in Table A1.4. The timber has rounded arrises not exceeding 3 mm radius. These sizes originated in North America and are commonly known as ALS/CLS. However, surfaced softwood is now also widely available from UK and Nordic sources.

Stud sizes for low rise buildings are most commonly 38 x 89 mm or 38 x 140 mm.

**Table A1.4 ALS/CLS sizes for softwood**

| Thickness (T2) mm | Width (T2) mm | | | | | | |
|---|---|---|---|---|---|---|---|
| | 63 | 89 | 114 | 140 | 184 | 235 | 285 |
| 38 | ✔ | ✔ | ✔ | ✔ | ✔ | ✔ | ✔ |

Sawn hardwood sizes are given in BS EN 1313-2 *Round and sawn timber – Permitted deviations and preferred sizes. Part 2 Hardwood sawn timber.* The Standards relating to hardwoods refer to BS EN 336 for tolerances on sizes for structural uses.

Preferred thicknesses for sawn hardwoods are given in BS 1313-2 as:

20,   27,   32,   40,   50,   60,   65,   70,   80,   100 mm

with additional sizes preferred in the UK:

19,   26,   38,   52,   63,   75.

Standard widths for sawn hardwoods are given in BS 1313-2 as:

50,   60,   70,   80,   90,   100,   120,   140,   160,   180,   200 etc

Preferred lengths for square edged hardwoods are in increments of 0.10 m for lengths over 1m.

The reduction of sawn hardwood sizes by processing for structural purposes is as given in BS EN 336.
For non-structural purposes, the reduction of hardwood sawn sizes by processing is included in a National Annex and depends upon the end use.

**Table A1.5 Reduction of basic hardwood sizes by processing two opposed faces (from BS1313-2)**

| End use or product | Reduction from basic size of width or thickness mm: | | | | |
|---|---|---|---|---|---|
| | 15 - 25 | 26 - 50 | 51 - 100 | 101 - 150 | 151 - 300 |
| Flooring, matchings, interlocked boarding and planed all round | 5 | 6 | 7 | 7 | 7 |
| Trim | 6 | 7 | 8 | 9 | 10 |
| Joinery and cabinet work | 7 | 9 | 10 | 12 | 14 |
| Permissible deviation for all finished sizes after processing is plus or minus 0.5 mm. | | | | | |

## A1.1.2 Strength grading and strength classes

The structural design code for timber, *BS 5268-2 Permissible stress design, materials and workmanship*, and its European equivalent, *DD ENV 1995-1-1 Eurocode 5: Design of timber structures* and through these the Building Regulations for all areas of the UK require structural timber to be strength graded and marked as such.

### A 1.1.2.1 Moisture content of strength graded timber

BS 5268-2 defines three Service Classes for structural timber, based on the temperature and humidity of the surrounding air:

♦ Service Class 1
Characterized by a moisture content corresponding to a temperature of 20° C and the relative humidity of the surrounding air only exceeding 65% for a few weeks each year. In such conditions most timber will attain an average moisture content not exceeding 12%.

♦ Service Class 2
Characterized by a moisture content corresponding to a temperature of 20° C and the relative humidity of the surrounding air only exceeding 85% for a few weeks each year. In such conditions most timber will attain an average moisture content not exceeding 20%.

♦ Service Class 3
Characterized by higher moisture contents than Service Class 2.

Timber is strength graded at two levels of moisture content: DRY (or for kiln dried material, KD) and WET (or Green, GRN).

The structural timber components used in conventional timber frame construction will be in Service Class 1 or 2 and for these purposes DRY graded timber must be specified. This is graded at an average moisture content of 20% or below. Timber in heated buildings will dry down to a moisture content of around 10% or less and so some shrinkage will occur. The implications are discussed in Section 9.3.
(Note that due to the difficulties of drying large sections, timber with a target thickness of over 100 mm is exempt from this requirement and may have to be graded and installed WET – ie over 20% moisture content. In this case, wet stresses must be used for structural design and extra care must be taken to account for shrinkage.).

So-called super-dried softwood is now becoming available under a variety of brand names. This is graded at an average moisture content of 12% or below and, although not yet widely available, may become popular for timber frame construction since it reduces the differential movement between the timber frame and masonry claddings, See Section 9.3.

## A 1.1.2.2 Softwood strength grading

Softwoods may be strength graded visually or by machine to one of the following standards:

- *BS EN 518: Structural timber - Grading - Requirements for visual grading standards.*
  Note: this standard defines the requirements for visual grading rules to be acceptable in Europe; it does not define grading rules as such.

- *BS 4978: Visual strength grading of softwood.*
  This standard defines the visual grading rules used in the UK for strength grading softwoods. The rules comply with the requirements of BS EN 518.
  Two grades are defined:
  GS - General structural and SS – Special structural.

- *BS EN 519: Structural timber - Grading - Requirements for machine strength graded timber and grading machines.*
  This defines the requirements for grading machines and details the additional visual assessment required for machine strength graded timber.

Machine grading is undertaken directly to Strength Classes (see below)

- *Economic Commission for Europe (ECE) Sawn timber.*
  *Recommended Standard for strength grading of coniferous sawn timber.*
  This standard is little used and is not considered further here.

Timber imported from Canada and the USA may be graded to their national standards. Timber strength graded to the following standards is accepted by BS 5268-2.

- *National grading rules for dimension lumber.* NLGA, Canada.

- *National grading rules for softwood dimension lumber.* NGRDL, USA.
  The grades included in BS 5268 Part 2 are:
  Structural Joist and Plank - Select structural (Sel), No 1, No 2, No 3
  Structural Light Framing - Select structural (Sel), No 1, No 2, No 3
  Light Framing - Construction (Const), Standard (Std), Utility (Util)
  Stud

- *North American export standard for machine stress rated lumber.*
  The grades included are:
  
  | | |
  |---|---|
  | 900f - 1.0E | 1200f - 1.2E |
  | 1450f - 1.3E | 1650f - 1.5E |
  | 1800f - 1.6E | 1950f - 1.7E |
  | 2100f - 1.8E | |

All structural timber used in the UK must be strength graded and marked under the supervision of a certification body approved by the UK Timber Grading Committee. The approved certification bodies are listed in a leaflet Approved Certification Bodies for the supply of strength graded timber, published by the Timber Trade Federation. The certification bodies oversee the training and certification of graders and the operation of grading machines. They also monitor the quality of grading carried out by the companies under their control. The certification body or grading agency logo or mark forms part of the grade stamp which must appear on all strength graded timber.

### A 1.1.2.3 Hardwood strength grading

Hardwoods used for structural purposes are strength graded in accordance with the requirements of BS 5756.

Tropical hardwoods are graded to a single strength grade; Hardwood structural, HS.

Temperate hardwoods are assigned to one of two groups, depending upon on the size of the section. Within each size grouping there are two grades:
Grades THA and THB apply to temperate hardwoods of large cross-section and TH1 and TH2 apply to temperate hardwoods with smaller cross sections. The actual sizes are defined in the Standard.

### A 1.1.2..4 Strength classes

Timbers of similar strength properties are grouped together into a series of Strength Classes which are defined in *BS EN 338 Structural timber – Strength classes*. This simplifies the design and specification process by enabling designs to be based on defined strength class limits without the need to identify and source a particular species and grade combination.

Fifteen Strength Classes are defined: nine for softwoods, prefixed C, and six for hardwoods, prefixed D. BS 5268-2 defines the species/grade combinations which satisfy the requirements for each strength class. The grade stresses appropriate to each strength class are given in the standard.

The softwood strength classes defined for general purpose use are C14 (weakest), C16, C18, C22, C24, C27, C30, C35 and C40. BS 5268-2 also defines additional strength classes for special purposes, such as TR26 for trussed rafters.
The TRADA *Wood Information Sheets 4 – 7 Guide to strength graded softwood* and *1 – 25 Introduction and supply of timber to BS 5268-2* give more information on strength grading and softwood strength classes.

The hardwood strength classes are D30, D40, D50, D60 and D70.

An individual species/ grade combination may have higher strength properties than those of the strength class to which they are assigned. The engineer can specify an individual species and grade combination to take advantage of this. Design values are given in BS 5268-2 for individual softwood species and species groups and for tropical and temperate hardwoods.

### A 1.1.2. 5 Marking

All structural timber must be marked with the following information:

♦ the strength grade and/or strength class

♦ the species or species combination

♦ information to identify the company (and/or the grader) and where appropriate the machine responsible for the grading. Timber machine graded to North American rules will include the phrase 'machine rated ' or 'MSR'

♦ the Standard number (eg BS 4978 or BS EN 519)

♦ the Certification body or Agency responsible for overseeing the grading (eg BM TRADA Certification)

♦ the timber condition; DRY, KD or WET, GRN.

## A1.2 Structural timber composites

Structural timber composites, as the name implies, are produced in structural-sized sections for use as beams and joists, columns and studs and as proprietary structural components. The 'family' of structural timber composites is growing but currently can be considered as comprising:

- Glued Laminated Timber or glulam
- Laminated Veneer Lumber or lvl
- Parallel Strand Lumber or psl
- Laminated Strand Lumber or lsl
- Engineered components, such as I beams.

The advantages of Structural Timber Composites include:

- availability in long lengths and in deep sections for long spans
- high strength and light weight
- consistent structural properties
- manufactured at low moisture content so shrinkage and distortion reduced
- maximum the use of the renewable timber resource.

Brief details of each type are given below; further information is included in the TRADA Technology publication, *Structural Timber Composites*. Information on glulam is included in Wood Information Sheets *1 – 6 Glued laminated timber – An introduction* and *1 – 38 Glued laminated timber – European Standards*.

### A1.2.1 Glulam

Glued laminated timber, of glulam is the best known and longest established of the Structural Timber Composites. Glulam components can be manufactured to meet virtually any architectural requirement. Common basic structural forms include:

- Straight, eg purlins, beams, lintels, columns
- Triangulated, eg A-frames, trusses girders
- Curved, eg arches, portals, domes.

Straight forms are available 'off the shelf'; other configurations are designed and manufactured to order. Glulam manufacture is undertaken to the requirements of *BS EN 386 Glued laminated timber, Performance requirements and minimum production requirements*.

The laminations are strength graded to BS 4978 or BS EN 519 before glulam manufacture. The grade stress for the glulam component is based on the strength class of the laminations. Glulam may be 'homogenous' with the laminations all of the same strength class, or 'combined', where the outer laminations are of a higher strength class. The requirements and the means of calculating the grade stress for the resulting components are given in BS 5268-2.

## A1.2.2 Laminated veneer lumber

Laminated Veneer Lumber is produced by bonding together veneers peeled from a log. The resulting long panels are then cut into structural sizes sections. Proprietary products are approved for use in the UK through independent third party certification schemes. Design information is available from the approval certificates or from the manufacturers.

## A1.2.3 Parallel strand lumber

Parallel strand lumber is manufactured by cutting peeled veneers into long strands which are glued under a heat and pressure in a quasi-extrusion process to form structural-sized sections in long lengths. Proprietary products are approved for use in the UK through independent third party certification schemes. Design information is available from the approval certificates or from the manufacturers.

## A1.2.4 Laminated strand lumber

Laminated strand lumber is produced by gluing together large flakes of wood under heat and pressure to produce structural sections. Proprietary products are approved for use in the UK through independent third party certification schemes. Design information is available from the approval certificates or from the manufacturers.

## A1.2.5 Engineered structural components

Structural components, such as I-beams, are now being produced as proprietary products. Typical products of this type are I-beams manufactured with the flanges made of softwood or LVL and the webs of plywood, OSB or hardboard. Other configurations which combine timber flanges with metal strutting webs are also available.

I-beams are being used for floor joists, since they combine large span capabilities with low moisture content, and in some cases for studs where high levels of insulation are required.

## A1.3 Wood-based panels

The introduction of European Standards (BS ENs) for wood-based panels has significantly changed the way that board materials are tested and specified in the UK. Inevitably such fundamental changes take some time for full implementation and we are still in a transition stage. Standards are still being developed; most significantly for the use of panels in timber frame construction, a series of performance standards for the use of boards in walls, floors and roofs.

The use of wood-based panels in timber frame in the UK has developed over many years, based on a combination of formal testing and experience in use. The requirements for the newly defined types of boards do not exactly match the previous British Standard designations (for example WBP bonding for plywoods). The guidance given in this document for OSB, particleboards and fibreboards is therefore based on the 'nearest fit' comparison of old and new grades as given in the Informative Annex to BS 7916. Notwithstanding the guidance given, designers and specifiers should always satisfy themselves that the materials specified are 'fit for purpose'.

### A1.3.1 Plywood

Plywoods suitable for structural use are listed in BS 5268-2 together with design information. These include specified grades of:

♦ American construction and industrial plywoods

♦ Canadian Douglas fir and softwood plywoods

♦ Finnish birch, birch faced and conifer plywoods

♦ Swedish softwood plywoods.

The marking which should appear on these plywoods is described and illustrated in BS 5268-2.

*BS EN 636 Plywood. Specifications* is produced in three parts, depending upon the conditions of use. Part 1 covers use in dry conditions, Part 2 in humid conditions and Part 3 in exterior conditions. The conditions are defined in *BS EN 335-1 Classification of hazard classes*.

A defining requirement for plywoods in each category relates to bonding quality which is laid down in BS EN 314-2 Plywood. Bonding quality. Requirements. Three classes are defined:

Bonding Class 1 is suitable for dry conditions, Bonding Class 2 for humid conditions and Bonding Class 3 for exterior use.

Further details about plywood standards are included in the Wood Information Sheets *2/4 – 48 Plywood – Key Standards listing, 2/3 – 49 Plywood – European Standards, 2/3 – 50 Plywood – European Standards – Test methods*.

Common sheet sizes of plywood are:
2440 x 1220 mm
2440 x 610 mm (normally t & g)
2500 x 1220 mm
3050 x 1525 mm
3050 x 1220 mm

Commonly used thicknesses range from 8 – 25 mm.

## A1.3.2 Oriented Strand Board (OSB)

OSB is manufactured from timber strands (flakes) measuring approximately 75 x 35 mm. These are blended with a synthetic resin and wax and formed into a three-layer mat. The grain of the strands in the outer layers are oriented along the length of the board and those of the inner layer across the board. The mat is then compressed using heat and pressure. Orientation of the strands in this way distributes the strength, stiffness and spanning capacity of the boards which are approximately twice as strong in the length as in the width.

Oriented strand board should comply with the requirements of BS EN 300 *Oriented strand board* which defines four types:

♦ OSB 1 General purpose boards and boards for interior fitments, including furniture, for use in dry conditions

♦ OSB 2 Load-bearing boards for use in dry conditions

♦ OSB 3 Load-bearing boards for use in humid conditions

♦ OSB 4 Heavy duty load-bearing boards for use in humid conditions.

Board sizes generally available are 2400 x 1200 mm and 2440 x 1220 mm in thicknesses of 6, 8, 11, 15, 18, 22 and 25 mm.

**Marking**

The marking which should appear on OSB is:

♦ the manufacturer's name, trademark or identification mark

♦ the Standard number, EN 300

♦ the type of board

♦ the nominal thickness

♦ the major axis, if this is not the length of the panel

♦ the formaldehyde class

♦ batch number or production week and year.

An additional voluntary colour coding may also appear. Coloured stripes are applied vertically, approximately 25 mm apart, to a stack of boards near to a corner, A combination of two colour bands define firstly, the suitability of the board for particular applications ie
White – general purpose boards
Yellow – load-bearing boards

and secondly, the environmental conditions for which the board is suited:
Blue – dry conditions
Green – humid conditions.

## A 1.3.3 Wood chipboard

Wood particles comprise the bulk of wood chipboard. These are generally coniferous softwoods although hardwoods, such as birch are sometimes used. The binders (adhesives) used are generally synthetic resins; in moisture resistant boards a melamine-urea-formaldehyde (MUF) is commonly used although phenol formaldehyde and polymeric methylene di-isocyanate (PMDI) resins may also be used.

General requirements for particleboards are laid down in *BS EN 312-1 Particleboards – Specifications. General requirements for all board types.* BS EN 312 Parts 2 – 7 cover particleboards suitable for use in different environmental conditions. The board types are defined as:

- P2 General purpose boards for use in dry conditions
- P3 Boards for interior fitments, including furniture
- P4 Load-bearing boards for use in dry conditions
- P5 Load-bearing boards for use in humid conditions
- P6 Heavy duty load-bearing boards for use in dry conditions
- P7 Heavy duty load-bearing boards for use in humid conditions

The conditions are defined in *BS EN 335-1 Hazard classes of wood and wood-based products against biological attack. Classification of hazard classes.*

**Marking**

The marking which should appear on each board is:

- the manufacturer's name, trademark or identification mark
- the Standard number, EN 312
- the type of board
- the nominal thickness
- the major axis, if this is not the length of the panel
- the formaldehyde class
- batch number or production week and year.

Chipboard may also be marked with the additional voluntary colour code marking described for OSB.

## A1.3.4 Cement-bonded particleboards

Cement-bonded particleboards are manufactured from wood (or other vegetable) particles bound with  hydraulic cement and possibly containing additives. Boards can be bonded with Ordinary Portland cement or with magnesium cements, such as magnesite. However, *BS EN 634-2 Cement-bonded particleboards. Specifications. Requirements for OPC bonded particleboards for use in dry, humid and exterior conditions* covers only Ordinary Portland cement bonded boards.

## A1.3.5 Fibreboards

The generic types of fibreboards are defined on the basis of their method of manufacture and their density in *BS EN 316 Wood fibreboards – Definition, classification and symbols.* Each generic type is further divided into use categories in the various parts of *BS EN 622 Fibreboards. Specifications,* see Table A1.6 and by its suitability for use in particular hazard classes, see Table A1.7. The detailed requirements for each type of board are defined in the relevant part of BS EN 622 as shown in Table A1.6. The hazard classes are defined in *BS EN 335-3 Durability of wood and wood products– Definition of hazard classes of biological attack. Application to wood-based products.*

## Table A1.6 Types of fibreboard

| Fibreboard type | Symbol | Density kg/m$^3$ | Requirements in: |
|---|---|---|---|
| WET PROCESS BOARDS | | | |
| Softboards | SB | less than 400 | BS EN 622-4 |
| Medium boards – Low density | MBL | more than 400, less than 560 | BS EN 622-3 |
| Medium boards – High density | MBH | more than 560, less than 900 | BS EN 622-3 |
| Hardboards | HB | 900 or more | BS EN 622-2 |
| DRY PROCESS BOARDS | | | |
| Medium density fibreboard | MDF | 450 or more | BS EN 622-5 |

## Table A1.7 Types of fibreboards suitable for use in particular hazard classes

| Board type | General purpose - Dry | Loadbearing - Dry | | General purpose Humid | Loadbearing - Humid | | General purpose Exterior |
|---|---|---|---|---|---|---|---|
| | | inst or short term load | all load durations - | | inst or short term load | all load durations | |
| Softboards | SB | SB.LS | | SB.H | SB.HLS | | SB.E |
| Medium | MBL | | | MBL.H | | | |
| boards | MBH | | MBH.LA1 MBH.LA2 | MBH.H | MBH.HLS1 MBH.HLS2 | | MBH.E |
| Hardboards | HB | | HB.LA | HB.H | | HB.HLA1 HB.HLA2 | HB.E |
| Dry process boards | MDF | | MDF.LA | MDF.H | MDF.HLS | | |

The load durations are defined in BS 5268-2.

## Marking

The marking for each type of board is defined in the relevant part of BS EN 622, see Table A1.9. In general terms all boards should be marked with at least the following information:

- the manufacturers name, trade mark or identification mark

- the number of the relevant standard and symbol of the board type

- the nominal thickness

- the batch number or production week and year.

An additional voluntary colour coding scheme is included in the standards although national colour schemes are not precluded. The recommended colour codes to be applied in stripes on a stack of boards, close to a corner are similar to those recommended for OSB and chipboard ie:

White – general purpose boards
Yellow – load-bearing boards

Blue – dry conditions
Green – humid conditions
Brown – exterior conditions.

# A1.4 Moisture content

The successful use of timber depends, to a significant extent, upon its moisture content at the time of installation being close to equilibrium with the temperature and relative humidity of its intended environment. In most situations, some fluctuations will occur and any chosen moisture content is a compromise, representing the mean equilibrium moisture content of the range of conditions likely to prevail over the life of a component or structure. More details about moisture content can be found in the *Wood Information Sheet 4 – 14 Moisture in timber.*

The British Standards for grading and design of structural timber recommend a moisture content of 20% for timber frame components (see section A1.1.2). However, the equilibrium moisture content of the timber frame in heated buildings will usually settle at a moisture content of around 10 - 13% after one or two heating seasons. Installing 'dry graded' timber at a moisture content of 20% means that the cross sections will shrink as the timber dries down to its equilibrium moisture content. This results in differential movement between the timber frame and separately supported claddings, such as brick, and allowance has to be made for this in the timber frame design; see Section 9.3.

Shrinkage can be minimised by the specification of timber kiln dried to around 12%, by the use of Structural Timber Composites which are manufactured at low moisture contents  or by the use of storey height panels, see Section 1.1.

## A1.4.1 Measuring moisture content

The moisture content of timber can be checked by using an electrical resistance moisture meter. Meters are available with insulated probes which can be driven into the timber to measure the moisture content below the surface. Insulated probes also overcome the effects of surface wetting which would 'short out' simple pin-type electrode heads and indicate too high a moisture content.

Readings given by moisture meters are influenced by the presence of salts, such as those from water-borne preservatives, flame retardant treatments and contamination by sea water. Such salts increase the conductivity of the timber and give a falsely high reading of moisture content. The magnitude of this effect is variable and it is not usually possible to adjust the readings. Therefore when the presence of such salts is suspected, moisture readings which are higher than expected should be treated with caution.

Panel products and Structural Timber Composites, with the exception of glulam, must be regarded as separate materials and not merely as the timber species from which they are made. The moisture content readings obtained with a resistance-type meter can be misleading and they should not be regarded with confidence unless the manufacturer has produced calibration charts for the particular product being tested.

## A1.5 Preservative treatment

There are many examples of existing untreated timber frame buildings in the UK , Scandinavia and North America which are performing satisfactorily. However, the potential disruption and cost of carrying out remedial work, should problems occur, leads to the recommendation that the softwood components listed below are treated with preservative when the timber species is of Durability class 3 (Moderately durable) or worse. Note the Durability ratings relate to the heartwood only and are defined in *BS EN 350-1 Guide to the principles and testing and classification of the natural durability of wood* and *BS 350-2 Guide to natural durability and treatability of selected wood species of importance in Europe*. Sapwood should always be treated.

♦ sole plates

♦ bottom members of wall frames resting directly on the dpc

♦ framing of external wall panels

♦ timber cavity barriers in external cavity walls (also protected by a separate dpc)

♦ timber in cold design flat roofs

♦ timber as a weather resistant cladding unless it is the heartwood of species of Durability Class 2 (durable) or better.

♦ cladding and tiling battens.

The housing warranty and guarantee authorities have specific requirements for both preservatives and methods of treatment for structural components in timber frame dwellings and for external joinery. The current editions of their manuals should be checked.

**Current recommendations**

Current recommendations for preservative treatment are given in *BS 5268-5 Preservative treatments for construction timber* or *BS 5589 Code of practice for the preservation of timber*, as appropriate. These give guidance on appropriate types of preservative and levels of treatment. Additional guidance is included in *BS 1282 Guide to choice, use and application of wood preservatives*. Treatment of individual timber members in the manufactured components listed above should normally be confined to organic solvents applied by the double vacuum method or timber treated at source by the boron process. Water-borne preservative treatments, such as copper chromium arsenic by the vacuum pressure process, should only be considered if sufficient time can be allowed for the timber to re-dry to the specified moisture content before component manufacture and installation. Guidance on preservative treatment is given in the *British Wood Preserving and Damp-proofing Association Manual*.

**Future recommendations**

European Standards follow a very different approach from the previous British Standards on preservation. Under the new system, the specifier defines the level of treatment which will give the required length of protection in a particular environment or hazard class. This is defined in terms of penetration requirements and preservative retention levels which are set out in *BS EN 351-1 Classification of preservative penetration and retention*. Nine penetration classes are identified.

Guidance on the combination of penetration and preservative retention required to give a level of protection to meet the required service life of a component in a particular hazard class is not yet available in a definitive form as a British Standard. Preliminary recommendations are available in a Draft for Development, *DD 239*. The European approach to the specification of preservative treatment will not be implemented in the UK until this guidance is available.

## A1.6 Care of timber and components

Timber dried to a level appropriate to its end use must be stored in such a way that moisture changes are minimal. Timber and timber components stacked under adequate cover, but not enclosed, on a dry base, may be stored for a week or two without major changes in moisture content. Stacks should be covered to protect the timber from rain and direct sunlight but the covering should allow free circulation of air to avoid the risk of condensation. Timber or timber components should never be stored on site without protection.

Delivery of timber frame components, including trussed rafters, should be scheduled to minimise storage on site. However, if components are not fixed in their final position directly from a trailer, then adequate storage on a dry base should be prepared before delivery.

Timber frame wall or floor panels should be stacked, sheathing or flooring side up, on bearers positioned to provide adequate support. The stack should be covered. Trussed rafters may be laid flat on sufficient bearers to give level support at close centres to prevent deformation and they should be covered. If trusses are stored in an upright position, they should be firmly supported. Bearers should be placed at the wall plate position with sufficient height to ensure that any rafter overhang clears the ground. Carcassing timber should be stacked on bearers to keep it off the ground on a level, well drained area and covered. Structural Timber Composites should be kept dry. Board materials of all types should be kept flat and dry.

The manufacture of wood-based panels produces boards at a moisture content lower than that likely to prevail, even in heated buildings. Boards should be conditioned before fixing, in accordance with the manufacturer's instructions, to the moisture content likely to be reached in use. Therefore wood-based panels delivered to site in strapped bundles should be broken open and the boards exposed to the atmosphere in a covered area for conditioning.

External joinery should be treated in a similar way to that recommended for structural components, with support being carefully chosen to avoid warp or twist caused by unnatural loading.

Internal joinery should be delivered and installed after the building is weatherproof. If it is necessary to store internal joinery, it should be kept in a dry store.

# Appendix 2 Materials data

## A2.1 Densities and weights of materials

The weight of materials can be obtained by sample tests, information from manufacturers and reference to *BS 648 Schedule of weights of building materials.*

Typical densities of commonly used materials are included below for reference. The weight (in kg/m²) of a specific thickness of material is obtained by multiplying the density by the thickness in metres.

For example: the weight of 22 mm chipboard flooring would be

$$750 \ (\text{kg/m}^3 \ \text{x} \ 0.022 \ (\text{m}) = 16.5 \ \text{kg/m}^2$$

Note: Values shown are typical though the density of individual products can vary considerably and these values should only be taken as a general guide. For detailed calculations the manufacturers' figures should be used.

**Table A2.1 Typical density of common materials**

| Material | | Typical density kg/m³ |
|---|---|---|
| Timber | Softwood | 350 - 550 |
| | Structural hardwood | 550 - 1000 |
| | Structural composite timber, eg LVL | 550 - 600 |
| Sheet materials | Sheathing/ flooring grade plywood | 530 |
| | Wood chipboard P5 | 750 |
| | Oriented strand board | 720 |
| | Cement bonded particleboard | 1250 |
| | Hardboard | 850 |
| | Tempered hardboard | 1000 |
| | Impregnated softboard | 400 |
| | MDF | 900 |
| | Plasterboard Type 1 | 950 |
| | Gypsum fibreboard | 1200 |
| | Mineral fibreboard | up to 1500 |
| | Glass | 2500 |
| Insulation | Mineral wool, glass | 12 |
| | Mineral wool, rock | 20 |
| | Mineral wool, as resilient layer | 60 – 100 |
| | Cellulose fibre | 36 |
| | Expanded polystyrene | 25 |
| | Extruded polystyrene | 35 |
| | Phenolic | 35 |
| | Polyisocyanurate | 32 |
| | Polyurethane | 32 |
| Gypsum plaster | | 1200 |
| Cement render | | 2500 |

There are some composite constructions which are more easily quoted as weights per square metre for guidance purposes including:

## Typical weights of composite constructions

| Material | | Typical weight kg/m$^2$ |
|---|:---:|:---:|
| Roofing felt | 3 layers felt and chippings | 37 |
| Tile battens | at 100 mm gauge | 3.4 |
| Concrete paving slabs | 50 mm thick | 117 |
| Ballast | 50 mm thick | 80 |
| Roofing | concrete interlocking tiles | 42 – 58 |
| | concrete plain tiles | 80 |
| | clay – machine-made tiles | 64 |
| | clay – hand-made tiles | 71 |
| | slates | 25 – 78 |
| | fibre cement slates | 25 |
| | insulated metal deck roofing | 20 - 30 |

## A 2.2 Vapour resistivity and vapour resistance values

The values quoted are typical mean values for materials commonly used in timber frame construction. Manufacturers may quote different figures for their products. When a range of values if shown, the lower value should be used when the board is used on the warm side of the construction and the higher value used when the board is located on the cold side. Values for materials not included in Table A2.2 should be obtained from the manufacturer.

The values for thin materials, such as metal foils and membranes are shown as a vapour resistance for the material. Other materials are shown as a vapour resistivity value.

Vapour resistance is calculated by multiplying the thickness in metres by the vapour resistivity.

All values are from *BS EN 12524 Building materials and products. Hygrothermal properties. Tabulated values*, except as noted

| Material | Vapour resistivity MNs/gm | Vapour resistance MNs/g |
|---|---|---|
| Plasterboard Type 1 | 20 | |
| Gypsum fibre reinforced board | 130 (a) | |
| Softwood | 100 | |
| Hardwood | 250 | |
| Expanded polystyrene | 300 | |
| Extruded polystyrene | 750 | |
| Cellulose fibre | 10 | |
| Mineral wool (glass or rock) | 5 | |
| Cement bonded particleboard | 150 | |
| Impregnated softboard (no film face) | 25 | |
| Mediumboard (high density) | 150 (a) | |
| MDF | 100 | |
| Oriented strand board (OSB) | 150 | |
| Plywood | 450 | |
| Tempered hardboard | 150 | |
| Wood chipboard | 100 | |
| Brickwork | 50 | |
| Blockwork | 50 | |
| Cement render | 50 | |
| Glass | | ∞ (c) |
| Vapour control plasterboard | | 60 (a) |
| Aluminium foil | | 7500 |
| 0.12 mm polythene sheet | | 250 |
| 0.25 mm polythene sheet | | 500 |
| Breather membrane – not greater than | | 0.6 (a) |
| Metal claddings | | ∞ (c) |
| Breather roof underlay | | 0.6 max |
| Roofing felt laid in bitumen | | 1000 (b) |
| Roofing felt underlay | | 50 (b) |

(a) Value from manufacturer
(b) Value from BS 5250
(c) For calculation assume arbitrary large value eg 100,000

## A 2.3 Thermal conductivity of materials

The values shown are typical design values. Manufacturers may provide more precise figures if required.

All values are from CIBSE Guide A3.

| Material | Thermal conductivity (W/mK) |
| --- | --- |
| Plasterboard Type I | 0.16 |
| Gypsum fibre reinforced board | 0.36 |
| Softwood | 0.13 |
| Hardwood | 0.14 |
| Cellulose fibre | 0.033 |
| Expanded polystyrene | 0.035 |
| Extruded polystyrene | 0.027 |
| Mineral wool (glass or rock) | 0.037 |
| Phenolic | 0.020 |
| Polyiscyanurate | 0.025 |
| Polyurethane | 0.025 |
| Cement bonded particleboard | 0.35 |
| Impregnated softboard | 0.055 |
| Mediumboard | 0.08 |
| Medium density fibreboard (MDF) | 0.12 |
| Oriented strand board (OSB) | 0.14 |
| Plywood (sheathing grade) | 0.14 |
| Tempered hardboard | 0.12 |
| Wood chipboard | 0.14 |
| Brickwork | 0.84 |
| Blockwork | 0.96 |
| Cement render | 1.00 |
| Glass | 1.05 |

# Appendix 3 Supervisor's check list

Site control should ensure the quality of the construction, the adherence to specifications and a smooth construction process to obtain the full benefits of the timber frame method.

This check list concentrates on the most important aspects of the assembly of the timber frame and the ancillary operations involved in completing the superstructure of the building. Building tolerances quoted are within acceptable limits using a reasonable degree of care.

## A3. I Concrete base and foundation walls

| | |
|---|---|
| A3.1.1 | Set out accurately, using a steel tape or equivalent. |
| A3.1.2 | Lengths of wall should be within +/- 10 mm. |
| A3.1.3 | Diagonals should be equal. Acceptable deviation is up to 10 m: +/- 5mm more than 10 m: +/- 10 mm |
| A3.1.4 | Ensure that walls or slab supporting sole plates are levelled to +/- 5 mm, and the perimeter lined within +/- 10 mm. |
| A3.1.5 | Level concrete slabs to +/- 5 mm from datum, and avoid exceeding 10 mm variation generally. |
| A3.1.6 | For suspended timber floors ensure that there is a dpm over the whole area of the underfloor and that there will be 150 mm between blinding or oversite concrete and the underside of joists and 75 mm to the underside of plates. Underfloor vents should be located at 2.0 m maximum centres and 450 mm maximum from corners. |
| A3.1.7 | Position underground ducts for plumbing stacks to rise clear of floor joists and trussed rafters. |

## A3.2 Sole plates (or bottom rail of panel if no sole plate)

| | |
|---|---|
| A3.2.1 | Check that these are pressure treated with preservative where specified and brush apply preservative to site cut ends and drilled holes. |
| A3.2.2 | Ensure that there is a dpc under sole plates lapped 100 mm at joints and overlapping the dpm. |
| A3.2.3 | Sole plates should be set out within +/- 10 mm in length or width defined by the drawings. Diagonals should be equal. Acceptable deviation is up to 10 m: +/- 5 mm; more than 10 m: +/- 10 mm. |
| A3.2.4 | The sole plates should not overhang the foundations by more than 10 mm or be set back from the foundation edge by more than 10 mm. |
| A3.2.5 | Sole plates must be level within +/- 5 mm. Fully bed the plates on mortar (and structural shims if necessary) if base is not level. Bedding should be approved by a structural engineer. |

234

## A3.3 Fixing down sole plates (or bottom rails of wall panels)

A3.3.1 — Type, number and centres of fixings to be as schedule and inserted in accordance with specification or manufacturers' recommendations, with adequate penetration to ensure that the plate or rail is rigidly secured to the base.

A3.3.2 — If mild steel brackets, shoes and straps have been specified, check that they are adequately protected by hot dip galvanising, or have equal corrosion resistance.

A3.3.3 — Replace any plates split or damaged during fixing.

## A3.4 Delivery of components

A3.4.1 — Check wall frames, floor joists, decking, floor panels and trussed rafters or loose rafters on delivery for:

- quality of material, strength grading marks/stamping and moisture resistance grade of decking, linings etc

- quality of assembly (correct nailing and jointing)

- correctly dimensioned within stated tolerances

- moisture content

- preservative treatment schedules (where applicable)

A3.4.2 — Also check any ancillary components fitted to wall frames, eg breather membrane, wall ties, cavity barriers, etc.

A3.4.3 — Unload and handle all components carefully.

A3.4.4 — Stack components off ground on level dry area to avoid soiling and distortion. Protect from rainwater and ground moisture but allow adequate ventilation.

## A3.5 Erecting timber frame

### Walls

A3.5.W1 — Lift panels on to sole plates (if provided), fix temporary bracing and loose tack.

Ensure that panels are correctly positioned and the right way up.

Plumb within +/- 10 mm over any storey height but not more than 10 mm cumulative over the building height.

Line within +/- 3 mm on the sole plate as the set-out template.

Ensure that inside faces of panels are flush.

Tightly butt-joint panels together.

Adjust temporary bracing to maintain accuracy.

A3.5.W2 — Nail panels together and to sole plate (or fix to base if no sole plate) as schedule.

Panel to panel fixings should be at maximum 300 mm centres vertically. Bottom rail to sole plate fixings should be at least one per stud bay.

| | |
|---|---|
| A3.5.W3 | Nail separate head binder (if specified) to top of wall panels and ensure that: |

- binders cover panel joints
- binder joints occur over studs
- binders are over the whole wall length.

| | |
|---|---|
| A3.5.W4 | For compartment walls use only light metal straps to connect wall leaves during construction, as rigid connections will impair sound performance of completed wall. Metal straps of maximum 3 mm thickness; one per storey height every 1.2 m. |
| A3.5.W5 | Ensure that any specified seals between wall panels and at panel/floor junctions are fitted. |

## Floors

| | |
|---|---|
| A3.5.FL1 | Ensure that walls are accurately aligned, braced temporarily and stable before installing floors. Bracing should remain until the floor is complete. |
| A3.5.FL2 | Ensure that joist dimensions, grading, spacing and direction of span are correct in the specified location and that trimmed openings for staircases and ducts are vertically aligned in the correct position and of the right size. |
| A3.5.FL3 | Ensure that the header joists align with wall panels and do not protrude into the cavity. |
| A3.5.FL4 | Double joists must be correctly located in position shown, eg under partitions or as trimmers, and securely fixed together as specification. |
| A3.5.FL5 | Ensure that metal joist hangers are of the correct type for their location and are firmly fixed in accordance with manufacturers' recommendations. |
| A3.5.FL6 | Avoid cutting the bottom edge of joists other than for hanger seating, or unless notching has been specified by the engineer. |
| A3.5.FL7 | Install strutting as specified within depth of joists and ensure that it is not oversize, causing distortion of the joists. |
| A3.5.FL8 | Ensure that solid blockings are used as firestops between joists where they bear on the compartment wall. |
| A3.5.FL9 | Non-loadbearing walls must be adequately supported by joists. |
| A3.5.FL10 | Ensure that joist notching and drilling is within limits specified. |
| A3.5.FL11 | Check clearance of timber components adjacent to flues and chimneys. |
| A3.5.FL12 | For compartment floors ensure that: |

- there is a gap at the floating floor perimeter with a resilient material in the gap
- there is a gap between the skirting and the floating floor deck
- there are no fixings penetrating the floor deck and resilient layer

## Floor decking

| | |
|---|---|
| A3.5.FL14 | Ensure that the correct thickness and type of floor decking and fixing is used in the specified location. |

| | |
|---|---|
| A3.5.FL14 | All ends and edges of sheets other than tongued and grooved should be fully supported on joists or noggings. Ensure specified expansion gap is around perimeter of chipboard and OSB decks. |
| A3.5.FL15 | All short edge joints should be staggered. |
| A3.5.FL16 | Glue sheet material decks to joists |
| A3.5.FL17 | Glue all tongued and grooved joints of sheet material decks and ensure that all fixings are driven below the surface of the boards. Tongued and grooved softwood boards should be cramped tight before nailing down. |
| A3.5.FL18 | Protect installed flooring from mechanical and water damage. |

## Roof framing

| | |
|---|---|
| A3.5.R1 | Ensure top storey walls are accurately aligned, temporarily braced and stable before installing roof. Bracing should remain until the roof is wind-braced and battened. |
| A3.5.R2 | Temporarily brace gable end wall panels and first truss. |
| A3.5.R3 | Do not distort or strain trussed rafters during installation, or damage truss plates in any way. |
| A3.5.R4 | Fix rafters or trussed rafters, parallel at specified centres and plumb within 10 mm in overall height. |
| A3.5.R5 | Ensure that roof bracing is installed in accordance with trussed rafter suppliers' instructions. All bracing should be fixed with a minimum of two nails at each connection. |
| A3.5.R6 | Ensure that hatch openings are correctly located and formed, and that tank supports are positioned in accordance with trussed rafter suppliers' instructions. |
| A3.5.R7 | With site constructed roofs ensure that the whole roof structure is fabricated and fixed in accordance with the specification and that rafters are birdsmouthed accurately. |
| A3.5.R8 | In habitable roofs where the ceiling is fixed to the underside of rafters, check insulation and ventilation provision are as specified and vapour control layer is correctly installed. Check that linings comply with the fire requirements. |
| A3.5.R9 | For flat roofs ensure that correct thickness and material of decking is used, and that the vapour control layer and ventilation is as specified. |
| A3.5.R10 | Do not install trussed rafters if incorrectly dimensioned, as they may distort wall panels. Trussed rafters must not be trimmed, cut or notched in any way without permission of the trussed rafter supplier or structural engineer. |
| A3.5.R11 | Check that tiling battens are of the correct gauge and size for the tile type and pitch. |
| A3.5.R12 | Check that roof flashings at upstands, eg at soil vent pipes, allow for differential movement. |
| A3.5.R13 | Check roof space ventilation. |

## A3.6 Site work on wall panels

### Frame

| | |
|---|---|
| A3.6.FR1 | Ensure that all site nailing is carried out as specified and that all bolts are fully tightened. |
| A3.6.FR2 | Ensure that all blockings, internal framing and noggings are correctly located and fixed flush. |
| A3.6.FR3 | Clear rubbish and timber offcuts from all cavities to be closed-in, eg compartment walls, framed walls and suspended floors. |

### Insulation

| | |
|---|---|
| A3.6.IN1 | Tightly fit insulation between all wall framing members avoiding any gaps. Fix insulation in position if friction is inadequate to hold material in place. |
| A3.6.IN2 | Ensure that there is an adequate overlap between ceiling insulation and wall panels to avoid a cold bridge, but ensure that ceiling level insulation does not block roof ventilation. |
| A3.6.IN3 | Check insulation to all pipes and tanks located outside insulated envelope and check that there is no insulation below cold water tanks in roof spaces. |
| A3.6.IN4 | Check compartment wall insulation. |

### Vapour control layer

| | |
|---|---|
| A3.6.VC1 | Vapour control layer should not be installed while moisture content of framing is above 20%. |
| A3.6.VC2 | For separate polythene membrane, laps should be 100 mm at all joints. Ensure that joints occur on studs or rails. |
| A3.6.VC3 | Return membrane into reveals, head and sill of all openings. |
| A3.6.VC4 | Check for puncturing or splitting of separate membrane during installation and ensure all holes and tears are repaired with adhesive pvc tape. |
| A3.6.VC5 | Ensure all service penetrations in the vapour control layer are sealed. |
| A3.6.VC6 | Check that any vapour control layer bonded to the plasterboard lining is undamaged, or repaired, before the lining is fixed. |

### Services

| | |
|---|---|
| A3.6.S1 | Do not notch any studs to accommodate service runs and ensure that notching of floor joists and drilling of studs and joists is within the limits specified. |
| A3.6.S2 | Do not run plumbing in external walls unless it is on the warm side of the insulation with no joints in the wall. Protect from nail damage. |
| A3.6.S3 | Ensure that all penetrations of the vapour control layer for services are tightly sealed. |

| | |
|---|---|
| A3.6.S4 | Where services have to be located in compartment walls, ensure that the necessary additional precautions are taken, eg additional backing plasterboard to outlets, to avoid any reduction in the fire and sound insulation of the wall. Note that no services may be run in separating walls in Scotland or Northern Ireland. |
| A3.6.S5 | Check that electric cables are correctly rated when located in or adjacent to insulation. |
| A3.6.S6 | Keep services clear of lining board nailing or protect with metal plates. |
| A3.6.S7 | Check that access is provided to pipe joints, stop cocks etc where required by Water Authority. |

## Linings

| | |
|---|---|
| A3.6.L1 | Plasterboard must be kept clean, dry and flat during storage. |
| A3.6.L2 | Test all plumbing and service connections in walls before linings are fixed. |
| A3.6.L3 | Ensure that the correct specification and thickness of board is used in the right location, eg fire resistant, moisture resistant, 'vapour check" board, etc. |
| A3.6.L4 | Follow manufacturers' recommendations for all fixings and jointing, including staggered joints when more than one layer is to be used. |
| A3.6.L5 | Ensure there is an adequate timber surface for fixing behind all board edges and at intermediate supports, and that all edges of plasterboard are supported where required. |
| A3.6.L6 | It is recommended that ceilings are lined before walls. |
| A3.6.L7 | Openings for electrical outlets should be accurately cut to the shape and size of outlet boxes, and, where plasterboard with an integral vapour control layer is used, any gap between plasterboard and outlet should be sealed. |

## Breather membrane

| | |
|---|---|
| A3.6.BM1 | Ensure that the breather membrane is of the correct specification, is fixed with stainless steel staples and lapped in accordance with manufacturers' instructions. Vertical laps min 150 mm, horizontal laps 100mm; overlap lowest timber member (sole plate) by 25 mm. |
| A3.6.BM2 | Additional pvc strips stapled over the breather membrane at stud positions will reinforce the membrane and simplify the correct location of wall ties. |
| A3.6.BM3 | Damaged areas of breather membrane should be repaired locally, with the replacement material lapped correctly under and over the existing material and securely stapled. |

## Cavity barriers and firestops

| | |
|---|---|
| A3.6.CBF1 | Locate cavity barriers in positions specified and ensure tight joints where ends of cavity barriers are butted together. |
| A3.6.CBF2 | Sleeved mineral wool cavity barriers should be fixed with stainless steel staples at spacings recommended by the manufacturers. |

| A3.6.CBF3 | Timber cavity barriers should be of treated timber and cut ends should be brush coated with preservative. A separate dpc should be fitted on the outside to protect the timber and a strip of mineral wool between the dpc and masonry will ensure a tight seal. Horizontal timber cavity barriers should be protected by a dpc, overlapped by the breather membrane above. |
| --- | --- |
| A3.6.CBF4 | Check internal cavity barriers in compartment walls where required at floor junctions. |
| A3.6.CBF5 | Ensure that firestops across the end of compartment walls are correctly fitted to close the cavity between frames. |
| A3.6.CBF6 | Ensure that firestops are fitted over compartment walls under the roof and across the eaves void and that the gaps between tiling battens are filled with mineral wool. |

## Damp proof courses and cavity trays

| A3.6.DPC1 | Fix dpcs around openings and return behind window and door frames, lapping to ensure that any water is diverted to outside. |
| --- | --- |
| A3.6.DPC2 | Ensure that horizontal dpcs are dressed up behind breather membrane and lapped minimum 100 mm. |
| A3.6.DPC3 | Dress flashings over cavity trays where these are installed. |

## Brick or block cladding

| A3.6.BC1 | Ensure that the cavity between masonry and sheathing is a nominal 50 mm ie +/- 10 mm. |
| --- | --- |
| A3.6.BC2 | Keep cavities clear of mortar droppings |
| A3.6.BC3 | Ensure that wall ties are stainless steel and suitable for use with timber frame. |
| A3.6.BC4 | Nail wall ties securely to timber studs at specified centres, and fully bed ends of ties in mortar joints. |
| A3.6.BC5 | To ensure ventilation and drainage of cavity, provide open perpends at minimum 1500 mm centres at base of wall, at horizontal cavity barriers, over lintels at minimum 900 mm centres (minimum 2 open perpends over window or door) and at cavity trays. |
| A3.6.BC6 | Ensure that there is sufficient clearance between window sills, soffits, verges, balconies, abutments etc, to allow for long-term shrinkage of timber frame, see Figure 9.1. |
| A3.6.BC7 | Ensure that all cavity barriers accurately close cavities |
| A3.6.BC8 | Ensure that all steel lintels are adequately protected from corrosion, solidly bedded, and clipped back to the timber frame (if this type is employed). Ensure that breather membrane overlaps the flashing over the lintel or the lintel if no flashing is used. |
| A3.6.BC9 | Check that cavity trays are installed where lean-to roofs abut masonry cladding. The breather membrane should dress over the tray and the tray dress over the roof flashing. |
| A3.6.BC10 | Check vertical movements joints in masonry cladding as required. |

## Other claddings

| | |
|---|---|
| A3.6.OC1 | Fix preservative treated battens and counterbattens as specified. Cut ends should be brush coated with preservative. |
| A3.6.OC2 | Ensure that moisture content of timber cladding is in accordance with specification before fixing as specified. |
| A3.6.OC3 | Provide sufficient gaps for differential movement between cladding and timber-frame at intermediate floors, or light cladding and masonry. |
| A3.6.OC4 | Ensure that there is a vented and drained cavity behind all cladding. |
| A3.6.OC5 | Check for movement joints in cement render cladding. |
| A3.6.OC6 | Ensure that fixings are the correct types and at correct centres. |

# References

## Regulations etc

UK PARLIAMENT Building and Buildings. **The Building Regulations** 1991. Statutory Instruments 1991 No 2768. London, HMSO. 1991

DEPARTMENT OF THE ENVIRONMENT, TRANSPORT AND THE WELSH OFFICE The Building Regulations 2000. **Approved Documents**: London, HMSO:
A **Structure**. 1992. amended 1994
B **Fire safety**. 2000
C **Site preparation and resistance to moisture**. 1992. Amended 2000
D **Toxic substances**. 1992 amended 1992, further amended 2000
E **Resistance to the passage of sound**. 1992. Amended 2000
F **Ventilation**. 1995 Edition, amended 2000
G **Hygiene**. 1992. Amended 2000
H **Drainage and waste disposal**. 1992. Amended 2000
J **Heat producing appliances** 1992. Amended 2000
K **Protection from falling, collision and impact**. 1998. Amended 2000
L **Conservation of fuel and power** 1995 Edition, amended 2000
M **Access and facilities for disabled people** 1999 Edition, amended 2000
N **Glazing – safety in relation to impact, opening and cleaning**. 1998. Amended 2000
Approved Document to support Regulation 7 – **Materials and workmanship**. 1999. Amended 2000

UK PARLIAMENT Building and buildings. **The Building Standards (Scotland) Regulations**. 1990. Statutory Instruments 1990 No 2179 (S187) London, HMSO. 1990 as amended by the Building Standards (Scotland) Amendment Regulations 1993, the Building Standards (Scotland) Amendment Regulations 1994, the Building Standards (Scotland) Amendment Regulations 1996, the Building (Scotland) Amendment Regulations 1997, and the Building Standards and Procedure Amendment (Scotland) Regulations 1999.

SCOTTISH EXECUTIVE **Technical Standards** for compliance with  Building Standards (Scotland) Regulations 1990, as amended by the Building Standards (Scotland) Amendment Regulations 1993, the Building Standards (Scotland) Amendment Regulations 1994, the Building Standards (Scotland) Amendment Regulations 1996, the Building (Scotland) Amendment Regulations 1997, and the Building Standards and Procedure Amendment (Scotland) Regulations 1999.

NORTHERN IRELAND PARLIAMENT **Building Regulations (Northern Ireland)** 1994 Statutory rules of Northern Ireland 1994 No 243. Belfast, HMSO. 1994

DEPARTMENT OF THE ENVIRONMENT OF NORTHERN IRELAND The Building Regulations (Northern Ireland). **Technical Booklets**:
C **Site preparation and resistance to moisture** 1994
D **Structure** 1994
E **Fire safety** 1994
F **Conservation of fuel and power** 1991
G **Sound** 1990
H **Stairs, ramps and guarding** 1994
L **Heat producing appliances** 1991
N **Drainage** 1990
P **Unvented hot water storage systems** 1994
R **Access and facilities for disabled people** 1994
V **Glazing** 1994

# British Standards

| | |
|---|---|
| BS EN 89: 2000 | Gas-fired storage water heaters for the production of domestic hot water |
| BS EN 26: 1998 | Gas-fired instantaneous water heaters for the production of domestic hot water, fitted with atmospheric burners |
| BS EN ISO 140-4: 1998 | Acoustics. Measurement of sound insulation in buildings and of building elements. Part 4 Field measurements of airborne sound insulation between rooms |
| BS EN ISO 140-6: 1998 | Acoustics. Measurement of sound insulation in buildings and of building elements. Part 6 Laboratory measurements of impact sound insulation of floors |
| BS EN ISO 140-7: 1998 | Acoustics. Measurement of sound insulation in buildings and of building elements. Part 7 Field measurements of impact sound insulation of floors |
| BS 187: 1978 | Specification for calcium silicate (sandlime and flintlime) bricks |
| BS EN 300: 1997 | Oriented strand boards (OSB). Definitions, classification and specifications |
| BS EN 301: 1992 | Adhesives, phenolic, aminoplastic for load-bearing timber structures - classification and performance requirements |
| BS EN 309: 1992 | Wood particleboards. Definition and classification |
| BS EN 310: 1993 | Wood-based panels - Determination of modulus of elasticity in bending and of bending strength |
| BS EN 312-1: 1997 | Particleboards. Specifications. Part 1 General requirements for all board types |
| BS EN 312-2: 1997 | Particleboards. Specifications. Part 2 Requirements for general purpose boards for use in dry conditions |
| BS EN 312-3: 1997 | Particleboards. Specifications. Part 3 Requirements for boards for interior fitments (including furniture) for use in dry conditions. |
| BS EN 312-4: 1997 | Particleboards. Specifications. Part 4 Requirements for load-bearing boards for use in dry conditions |
| BS EN 312-5: 1997 | Particleboards. Specifications. Part 5 Requirements for load-bearing boards for use in humid conditions |
| BS EN 312-6: 1997 | Particleboards. Specifications. Part 6 Requirements for heavy duty load-bearing boards for use in dry conditions |

| | |
|---|---|
| BS EN 312-7: 1997 | Particleboards. Specifications. Part 7 Requirements for heavy duty load-bearing boards for use in humid conditions |
| BS EN 313-1: 1996 | Plywood – Classification and terminology Part 1 Classification |
| BS EN 313-2: 2000 | Plywood – Classification and terminology Part 2 Terminology |
| BS EN 314- 2: 1993 | Plywood Part 2 Bonding quality. Requirements |
| BS EN 315: 2000 | Plywood - Tolerances for dimensions |
| BS EN 316: 1999 | Wood fibreboards - Definitions, classification and symbols |
| BS EN 322: 1993 | Wood-based panels - Determination of moisture content |
| BS EN 335-1: 1992 | Durability of wood and wood products. Definition of hazard classes of biological attack. Part 1 General |
| BS EN 335-2 1992 | Hazard classes of wood and wood-based products against biological attack Part 2 Guide to the application of hazard classes to solid wood |
| BS EN 335-3: 1996 | Durability of wood and wood products. Definition of hazard classes biological attack Part 3 Application to wood-based panels |
| BS EN 336: 1995 | Structural timber. Coniferous and poplar. Sizes. Permissible deviations |
| BS EN 338: 1995 | Structural timber. Strength classes |
| BS EN 350-1: 1994 | Durability of wood and wood based products  - natural durability of solid wood - Guide to the principles of testing and classifcation of the natural durability of wood |
| BS EN 350-2: 1994 | Durability of wood and wood based products  - natural durability of solid wood - Guide to  natural durability and treatability of selected wood species of importance in Europe |
| BS EN 351-1: 1996 | Durability of wood and wood-based products.  Preservative-treated solid wood.  Classification of preservative penetration and retention |
| BS EN 385: 1995 | Finger jointed structural timber. Performance requirements and minimum production requirements |
| BS EN 386: 1995 | Glued laminated timber, Performance requirements and minimum production requirements |
| BS EN 390: 1995 | Glued laminated timber. Sizes. Permissible deviations |
| BS EN 460: 1994 | Durability of wood and wood-based products. Natural durability of solid wood. Guide to the durability requirements for wood to be used in hazard classes |
| BS 476-3: 1975 | Fire tests on building materials and structures Part 3 External fire exposure roof test |
| BS 476-4: 1970 | Fire tests on building materials and structures Part 4 Non-combustibility test for materials |
| BS 476-6: 1989 | Fire tests on building materials and structures Part 6 Method of test for fire propagation for products |
| BS476-7: 1997 | Fire tests on building materials and structures Part 7 Method of test to determine the classification of the surface spread of flame of products |
| BS 476-11: 1982 | Fire tests on building materials and structures Part 11 Method for assessing the heat emission from building materials |
| BS 476-20: 1987 | Fire tests on building materials and structures Part 20 Method for determination of the fire resistance of elements of building construction (general principles) |
| BS 476-21: 1987 | Fire tests on building materials and structures Part 21 Methods for determination of the fire resistance of loadbearing elements of construction |

| | |
|---|---|
| BS 476-22: 1987 | Fire tests on building materials and structures Part 22 Methods for determination of the fire resistance of non-loadbearing elements of construction |
| BS 476-23: 1987 | Fire tests on building materials and structures Part 23 Methods for determination of the contribution of components to the fire resistance of a structure |
| BS 476-24: 1987 | Fire tests on building materials and structures Part 24 Method for the determination of the fire resistance of ventilation ducts |
| BS EN 518:1995 | Structural timber. Grading. Requirements for visual strength grading standards |
| BS EN 519: 1995 | Structural timber. Grading. Requirements for machine strength graded timber and grading machines |
| BS EN 599-1: 1997 | Durability of wood and wood-based products. Performance of preventive wood preservatives as determined by biological tests. Specification according to hazard class |
| BS EN 622-1: 1997 | Fibreboards - Specifications.  General requirements |
| BS EN 622-2: 1997 | Fibreboards - Specifications.  Requirements for hardboards |
| BS EN 622-3: 1997 | Fibreboards - Specifications.  Requirements for medium boards |
| BS EN 633: 1994 | Cement bonded particleboards. Definitions and classification |
| BS EN 634-1: 1995 | Cement-bonded particleboards. Specification. General requirements |
| BS EN 634-2: 1997 | Requirements for OPC bonded particleboards for use in dry, humid and exterior conditions |
| BS EN 636-1:1997 | Plywood for use in dry conditions |
| BS EN 636-2: 1997 | Plywood for use in humid conditions |
| BS EN 636-3: 1997 | Plywood for use in exterior conditions |
| BS 648: 1964 | Schedule of weights of building materials. |
| BS EN ISO 717-1: 1997 | Acoustics. Rating of sound insulation in buildings and of building elements. Part 1 Airborne sound insulation |
| BS EN ISO 717-2: 1997 | Acoustics. Rating of sound insulation in buildings and of building elements. Part 2 Impact sound insulation |
| BS 747: 2000 | Reinforced bitumen sheets for roofing – Specification |
| BS EN 778: 1998 | Domestic gas-fired forced convection air heaters for space heating not exceeding anet heat input of 70 kW, without a fan to assist transportation of combustion air and/or combustion |
| BS EN 912:2000 | Timber fasteners. Specifications for connectors for timber |
| BS EN 942: 1996 | Timber in joinery. General classification of timber quality |
| BS EN 1059: 1999 | Timber structures. Product requirements for prefabricated trusses using punched metal plate fasteners |
| BS 1088 & BS 4079: 1966 | Specifications for plywood for marine craft |
| BS 1186-2: 1988 | Timber for and workmanship in joinery. Part 2 Specification for workmanship |
| BS 1186-3: 1990 | Timber for and workmanship in joinery. Part 3 Specification for wood trim and its fixing |
| BS 1202-1: 1974. | Specification for nails.  Steel nails |
| BS 1230-1: 1985 | Gypsum plasterboard. Part 1 Specification for plasterboard excluding materials submitted to secondary operations |

| | |
|---|---|
| BS 1297: 1987 | Specification for tongued and grooved softwood flooring |
| BS 1313-1: 1997 | Round and sawn timber – Permitted deviations and preferred sizes. Part 1 Softwood sawn timber |
| BS 1313-2: 1999 | Round and sawn timber – Permitted deviations and preferred sizes. Part 2 Hardwood sawn timber |
| BS EN 1363-1: 1999 | Fire resistance tests. Part 1 General requirements |
| BS EN 1364-1: 1999 | Fire resistance test for non-loadbearing elements. Part 1 Walls |
| BS EN 1364-2: 1999 | Fire resistance test for non-loadbearing elements. Part 2 Ceilings |
| BS EN 1365-1: 1999 | Fire resistance tests for loadbearing elements. Part 1 Walls |
| BS EN 1365-2: 2000 | Fire resistance tests for loadbearing elements. Part 2 Floors and roofs |
| BS EN 1365-3: 2000 | Fire resistance tests for loadbearing elements. Part 3 Beams |
| BS EN 1365-4: 1999 | Fire resistance tests for loadbearing elements. Part 4 Columns |
| BS EN 1634-1 2000 | Fire resistance tests for door and shutter assemblies. Part 1 Fire doors and shutters |
| BS 3921: 1985 (1995) | Specification for clay bricks |
| BS 4016: 1997 | Specification for flexible building membranes (breather type) |
| BS 4978: 1996 | Specification for visual strength grading of softwood |
| BS 5234-1: 1992. | Partitions (including matching linings). Code of practice for design and installation |
| BS 5234-2: 1992. | Partitions (including matching linings). Specification for performance requirements for strength and robustness including methods of test |
| BS 5250: 1989 | Code of practice for control of condensation in buildings |
| BS 5258-1: 1986 | Safety of domestic gas appliances. Part 1 Specification for central heating boilers and circulators (Superseded by BS EN 297, but remains current) |
| BS 5258-5: 1989 | Safety of domestic gas appliances. Part 5 Specification for gas fires |
| BS 5258-7: 1977 | Safety of domestic gas appliances. Part 7 Specification for storage water heaters |
| BS 5258-8: 1980 | Safety of domestic gas appliances. Part 8 Combined appliances: gas fire/back boiler |
| BS 5262: 1991 | Code of practice for external renderings |
| BS 5268-2: 1996 | Structural use of timber. Part 2 Code of practice for permissible stress design, materials and workmanship |
| BS 5268-3: 1998 | Structural use of timber Part 3 Code of practice for trussed rafter roofs |
| BS 5268-4 Section 4.1: 1978 | Structural use of timber. Part 4 Fire resistance of timber structures. Section 4.1 Recommendations for calculating fire resistance of timber members |
| BS 5268-4 Section 4.2: 1990 | Structural use of timber. Part 4 Fire resistance of timber structures. Section 4.2 Recommendations for calculating the fire resistance of timber stud walls and joisted floor constructions |
| BS 5268-5: 1989 | Structural use of timber Part 5 Code of practice for the preservative treatment of structural timber |
| BS 5268-6 Section 6.1: 1996 | Structural use of timber Part 6 Code of practice for timber framed walls. Section 6.1 Dwellings not exceeding four storeys |
| BS 5328-1: 1997 | Concrete. Part 1 Guide to specifying concrete |
| BS 5328-2: 1997 | Concrete. Part 2 Methods for specifying concrete mixes |
| BS 5386-1: 1976 | Specification for gas burning appliances.Part 1 Gas burning appliances for instantaneous production of hot water for domestic use |

| | |
|---|---|
| BS 5440-2: 2000 | Installation and maintenance of flues and ventilation for gas appliances of rated input not exceeding 70 kW net (1st 2nd and 3rd family gases). Part 2 Specification for installation and maintenance of ventilation for gas appliances |
| BS 5442-3: 1979 | Adhesives for construction. Classification of adhesives for construction. Part 3 Adhesives for use with wood |
| BS 5450: 1977 | Sizes of hardwoods and methods of measurement |
| BS 5531: 1988. | Code of practice for safety in erecting structural frames |
| BS 5534-1: 1997 | Code of practice for slating and tiling (including shingles). Part 1 Design |
| BS 5588-0: 1996. | Fire precautions in the design construction and use of building. Guide to fire safety codes of practice for particular premises/applications |
| BS 5588-1: 1990. | Fire precautions in the design construction and use of building. Code of practice for residential buildings |
| BS 5588-11: 1997. | Fire precautions in the design construction and use of building. Code of practice for shops, offices, industrial, storage and other similar buildings |
| BS 5589: 1989 | Code of practice for the preservation of timber |
| BS 5628-1 1992 | Code of practice for use of masonry. Part 1 Structural use of unreinforced masonry |
| BS 5628-2: 1995 | Code of practice for use of masonry. Part 2 Structural use of reinforced and prestressed masonry |
| BS 5628 3: 1985 | Code of practice for use of masonry. Part 3 Materials and components, design and workmanship |
| BS ISO TR 5658-1: 1997. | Reaction to fire tests. Spread of flame. Guidance on flame spread |
| BS ISO 5658-2: 1996. | Reaction to fire tests. Spread of flame.  Lateral spread on building products in vertical configuration |
| BS 5756: 1997 | Specification for visual strength grading of hardwood |
| BS 5977-2: 1983 | Lintels. Specification for prefabricated lintels |
| BS 6073-1: 1981 | Precast concrete masonry units. Part 1 Specification for precast concrete masonry units |
| BS 6073-2: 1981 | Precast concrete masonry units. Part 2 Method for specifying precast concrete masonry units |
| BS 6399-1: 1996 | Loading for buildings. Part 1 Code of practice for dead and imposed loads |
| BS 6399-2: 1997 | Loading for buildings. Part 2 Code of practice for wind loads |
| BS 6399-3: 1988 | Loading for buildings. Part 3 Code of practice for imposed roof loads |
| BS 6400: 1997 | Specification for installation of domestic sized gas meters (2nd and 3rd family gases) |
| BS 6891: 1998 | Specification for installation of low pressure gas pipework of up to 28 mm (RI) in domestic premises (2nd family gas) |
| BS 7671:1992 | Requirements for electrical installations |
| BS 7916: 1998 | Code of practice for the selection and application of particleboard, oriented strand board (OSB, cement bonded wood particleboard and wood fibreboards for specific purposes |
| BS 8000-1: 1989 | Workmanship on building sites Part 1 Code of practice for excavation and filling |

| | |
|---|---|
| BS 8000-2: 1990 Section 2.2 | Workmanship on building sites Part 2 Code of practice for concrete work. Section 2.2 Sitework with insitu and precast concrete |
| BS 8000-3: 1989 | Workmanship on building sites Part 3 Code of practice for masonry |
| BS 8000-4: 1989 | Workmanship on building sites Part 4 Code of practice for waterproofing |
| BS 8000-5: 1990 | Workmanship on building sites Part 5 Code of practice for carpentry, joinery and general fixings |
| BS 8000-6: 1990 | Workmanship on building sites Part 6 Code of practice for slating, tiling of roofs and claddings |
| BS 8000-7: 1990 | Workmanship on building sites Part 7 Code of practice for glazing |
| BS 8000-8: 1994 | Workmanship on building sites Part 8 Code of practice for plasterboard partitions and dry linings |
| BS 8000-9: 1999 | Workmanship on building sites Part 9 Cementitious levelling screeds and wearing screads. Code of practice |
| BS 8000-10: 1995 | Workmanship on building sites Part 10 Code of practice for plastering and rendering |
| BS 8004: 1986 | Code of practice for foundations |
| BS 8102: 1990 | Code of practice for protection of structures against water from the ground |
| BS 8103-1: 1995 | Structural design of low-rise buildings Part 1 Code of practice for stability, site investigations, foundations and ground floor slabs for housing |
| BS 8103-3: 1996 | Structural design of low-rise buildings Part 2 Code of practice for timber floors and roofs for housing |
| BS 8103-4: 1995 | Structural design of low-rise buildings. Code of practice for suspended concrete floors for housing |
| BS 8201: 1987. | Code of practice for flooring of timber, timber products and wood based panel products |
| BS 8212: 1995 | Code of practice for dry lining and partitioning using gypsum plasterboard |
| BS 8233: 1999. | Sound insulation and noise reduction for buildings.  Code of practice |
| BS ISO/TR 11696-1:1999 | Uses of reaction to fire test results.  Part 1: Application of test results to predict fire performance of internal linings and other building products |
| BS ISO/TR 11696-2: 1999 | Uses of reaction to fire test results.  Part 2: Fire hazard assessment of construction products |
| BS ISO TR 11925-1: 1999 | Reaction to fire test – Ignitability of building products subjected to direct impingement of flame – Guidance on ignitability |
| BS ISO 11925-2: 1997. | Reaction to fire tests - Ignitability of building products subjected to direct impingement of flame. Single flame source test |
| BS ISO 11925-3: 1997. | Reaction to fire tests - Ignitability of building products subjected to direct impingement of flame. Multi-source test |
| BS ISO/TR 14696:1999 | Reaction to fire tests.  Determination of fire parameters of materials, products and assemblies using an intermediate scale heat release calorimeter (ICAL) |
| BS ISO/TR 14697: 1997. | Fire tests - Guidance on the choice of substrates for building products |
| BS EN ISO 13370: 1998 | Thermal performance of buildings. Heat transfer via the ground. Calculation methods |

## Drafts for Development

| | |
|---|---|
| DD 140-2: 1987 | Wall ties. Recommendations for design of wall ties |
| DD 239: 1998 | Recommendations for the preservation of timber |
| DD ENV 1099: 1998 | Plywood. Biological durability. Guidance for the assessment of plywood for use in different hazard classes |
| DD ENV1991-1: 1996 | Eurocode 1 Basis of design and actions on structures. Basis of design |
| DD ENV 1991-2-1: 1996 | Actions of structures. Densities, self weight and imposed loads |
| DD ENV 1991-2-2: 1996 | Basis of design and actions on structures. Actions on structures exposed to fire |
| DD ENV 1991-2-3: 1996 | Basis of design and actions on structures. Actions on structures. Snow loads |
| DD ENV 1991-2-4: 1997 | Basis of design and actions on structures. Actions on structures. Wind actions |
| DD ENV 1991-2-6: 2000 | Basis of design and actions on structures. Actions during execution |
| DD ENV 1995-1-1: 1994 | Eurocode 5 Design of timber structures. General rules and rules for buildings |
| DD ENV 1995-1-2: 2000 | General rules. Structural fire design |

# Overseas Standards

### Canadian Standards Association, Rexdale, Ontario

| | |
|---|---|
| CSA 0121-M1978 | Douglas fir plywood. 1978 |
| CSA 0141-1991 | Canadian softwood lumber. 1991 |
| CSA 0151-M1978 | Canadian softwood plywood. 1978 |

National Grading Rules for Softwood Dimension Lumber (NGRDL)

National grading rules for softwood dimension lumber. Portland, USA 1975

### National Lumber Grades Authority, New Westminster, BC

National grading rules for dimension lumber. Burnaby, BC. 1994

Standard grading rules for Canadian Lumber. 2000

Interpretations and the European Union Visual Grade requirements Annex. 2000

### National Lumber Grades Authority, Southern pine inspection Bureau, West Coast Lumber Inspection Bureau, Western Wood Products Association

North American export standard for machine stress rated lumber. Burnaby BC. (NLGA) 1987 and supplement 1992

### National Institute for Standards and Technology (NIST), Washington

| | |
|---|---|
| PS 1-95 | American construction and industrial plywood. 1996 |
| PS 20-70, 20-94, 20-99 | American softwood lumber standard. |

# TRADA and TRADA Technology Publications

*TRADA and TRADA Technology produce a wide range of publications relating to timber and its uses. For details and prices visit the website www.trada.co.uk or contact the TRADA Information Centre on 01494 569602. A full list of publications is available on request.*

## Books and Reports

| | |
|---|---|
| Report 1/2000 | Acoustic performance of party floors and walls in timber framed buildings |
| Report 2/2000 | Timber frame: Re-engineering for affordable housing |
| Report 1/2001 | Timber frame walls and floors: Fire resistance of service penetrations |
| AD 1 | Timber intermediate floors for dwellings. 1992 Approved Document to the England and Wales Building Regulations |
| TBL 61 | Energy efficient housing - A timber frame approach. 1989 |
| A Batsford/TRADA book | Timber in construction. ed J G Sunley and Barbara Bedding. 1985 |
| GD 8 | Bracing for non-domestic timber trussed rafter roofs. Timber Engineering Guidance Document. 1999 |

## Wood Information Sheets

| | |
|---|---|
| WIS 0 - 3 | Introduction to timber framed housing |
| WIS 0 - 5 | Timber framed housing - materials specification |
| WIS 0 - 7 | Timber frame - energy efficient housing |
| WIS 0 - 8 | Timber frame construction - site control |
| WIS 0 -10 | Surveys of timber frame houses. |
| WIS 0 -11 | Improving the thermal performance of existing timber framed buildings |
| WIS 0 -12 | Room in the roof construction for new dwellings |
| WIS 1 -10 | Principles of pitched roof construction. |
| WIS 1 - 17 | Structural use of hardwoods |
| WIS 1 -20 | External timber cladding. |
| WIS 1 -25 | Introduction and supply of timber to BS 5268 Part 2. |
| WIS 1 -29 | Trussed rafters. |
| WIS 1 - 33 | The performance of joinery products |
| WIS 1 - 35 | Breather membranes for timber frame walls |
| WIS 2/3 - 1 | Finishes for exterior timber |
| WIS 2/3 - 3 | Flame retardant treatments for timber |
| WIS 2/3 - 11 | Specification and treatment of exterior plywood |
| WIS 2/3 - 16 | Preservative treatment for timber - A guide to specification |
| WIS 2/3 - 20 | Edge sealants for wood-based board products |
| WIS 2/3 - 21 | Wood preservation - processing and site control |

| WIS 2/3 - 23 | Introduction to wood-based panel products |
| WIS 4 - 7 | Guide to strength graded softwood. |
| WIS 4 - 11 | Timber and wood-based sheet materials in fire |
| WIS 4 - 12 | Care of timber and wood-based products on building sites |
| WIS 4 -15 | Condensation control in dwellings. |
| WIS 4 - 16 | Timber in joinery |
| WIS 4 - 18 | Moisture meters for wood |
| WIS 4 - 19 | European standards on timber |

*Prices of these publications and a complete list of other items is available via the website www.trada.co.uk or from the TRADA Information Centre, telephone 01494 569602.*

## Other publications

### British Cement Association, Crowthorne
| Approved Document. | Basements for dwellings.  1997 |
| BCA Guide | Strip foundations for houses. 1993 |
| Appearance Matters 2. | External rendering. W Monks. 1992 |

### Brick Development Association, Windsor.
| Design Note 7. | Brickwork durability. 1986 |
| Design Note 15. | Brick cladding for timber frame construction. 1992 |
| Technical Information Papers 10 | Brickwork dimensions table |

### British Gypsum Ltd, Nottingham
| The White Book. | Technical Manual of Building Products. 2000 |

### Building Research Establishment, Garston
| BR 128 | Guidelines for the construction of fire-resisting structural elements. 1988 |
| BR 211 | Radon: guidance on protective measures for new dwellings. 1999 |
| BR 212. | Construction of new buildings on gas-contaminated land. 1991 |
| BR 278 | Environmental standard: homes for a greener world. 1995 |
| BR 350 | BREEAM for offices. 1998 |
| BR 351 | The green guide to specification. An environmental profiling system for building materials and components. 1998 |
| BR 389 | ECOHOMES: The environmental rating for homes. 2000 |
| BR 390 | The green guide to housing specification. 2000 |

*BRE publications can be purchased via the website www.trada.co.uk or from the TRADA Information Centre 01494 569602.*

### Chartered Institution of Building Services Engineers, London
| CIBSE Guide A. | Environmental design. 1999 (Section A3 Thermal properties of building structures) |

**Department of the Environment, Transport and the Regions, London**

Constructing the team. Sir Michael Latham. 1993

Rethinking construction. Sir John Egan. 1998

Accessible thresholds in new housing. 1999

**Institution of Gas Engineers, London**

Gas in timber frame buildings. 1998

**National House-building Council, Amersham**

NHBC Standards Volumes 1 and 2

**Zurich Mutual**

Technical manual

# Index